The Abnormal Personality
Through Literature

Much madness is divinest sense
To a discerning eye;
Much sense the starkest madness.
'Tis the majority
In this, as all, prevails.
Assent, and you are sane:
Demur,—you're straightway dangerous,
And handled with a chain.

Emily Dickinson

The Abnormal Personality
Through Literature

edited by ALAN A. STONE, M.D.
Associate in Psychiatry, Harvard Medical School

and SUE SMART STONE

Prentice-Hall, Inc., *Englewood Cliffs, New Jersey*

Prentice-Hall Series in Psychology

RICHARD S. LAZARUS, *Editor*

PRENTICE-HALL INTERNATIONAL, INC., *London*
PRENTICE-HALL OF AUSTRALIA, PTY., LTD., *Sydney*
PRENTICE-HALL OF CANADA, LTD., *Toronto*
PRENTICE-HALL OF INDIA (PRIVATE) LTD., *New Delhi*
PRENTICE-HALL OF JAPAN, INC., *Tokyo*

to KAREN, DOUGLAS, *and* DAVID

Introduction

Dostoevsky, in the introduction to his great novel *The Brothers Karamazov*, called himself a "biographer." He was, of course, much more than that—a psychologist, a philosopher, a mystic, a poet, a novelist, and a man of extraordinary genius who explored the depths of his own heart and soul. He was, as one critic has said, a man capable of uncovering "the abyss in man and in the universe." These awesome talents were poured into Dostoevsky's "biographies," as he portrayed motives, feelings, passions, the good and the evil, all of human nature that was accessible to his gift. Dostoevsky is only one of the literary greats who turned his talents towards "biography," and thus "fiction" has paradoxically become one of the richest and most profound sources of man's realistic view of man.

Those psychological sciences which focus on human thought and behavior have long recognized this fact. Sigmund Freud, speaking of creative writers, said, "One may heave a sigh at the thought that it is vouchsafed to a few with hardly an effort, to salve from the whirlpool of their emotions the deepest truths, to which we others have to force our way. . . ." And again, "Imaginative writers are valuable colleagues. . . . In the knowledge of the human heart they are far ahead of us common folk, because they draw on sources that we have not yet made accessible to science." The contemporary psychological sciences have in the main been cast in a humanistic tradition and therefore they have maintained their ties with literature. Few investigators have, however, been able to use these valuable colleagues as profitably as did Freud. Most psychologists, psychoanalysts, and psychiatrists have instead turned their skills towards analyzing the personal idiosyncrasies of their literary colleagues rather than using them as valuable collaborators.

The reasons that this collaboration has not been pursued can in part be ascribed to the fact that most literature seeks to understand the general in terms of the unique, while contemporary psychology, like most "modern sciences," tries to explain the unique in terms of the general.

This scientific goal is nowhere more apparent than in the classification of abnormal personality. Contemporary psychology and psychiatry set themselves the task of assessing the relevant aspects of each unique life and assigning to this pathology a diagnostic label. Such labels at best are helpful in the management of some emotionally disturbed persons because they suggest either a particular prognosis or a preferable type of treatment. In many instances these labels have no such immediate value and gratify only a common human belief that in naming something one has gained a measure of control. Unhappily, these diagnostic labels have acquired an inordinate significance in professional and nonprofessional circles as well. Diagnostic labels are applied in a social context with the emotional value of sophisticated insults.

The tendency to categorize the unique in terms of the general frequently pervades "case histories" meant to illustrate the different types of abnormality. When the psychologist or psychiatrist attempts the task of biography, he is apt to focus on certain predetermined general pathological mechanisms; thus his portrait is inevitably in a sense a fiction. He has placed a predetermined mold on the unique features of an individual, and the result is too often a scientific caricature. The writer views abnormality within a different framework, and often finds in the pathological the individualistic, the creative, and the spiritual.

Dostoevsky portrayed pathology, and much of it is recognizable by our modern psychological sciences. But he also saw this as only part of a life, only part of a social context. Furthermore, psychopathology for Dostoevsky could be approached from many directions and each perspective provided a new and different impression for the beholder—and not all of them seemed equally pathological.

This book, then, will attempt to renew the valuable collaboration with literature. It will attempt to present "the outward forms" of abnormal personality utilizing the portraits drawn in literature. None of these portraits is as stereotyped as the ordinary case history presented to illustrate an abnormal personality. They are, however, closer to the reality of human nature, which resists oversimplified classification. It is hoped these examples from fiction will permit the reader to grasp the traditional classification of psychological disorders as they can be identified within the vivid delineation of human lives and human relationships.

The literary sources of this book arise mainly from Russian, French, English, German, and American fiction, with lesser contributions from the Spanish, Japanese, Italian, Swedish, and Irish cultures. The range of selections reflects in part the fact that certain national literatures are more preoccupied than others with the exploration of psychological motivation. The choices inevitably also reflect the availability of good translations, and the willingness or reluctance of writers, their heirs, and agents to permit the inclusion of excerpts in a collection such as this.

It is a verity that literary genius is not equally distributed amongst writers of fiction. Some lesser authors found their way into this collection and take their place alongside men of extraordinary genius. Nonetheless, within the range of the compilers' search, their taste, and their judgment, each excerpt discovers something about human personality that is worth remembering.

Contents

one

The Three Major Types of Abnormality   1

I.   Psychosis: The Break with Reality   2

    WARD NO. 6, *Anton Chekhov*   3

II.   Neurosis: The Symptoms of Anxiety   7

    BEATRICE TRUEBLOOD'S STORY, *Jean Stafford*   8

III.   Character Disorder: The Compromise with Reality   20

    THE OVERCOAT, *Nicolai Gogol*   21

two

The Struggle with Impulse   33

    THE HUNCHBACK OF NOTRE DAME, *Victor Hugo*   34

    THE WAY TO THE CHURCHYARD, *Thomas Mann*   40

    STUDS LONIGAN, *James T. Farrell*   47

three

Psychosis. The Break with Reality   49

I.   Schizophrenia   49

    LOUIS LAMBERT, *Honoré de Balzac*   52

HAMLET, *William Shakespeare*   65

THE DIARY OF A MADMAN, *Nicolai Gogol*   69

TENDER IS THE NIGHT, *F. Scott Fitzgerald*   75

THE ROOM, *Jean-Paul Sartre*   79

II.   The Affective Psychoses   87

MADAME BOVARY, *Gustave Flaubert*   88

THE ARLESIAN GIRL, *Alphonse Daudet*   89

AN OLD MAN DIES, *Luise Rinser*   92

THE ETERNAL HUSBAND, *Fyodor Dostoevsky*   98

FOMA GORDEYEV, *Maxim Gorky*   104

III. Senility   113

THE LOST PHOEBE, *Theodore Dreiser*   114

four

Psychotic Symptoms   126

I.   Hallucinations   126

THE TELL-TALE HEART, *Edgar Allan Poe*   127

II.   Visual Hallucinations in Schizophrenia   131

THE BLACK MONK, *Anton Chekhov*   131

III. Disturbances in the Body Image   136

THE NOTEBOOKS OF MALTE LAURIDS BRIGGE, *Rainer Maria Rilke*   136

IV.   Ideas of Reference   141

THE NOTEBOOKS OF MALTE LAURIDS BRIGGE, *Rainer Maria Rilke*   142

V.   Paranoid Jealousy   143

THE HEART'S REASONS, *Eduardo Mallea*   143

VI.   Autism   152

SILENT SNOW, SECRET SNOW, *Conrad Aiken*   153

VII.   Idiot Savant   158

      JOHNNY BEAR, *John Steinbeck*   159

five

The Neuroses: Anxiety and Its Manifestations   161

I.   Hysteria   162

      THE BARRETTS OF WIMPOLE STREET, *Rudolf Besier*   163

II.   Obsessive-Compulsive Neurosis   169

      PNIN, *Vladimir Nabokov*   170

III.   Phobias   174

      THE END OF THE PARTY, *Graham Greene*   175

IV.   Neurotic Depression   182

      THE VAGABOND, *Collette*   182

V.   The Traumatic Neurosis   186

      FLOTSAM AND JETSAM, *W. Somerset Maugham*   186

six

Neurotic Symptoms   191

I.   Anxiety Attacks   191

      PIGEON FEATHERS, *John Updike*   192

II.   Obsessions   193

      THE NOTEBOOKS OF MALTE LAURIDS BRIGGE, *Rainer Maria Rilke*   193

      BARTLEBY THE SCRIVENER, *Herman Melville*   194

III.   Compulsive Thoughts   195

      THE SCARLET LETTER, *Nathaniel Hawthorne*   195

IV.   Depression   197

       Two Poems, *Emily Dickinson*   198

V.   Reaction Formation   199

       Tobias Mindernickel, *Thomas Mann*   199

VI.   Repression   205

       The Mill on the Floss, *George Eliot*   206

VII.   Hypomania   208

       The Soft Touch of Grass, *Luigi Pirandello*   209

VIII. Displacement   212

       Counterparts, *James Joyce*   213

IX.   Depersonalization   214

       Swann's Way, *Marcel Proust*   215

       Flight, *John Updike*   217

X.   Repetition Compulsion   218

       An Enigmatic Nature, *Anton Chekhov*   219

XI.   Action as Symptom   220

       Escape, *Luigi Pirandello*   221

       The Wrysons, *John Cheever*   225

                                 seven
       Character Disorders   227

I.   Disturbances of Personality Pattern   227

       Oblomov, *Ivan Goncharov*   228

       Paul's Case, *Willa Cather*   231

       The Amazon, *Nikolai Leskov*   247

       The Man Who Shot Snapping Turtles, *Edmund Wilson*   256

II.   Sociopathic Personality Disturbances   258

GÁLVEZ THE ABSURD, *Pio Baroja*   259

CONFESSIONS OF FELIX KRULL, CONFIDENCE MAN, *Thomas Mann*   264

III.   Disturbances of Personality Traits   272

THE MAN IN THE CASE, *Anton Chekhov*   272

eight

The Problem of Identity: An Approach to the Study of Social Adaptation   276

I.   Childhood—The Problem of Self Determination   277

A HIGH WIND IN JAMAICA, *Richard Hughes*   277

II.   Adolescence—The Problem of Sexual Identity   280

THE MAN WHO BECAME A WOMAN, *Sherwood Anderson*   280

III a.   Young Adulthood—The Problem of Vocational Identification   287

THE RUIN OF HUMANITY, *Alberto Moravia*   288

III b.   Young Adulthood—The Problem of Social Identity   292

MISS JULIE, *August Strindberg*   292

IV.   Adulthood—The Problem of Hardening of Identity   305

THE GOLOVLYOVS, *M. Saltykov-Schedrin*   305

V.   Adulthood and Old Age—The Problem of Identity in Death   309

THE DEATH OF IVAN ILYCH, *Leo Tolstoy*   310

nine

Perversions: The Deviations of Sexual Thought and Behavior   318

I.   Homosexuality   319

THE PRUSSIAN OFFICER, *D. H. Lawrence*   320

II.   Pedophilia   326

       DEATH IN VENICE, *Thomas Mann*   327

       AN ENCOUNTER, *James Joyce*   332

III.   Transvestism   334

       BALTHAZAR, *Lawrence Durrell*   335

IV.   Sadism and Masochism   338

       THE HOUSE OF THE DEAD, *Fyodor Dostoevsky*   338

V.   Voyeurism   342

       THE ASSISTANT, *Bernard Malamud*   342

VI.   Exhibitionism   344

       THE CONFESSIONS OF JEAN-JACQUES ROUSSEAU,
            Jean-Jacques Rousseau   344

VII.   Chronic Alcoholism   346

       BIG BLONDE, *Dorothy Parker*   347

VIII. Addiction   354

       MAN'S FATE, *Andre Malraux*   355

       THE MAN WITH THE GOLDEN ARM, *Nelson Algren*   357

ten

The Psychotherapeutic Process   362

I.   Catharsis   362

       GRIEF, *Anton Chekhov*   363

II.   Insight   367

       OBLOMOV, *Ivan Goncharov*   368

III.   Emotional Support   370

       THE BEGGAR, *Anton Chekhov*   370

       THE SACRED TABLE, *T. C. Worsley*   376 *eleven*

The Abnormal Personality in Childhood   392

THE INSANE, *William Carlos Williams*   393

THE DOWNWARD PATH TO WISDOM, *Katherine Anne Porter*   396

COMING HOME, *Elizabeth Bowen*   405

FIRST LOVE, *Isaac Babel*   409

twelve

Psychiatry and the Law   415

HAN'S CRIME, *Shiga Naoya*   416

The Abnormal Personality
Through Literature

CHAPTER one

The Three Major Types of Abnormality

The mystery of mental illness, like all unsolved mysteries, has troubled mankind for centuries. The obscure nature of the causes and the bizarre nature of the symptoms have led to wild speculation, to dogmatic assertions, and to bitter controversy. Physicians and philosophers in the late medieval period risked religious persecution when they challenged the belief that "the possessed" harbored devils. In Europe thousands of men and women who would now be considered insane were tortured, exorcized, and killed, based on the judgment that their hallucinations or delusions represented a possession by the devil. America was not spared this inquisition of ignorance. Some of the people persecuted as Salem's witches were in fact the victims of a rare hereditary disease, Huntington's Chorea, ironically brought over on the Mayflower by an affected family. This neurologic disease usually begins after thirty and causes uncontrolled movements of groups of muscles. These movements were interpreted by the trials of persecution as possession by the devil.

The social and political reforms which followed the great western renaissance produced changes in the treatment of the insane. France and Italy were among the first to provide so-called "moral treatment," which attempted to preserve the humanity of the afflicted rather than to destroy the supernatural incubus. As retreats, hospitals, lazarettos, clinics, and asylums were set up, large numbers of patients became available for study, thus for the first time permitting detailed nosological investigation. Insanity had become the province of the scientist rather than the ecclesiast.

Psychiatric nosology was predictably superimposed on the prevailing medical concepts of disease and diagnosis. Medical diagnoses were based on a careful classification of symptoms occurring in some sequence and called a syndrome. Years later scientific study might identify an infectious microbe or diseased organ that was responsible for part or all of the group of patients suffering with a particular syndrome.

Thus in the 18th and 19th centuries physicians began to categorize mental patients on the basis of their symptoms. This early phase of nosology culminated in the work of Emil Kraepelin. In 1898 Kraepelin extracted from the diffuse symptoms of insanity one major syndrome which shared certain symptoms and prognosis. This classical syndrome he called "Dementia Praecox," later to be known generally as schizophrenia. Kraepelin's work is generally considered the foundation of modern "medically oriented" psychiatric nosology.

Since that time psychiatrists preoccupied with minor variations have produced an incredibly complicated array of categories of mental illness. However, three major nosological entities seem to have transcended this complexity and have both theoretical and utilitarian value: psychosis, neurosis, and character disorder.

Psychosis: The Break with Reality

I. The person suffering from a psychosis, the psychotic, is characteristically the most disturbed of the mentally ill. He corresponds to what the layman readily understands as crazy. A major distinguishing factor is that the psychotic has "lost touch with reality." Because of the pressures of his illness, he has replaced some important aspect of the real world by a creation of his own deranged mind. He is the victim of a complicated plot; he is in communication with divine authority; unseen voices speak to him; it has been revealed to him that he is in fact a king; he denies a death or insists on the reality of one that has not occurred; he is too evil to eat or drink; his heart is migrating through his body; people are accusing him of abnormal sexual acts. In subsequent chapters we will discuss the various types of psychoses and present

examples. Here, however, to illustrate the break with reality we
have chosen a selection from Chekhov, himself a physician
as well as an author. This case portrays a paranoid
schizophrenic collapse, one major form of psychosis. The case
is remarkably accurate in its description of the prepsychotic
personality, as well as the age at onset of the illness and the
typical life situation in which it is apt to occur.

WARD NO. 6

Anton Chekhov   *(1860–1904)*

Some twelve or fifteen years ago an official called Gromov,
a highly respectable and prosperous person, was living in his own house
in the principal street of the town. He had two sons, Sergey and Ivan.
When Sergey was a student in his fourth year he was taken ill with galloping consumption and died, and his death was, as it were, the first of a
whole series of calamities which suddenly showered on the Gromov
family. Within a week of Sergey's funeral the old father was put on his
trial for fraud and misappropriation, and he died of typhoid in the prison
hospital soon afterwards. The house, with all their belongings, was sold by
auction, and Ivan Dmitritch and his mother were left entirely without
means.

Hitherto in his father's lifetime, Ivan Dmitritch, who was studying in
the University of Petersburg, had received an allowance of sixty or seventy rubles a month, and had had no conception of poverty; now he had
to make an abrupt change in his life. He had to spend his time from morning to night giving lessons for next to nothing, to work at copying, and
with all that to go hungry, as all his earnings were sent to keep his mother.
Ivan Dmitritch could not stand such a life; he lost heart and strength,
and, giving up the university, went home.

Here, through interest, he obtained the post of teacher in the district
school, but could not get on with his colleagues, was not liked by the
boys, and soon gave up the post. His mother died. He was for six months
without work, living on nothing but bread and water; then he became a
court usher. He kept this post until he was dismissed owing to his illness.

He had never even in his young student days given the impression of
being perfectly healthy. He had always been pale, thin, and given to
catching cold; he ate little and slept badly. A single glass of wine went to
his head and made him hysterical. He always had a craving for society,
but, owing to his irritable temperament and suspiciousness, he never be-

"Ward No. 6" by Anton Chekhov. Reprinted with permission of the publisher from
The Horse Stealers and Other Stories by Anton Chekhov. Copyright 1921 by The
Macmillan Company, renewed 1949 by David Garnett.

came very intimate with anyone, and had no friends. He always spoke
with contempt of his fellow-townsmen, saying that their coarse ignorance
and sleepy animal existence seemed to him loathsome and horrible. He
spoke in a loud tenor, with heat, and invariably either with scorn and
indignation, or with wonder and enthusiasm, and always with perfect
sincerity. Whatever one talked to him about he always brought it round
to the same subject: that life was dull and stifling in the town; that the
townspeople had no lofty interests, but lived a dingy, meaningless life,
diversified by violence, coarse profligacy, and hypocrisy; that scoundrels
were well fed and clothed, while honest men lived from hand to mouth;
that they needed schools, a progressive local paper, a theatre, public lec-
tures, the co-ordination of the intellectual elements; that society must see
its failings and be horrified. In his criticisms of people he laid on the colors
thick, using only black and white, and no fine shades; mankind was divided
for him into honest men and scoundrels: there was nothing in between.
He always spoke with passion and enthusiasm of women and of love, but
he had never been in love.

In spite of the severity of his judgments and his nervousness, he was
liked, and behind his back was spoken of affectionately as Vanya. His innate refinement and readiness to be of service, his good breeding, his moral
purity, and his shabby coat, his frail appearance and family misfortunes,
aroused a kind, warm, sorrowful feeling. Moreover, he was well educated
and well read; according to the townspeople's notions, he knew everything, and was in their eyes something like a walking encyclopedia.

He had read a great deal. He would sit at the club, nervously pulling
at his beard and looking through the magazines and books; and from his
face one could see that he was not reading, but devouring the pages without giving himself time to digest what he read. It must be supposed that
reading was one of his morbid habits, as he fell upon anything that came
into his hands with equal avidity, even last year's newspapers and calen-
dars. At home he always read lying down.

One autumn morning Ivan Dmitritch, turning up the collar of his
greatcoat and splashing through the mud, made his way by side-streets and
back lanes to see some artisan, and to collect some payment that was owing. He was in a gloomy mood, as he always was in the morning. In one
of the side-streets he was met by two convicts in fetters and four soldiers
with rifles in charge of them. Ivan Dmitritch had very often met convicts
before, and they had always excited feelings of compassion and discomfort in him; but now this meeting made a peculiar, strange impression on
him. It suddenly seemed to him for some reason that he, too, might be put
into fetters and led through the mud to prison like that. After visiting the
artisan, on the way home he met near the post office a police superin-
tendent of his acquaintance, who greeted him and walked a few paces
along the street with him, and for some reason this seemed to him sus-

picious. At home he could not get the convicts or the soldiers with their rifles out of his head all day, and an unaccountable inward agitation prevented him from reading or concentrating his mind. In the evening he did not light his lamp, and at night he could not sleep, but kept thinking that he might be arrested, put into fetters, and thrown into prison. He did not know of any harm he had done, and could be certain that he would never be guilty of murder, arson, or theft in the future either; but was it not easy to commit a crime by accident, unconsciously, and was not false witness always possible, and, indeed, miscarriage of justice? It was not without good reason that the agelong experience of the simple people teaches that beggary and prison are ills none can be safe from. A judicial mistake is very possible as legal proceedings are conducted nowadays, and there is nothing to be wondered at in it. People who have an official, professional relation to other men's sufferings—for instance, judges, police officers, doctors—in course of time, through habit, grow so callous that they cannot, even if they wish it, take any but a formal attitude to their clients; in this respect they are not different from the peasant who slaughters sheep and calves in the back-yard, and does not notice the blood. With this formal, soulless attitude to human personality the judge needs but one thing—time—in order to deprive an innocent man of all rights of property, and to condemn him to penal servitude. Only the time spent on performing certain formalities for which the judge is paid his salary, and then—it is all over. Then you may look in vain for justice and protection in this dirty, wretched little town a hundred and fifty miles from a railway station! And, indeed, is it not absurd even to think of justice when every kind of violence is accepted by society as a rational and consistent necessity, and every act of mercy—for instance, a verdict of acquittal—calls forth a perfect outburst of dissatisfied and revengeful feeling?

In the morning Ivan Dmitritch got up from his bed in a state of horror, with cold perspiration on his forehead, completely convinced that he might be arrested any minute. Since his gloomy thoughts of yesterday had haunted him so long, he thought, it must be that there was some truth in them. They could not, indeed, have come into his mind without any grounds whatever.

A policeman walking slowly passed by the windows: that was not for nothing. Here were two men standing still and silent near the house. Why were they silent? And agonizing days and nights followed for Ivan Dmitritch. Everyone who passed by the windows or came into the yard seemed to him a spy or a detective. At midday the chief of the police usually drove down the street with a pair of horses; he was going from his estate near the town to the police department; but Ivan Dmitritch fancied every time that he was driving especially quickly, and that he had a peculiar expression: it was evident that he was in haste to announce that there was a very important criminal in the town. Ivan Dmitritch started at every ring at the bell and knock at the gate, and was agitated whenever he came upon anyone new at his landlady's; when he met police officers and gendarmes he smiled and began whistling so as to seem unconcerned. He could not sleep for whole nights in succession expecting to be arrested, but he snored loudly and sighed as though in deep sleep, that his landlady might think he was asleep; for if he could not sleep it meant that he was tormented by the stings of conscience—what a piece of evidence! Facts and common sense persuaded him that all these terrors were nonsense and morbidity, that if one looked at the matter more broadly there was nothing really terrible in arrest and imprisonment—so long as the conscience is at ease; but the more sensibly and logically he reasoned, the more acute and agonizing his mental distress became. It might be compared with the story of a hermit who tried to cut a dwelling-place for himself in a virgin forest; the more zealously he worked with his axe, the thicker the forest grew. In the end Ivan Dmitritch, seeing it was useless, gave up reasoning altogether, and abandoned himself entirely to despair and terror.

He began to avoid people and to seek solitude. His official work had been distasteful to him before: now it became unbearable to him. He was afraid they would somehow get him into trouble, would put a bribe in his pocket unnoticed and then denounce him, or that he would accidentally make a mistake in official papers that would appear to be fraudulent, or would lose other people's money. It is strange that his imagination had never at other times been so agile and inventive as now, when every day he thought of thousands of different reasons for being seriously anxious over his freedom and honor; but, on the other hand, his interest in the outer world, in books in particular, grew sensibly fainter, and his memory began to fail him.

In the spring when the snow melted there were found in the ravine near the cemetery two half-decomposed corpses—the bodies of an old woman and a boy bearing the traces of death by violence. Nothing was talked of but these bodies and their unknown murderers. That people might not think he had been guilty of the crime, Ivan Dmitritch walked about the streets, smiling, and when he met acquaintances he turned pale, flushed, and began declaring that there was no greater crime than the murder of the weak and defenceless. But this duplicity soon exhausted him, and after some reflection he decided that in his position the best thing to do was to hide in his landlady's cellar. He sat in the cellar all day and then all night, then another day, was fearfully cold, and waiting till dusk, stole secretly like a thief back to his room. He stood in the middle of the room till daybreak, listening without stirring. Very early in the morning, before sunrise, some workmen came into the house. Ivan Dmitritch knew perfectly well that they had come to mend the stove in the kitchen, but terror told him that they were police officers disguised as workmen. He slipped stealthily out of the flat, and, overcome by terror, ran along the street without his cap and coat. Dogs raced after him barking, a peasant shouted somewhere behind him, the wind whistled in his ears, and it seemed to Ivan Dmitritch that the force and violence of the whole world was massed together behind his back and was chasing after him.

He was stopped and brought home, and his landlady sent for a doctor. Doctor Andrey Yefimitch, of whom we shall have more to say hereafter, prescribed cold compresses on his head and laurel drops, shook his head, and went away, telling the landlady he should not come again, as one should not interfere with people who are going out of their minds. As he had not the means to live at home and be nursed, Ivan Dmitritch was soon sent to the hospital, and was there put into the ward for venereal patients. He could not sleep at night, was full of whims and fancies, and disturbed the patients, and was soon afterwards, by Andrey Yefimitch's orders, transferred to Ward No. 6.

Within a year Ivan Dmitritch was completely forgotten in the town, and his books, heaped up by his landlady in a sledge in the shed, were pulled to pieces by boys.

Neurosis: The Symptoms of Anxiety

II. The second major nosological category is the neurosis. The neurotic classically suffers either from anxiety or some symptom which protects him from his feelings of anxiety. He maintains contact with reality, but has some handicap which often both he and the people around him recognize as unusual, unnecessary, or sick. For example: he is afraid of certain harmless animals; he fears heights; during unexpected moments his heart pounds and he may have a sudden terrifying fear of impending death; he may act weak and sickly or become blind or paralyzed without a physical cause; he may wash his hands countless numbers of times; unexpected, unwanted thoughts of death or sex may rush into his mind; or he is frequently dissatisfied without cause.

The Two Major Types of Neurosis

1. *The direct manifestation of anxiety* is seen in the neurotic *anxiety attack*. The person experiences a feeling of impending death as his heart beats wildly in palpitations. His

skin becomes clammy as it cools and perspires, his breathing
pattern alters and becomes irregular, his hands tremble, and
there may be physical sensations in the stomach, chest, or throat.

2. *The protection against anxiety* is seen most directly
in the so-called *hysterical conversion,* where the anxiety and
conflict are converted into a physical symptom without physical
cause. A striking aspect is the absence of anxiety as the patient
presents his new found symptom with an apparent lack of
concern. The anxiety is thought to be masked by conversion
to a physical symptom which the patient somehow finds
singularly nonthreatening. This lack of concern has been called
by French psychiatrists "La Belle Indifference" (the beautiful
indifference).

Jean Stafford, in her short story, demonstrates all of the
important features of this most classic form of neurosis, the
conversion hysteria. We are shown the childhood frustrations
repeated in the present which shape the special quality of the
symptom. We see the strange absence of anxiety at the sudden
onset of the symptom, and the way that life goes on with
limitations, but without the break with reality. Finally, one
sees that the elimination of a symptom such as this by brief
treatment is not a total cure, but only allows the patient to
return to the vicissitudes of his life situation and the problems
produced by his own character.

Beatrice Trueblood's Story

Jean Stafford   (1915–   )

When Beatrice Trueblood was in her middle thirties and
on the very eve of her second marriage, to a rich and reliable man—when,
that is, she was in the prime of life and on the threshold of a rosier phase
of it than she had ever known before—she overnight was stricken with
total deafness.

"The vile unkindness of fate!" cried Mrs. Onslager, the hostess on
whose royal Newport lawn, on a summer day at lunchtime, poor Beatrice
had made her awful discovery. Mrs. Onslager was addressing a group of

Reprinted from "Beatrice Trueblood's Story," by Jean Stafford, by permission of
Farrar, Straus & Giroux. Copyright 1955 by *The New Yorker Magazine,* © 1956 by
Farrar, Straus & Giroux.

house guests a few weeks after the catastrophe and after the departure of its victim—or, more properly, of its victims, since Marten ten Brink, Mrs. Trueblood's fiancé, had been there, too. The guests were sitting on the same lawn on the same sort of dapper afternoon, and if the attitudes of some of Mrs. Onslager's audience seemed to be somnolent, they were so because the sun was so taming and the sound of the waves was a glamorous lullaby as the Atlantic kneaded the rocks toward which the lawn sloped down. They were by no means indifferent to this sad story; a few of them knew Marten ten Brink, and all of them knew Beatrice Trueblood, who had been Mrs. Onslager's best friend since their girlhood in St. Louis.

"I'm obliged to call it fate," continued Mrs. Onslager. "Because there's nothing wrong with her. All the doctors have reported the same thing to us, and she's been to a battalion of them. At first she refused to go to anyone on the ground that it would be a waste of money, of which she has next to none, but Jack and I finally persuaded her that if she didn't see the best men in the country and let us foot the bills, we'd look on it as unfriendliness. So, from Johns Hopkins, New York Hospital, the Presbyterian, the Leahy Clinic, and God knows where, the same account comes back: there's nothing physical to explain it, no disease, no lesion, there's been no shock, there were no hints of any kind beforehand. And I'll not allow the word 'psychosomatic' to be uttered in my presence—not in this connection, at any rate—because I know Bea as well as I know myself and she is not hysterical. Therefore, it has to be fate. And there's a particularly spiteful irony in it if you take a backward glance at her life. If ever a woman deserved a holiday from tribulation, it's Bea. There was first of all a positively hideous childhood. The classic roles were reversed in the family, and it was the mother who drank and the father who nagged. Her brother took to low life like a duck to water and was a juvenile delinquent before he was out of knickers—I'm sure he must have ended up in Alcatraz. They were unspeakably poor, and Bea's aunts dressed her in their hand-me-downs. It was a house of the most humiliating squalor, all terribly genteel. You know what I mean—the mother prettying up her drunkenness by those transparent dodges like 'Two's my limit,' and keeping the gin in a Waterford decanter, and the father looking as if butter wouldn't melt in his mouth when they were out together publicly, although everyone knew that he was a perfectly ferocious tartar. Perhaps it isn't true that he threw things at his wife and children and whipped them with a razorstrop—he didn't have to, because he could use his tongue like a bludgeon. And then after all that horror, Bea married Tom Trueblood—really to escape her family, I think, because she couldn't possibly have loved him. I mean it isn't possible to love a man who is both a beast and a fool. *He* was drunker than her mother ever thought of being; he was obscene, he was raucous, his infidelities to that good, beautiful girl were of a vulgarity that caused the mind to boggle. I'll never know how she managed to live with him for seven mortal years. And then at last, after all those tempests, came Marten ten Brink, like redemption itself. There's nothing sensational in Marten, I'll admit. He's rather a stick, he was born rather old, he's rather jokeless and bossy. But, oh, Lord, he's so *safe*, he was so protective of her, and he is so scrumptiously rich! And two months before the wedding *this* thunderbolt comes out of nowhere. It's indecent! It makes me so angry!" And this faithful friend shook her pretty red head rapidly in indignation, as if she were about to hunt down fate with a posse and hale it into court.

"Are you saying that the engagement has been broken?" asked Jennie Fowler, who had just got back from Europe and to whom all this was news.

Mrs. Onslager nodded, closing her eyes as if the pain she suffered were unbearable. "They'd been here for a week, Marten and Bea, and we were making the wedding plans, since they were to be married from my house. And the very day after this gruesome thing happened, she broke the engagement. She wrote him a note and sent it in to his room by one of the maids. I don't know what she said in it, though I suppose she told him she didn't want to be a burden, something like that—much more gracefully, of course, since Bea *is* the soul of courtesy. But whatever it was, it must have been absolutely unconditional, because he went back to town before dinner the same night. The letter I got from him after-ward scarcely mentioned it—he only said he was sorry his visit here had ended on 'an unsettling note.' I daresay he was still too shocked to say more."

*   *   *

Jack Onslager gazed through half-closed eyes at his wholesome, gabbling wife—he loved her very much, but her public dicta were always overwrought and nearly always wrong—and then he closed his eyes tight against the cluster of his guests, and he thought how blessed it would be if with the same kind of simple physical gesture one could also tempo-rarily close one's ears. One could decline to touch, to taste, to see, but it required a skill he had not mastered to govern the ears. Those stopples made of wax and cotton would be insulting at a party; besides, they made him claustrophobic, and when he used them, he could hear the interior workings of his skull, the boiling of his brains in his brainpan, a rustling behind his jaws. He would not like to go so far as Beatrice had gone, but he would give ten years of his life (he had been about to say he would give his eyes and changed it) to be able, when he wanted, to seal himself into an impenetrable silence.

To a certain extent, however, one could insulate the mind against the invasion of voices by an act of will, by causing them to blur together into a general hubbub. And this is what he did now; in order to consider Mrs. Trueblood's deafness, he deafened himself to the people who were talking about it. He thought of the day in the early summer when the extraordinary thing had taken place.

It had been Sunday. The night before, the Onslagers and their house-party—the young Allinghams, Mary and Leon Herbert, Beatrice and ten Brink—had gone to a ball. It was the kind of party to which Onslager had never got used, although he had been a multimillionaire for twenty years and not only had danced through many such evenings but had been the host at many more, in his own houses or in blazoned halls that he had hired. He was used to opulence in other ways, and took for granted his boats and horses and foreign cars. He also took for granted, and was bored by, most of the rites of the rich: the formal dinner parties at which the protocol was flawlessly maneuvered and conversation moved on stilts and the food was platitudinous; evenings of music to benefit a worthy cause (How papery the turkey always was at the buffet supper after the Grieg!); the tea parties to which one went obediently to placate old belles who had lost their looks and their husbands and the roles that, at their first assembly, they had assumed they would play forever. Well-mannered and patient, Onslager did his duty suavely, and he was seldom thrilled.

But these lavish, enormous midsummer dancing parties in the fabulous, foolish villas on Bellevue Avenue and along the Ocean Drive did make his backbone tingle, did make him glow. Even when he was dancing, or proposing a toast, or fetching a wrap for a woman who had found the garden air too cool, he always felt on these occasions that he was static, looking at a colossal *tableau vivant* that would vanish at the wave of a magic golden wand. He was bewitched by the women, by all those *soignée* or demure or jubilant or saucy or dreaming creatures in their caressing, airy dresses and their jewels whose priceless hearts flashed in the light from superb chandeliers. They seemed, these dancing, laughing incandescent goddesses, to move in inaccessible spheres; indeed, his wife, Priscilla, was transfigured, and, dancing with her, he was moon-struck. No matter how much he drank (the champagne of those evenings was invested with a special property—one tasted the grapes, and the grapes had come from celestial vineyards), he remained sober and amazed and, in spite of his amazement, so alert that he missed nothing and recorded everything. He did not fail to see, in looks and shrugs and the clicking of glasses, the genesis of certain adulteries, and the demise of others in a glance of contempt or an arrogant withdrawal. With the accuracy of the uninvolved bystander, he heard and saw amongst these incredible women moving in the aura of their heady perfume their majestic passions—tragic heartbreak, sublime fulfillment, dangerous jealousy, the desire to murder. When, on the next day, he had come back to earth, he would reason that his senses had devised a fiction to amuse his mind, and that in fact he had witnessed nothing grander than flirtations and impromptu pangs as ephemeral as the flowers in the supper room.

So, at the Paines' vast marble house that night, Onslager, aloof and beguiled as always, had found himself watching Beatrice Trueblood and Marten ten Brink with so much interest that whenever he could he guided his dancing partner near them, and if they left the ballroom for a breath of air on a bench beside a playing fountain, or for a glass of champagne, he managed, if he could do so without being uncivil to his interlocutor and without being observed by them, to excuse himself and follow. If he had stopped to think, this merciful and moral man would have been ashamed of his spying and eavesdropping, but morality was irrelevant to the spell that enveloped him. Besides, he felt invisible.

Consequently, he knew something about that evening that Priscilla did not know and that he had no intention of telling her, partly because she would not believe him, partly because she would be displeased at the schoolboyish (and parvenu) way he put in his time at balls. The fact was that the betrothed were having a quarrel. He heard not a word of it—not at the dance, that is—and he saw not a gesture or a grimace of anger, but he nevertheless knew surely, as he watched them dance together, that ten Brink was using every ounce of his strength not to shout, and to keep in check a whole menagerie of passions—fire-breathing dragons and bone-crushing serpents and sabretoothed tigers—and he knew also that Beatrice was running for dear life against the moment when they would be unleashed, ready to gobble her up. Her broad, wide-eyed, gentle face was so still it could have been a painting of a face that had been left behind when the woman who owned it had faded from view, and Bea's golden hand lay on ten Brink's white sleeve as tentatively as a butterfly. Her lover's face, on the other hand, was—Onslager wanted to say "writhing," and the long fingers of the hand that pressed against her back were splayed out and rigid, looking grafted onto the sunny flesh beneath the diaphanous blue stuff of her dress. He supposed that another observer might with justification have said that the man was animated and that his fiancée was becomingly engrossed in all he said, that ten Brink was in a state of euphoria as his wedding approached, while Beatrice moved in a wordless haze of happiness. He heard people admiringly remark on the compatibility of their good looks; they were said to look as if they were "dancing on air"; women thanked goodness that Mrs. Trueblood had come at last into a safe harbor, and men said that ten Brink was in luck.

As soon as the Onslagers and their guests had driven away from the ball and the last echo of the music had perished and the smell of roses had been drowned by the smell of the sea and the magic had started to wane from Onslager's blood, he began to doubt his observations. He was prepared to elide and then forget his heightened insights, as he had always done in the past. The group had come in two cars, and the Allinghams were with him and Priscilla on the short ride home. Lucy Allingham, whose own honeymoon was of late and blushing memory, said, with mock petulance, "I thought *young* love was supposed to be what caught the eye. But I never saw anything half so grand and wonderful as the looks of those two." And Priscilla said, "How true! How magnificently right you are, Lucy! They were radiant, both of them."

Late as it was, Priscilla proposed a last drink and a recapitulation of the party—everyone had found it a joy—but ten Brink said, "Beatrice and I want to go down and have a look at the waves, if you don't mind," and when no one minded but, on the contrary, fondly sped them on their pastoral way, the two walked down across the lawn and presently were gone from sight in the romantic mist. Their friends watched them and sighed, charmed, and went inside to drink a substitute for nectar.

Hours later (he looked at his watch and saw that it was close on five o'clock), Jack woke, made restless by something he had sensed or dreamed, and, going to the east windows of his bedroom to look at the water and see what the sailing would be like that day, he was arrested by the sight of Beatrice and Marten standing on the broad front steps below. They were still in their evening clothes. Beatrice's stance was tired; she looked bedraggled. They stood confronting each other beside the balustrade; ten Brink held her shoulders tightly, his sharp, handsome (but, thought Onslager suddenly, Mephistophelean) face bent down to hers.

"You mustn't think you can shut your mind to these things," he said. "You can't shut your ears to them." Their voices were clear in the hush of the last of the night.

"I am exhausted with talk, Marten," said Beatrice softly. "I will not hear another word."

An hour afterward, the fairest of days dawned on Newport, and Jack Onslager took out his sloop by himself in a perfect breeze, so that he saw none of his guests until just before lunch, when he joined them for cocktails on the lawn. Everyone was there except Beatrice Trueblood, who had slept straight through the morning but a moment before had called down from her windows that she was nearly ready. It was a flawless day to spend beside the sea: the chiaroscuro of the elm trees and the sun on the broad, buoyant lawn shifted as the sea winds disarrayed the leaves, and yonder, on the hyacinthine water, the whitecaps shuddered and the white sails swelled; to the left of the archipelago of chairs and tables where they sat, Mrs. Onslager's famous rosary was heavily in bloom with every shade of red there was and the subtlest hues of yellow, and her equally famous blue hydrangeas were at their zenith against the house, exactly the color of this holiday sky, so large they nodded on their stems like drowsing heads.

The Allinghams, newly out of their families' comfortable houses in St. Louis and now living impecuniously in a railroad flat in New York that they found both adventurous and odious, took in the lawn and

seascape with a look of real greed, and even of guile, on their faces, as if
they planned to steal something or eat forbidden fruit.

In its pleasurable fatigue from the evening before and too much sleep
this morning, the gathering was momentarily disinclined to conversation,
and they all sat with faces uplifted and eyes closed against the sun. They
listened to the gulls and terns shrieking with their evergreen gluttony;
they heard the buzz-saw rasp of outboard motors and the quick, cleaving
roar of an invisible jet; they heard automobiles on the Ocean Drive, a
power mower nasally shearing the grass at the house next door, and from
that house they heard, as well, the wail of an infant and the panicky barking of an infant dog.

"I wish this day would never end," said Lucy Allingham. "This is
the kind of day when you want to kiss the earth. You want to have an
affair with the sky."

"Don't be maudlin, Lucy," said her husband. "And above all, don't
be inaccurate." He was a finicking young cub who had been saying things
like this all weekend.

Onslager's own wife, just as foolishly euphoric but with a good deal
more style, simply through being older, said, "Look, here comes Beatrice.
She looks as if her eyes were fixed on the Garden of Eden before the Fall
and as if she were being serenaded by angels."

Marten ten Brink, an empiricist not given to flights of fancy, said, "Is
that a depth bomb I hear?"

No one answered him, for everyone was watching Beatrice as she
came slowly, smiling, down the stone steps from the terrace and across
the lawn, dulcifying the very ground she walked upon. She was accompanied by Mrs. Onslager's two Siamese cats, who cantered ahead of her,
then stopped, forgetful of their intention, and closely observed the life
among the blades of grass, then frolicked on, from time to time emitting
that ugly parody of a human cry that is one of the many facets of the
Siamese cat's scornful nature. But the insouciant woman paid no attention
to them, even when they stopped to fight each other, briefly, with noises
straight from Hell.

"You look as fresh as dew, dear," said Priscilla. "Did you simply
sleep and sleep?"

"Where on earth did you get that fabric?" asked Mrs. Herbert.
"Surely not here. It must have come from Paris. Bea, I do declare your
clothes are always the ones I want for myself."

"Sit here, Beatrice," said ten Brink, who had stood up and was indicating the chair next to himself. But Beatrice, ignoring him, chose another chair. The cats, still flirting with her, romped at her feet; one of
them pretended to find a sporting prey between her instep and her heel,
and he pounced and buck-jumped silently, his tail a fast fierce whip.
Beatrice, who delighted in these animals, bent down to stroke the lean

flanks of the other one, momentarily quiescent in a glade of sunshine.

"What do you think of the pathetic fallacy, Mrs. Trueblood?" said Peter Allingham, addressing her averted head. "Don't you think it's pathetic?" By now, Onslager was wishing to do him bodily harm for his schoolmasterish teasing of Lucy.

"Monkeys," murmured Beatrice to the cats. "Darlings."

"Beatrice!" said Marten ten Brink sharply, and strode across to whisper something in her ear. She brushed him away as if he were a fly, and she straightened up and said to Priscilla Onslager, "Why is everyone so solemn? Are you doing a charade of a Quaker meeting?"

"Solemn?" said Priscilla, with a laugh. "If we seem solemn, it's because we're all smitten with this day. Isn't it supreme? Heaven can't possibly be nicer."

"Is this a new game?" asked Beatrice, puzzled, her kind eyes on her hostess's face.

"Is what a new game, dear?"

"What *is* going on?" She had begun to be ever so slightly annoyed. "Is it some sort of silence test? We're to see if we can keep still till teatime? Is it that? I'll be delighted—only, for pity's sake, tell me the rules and the object."

"Silence test! Sweetheart, you're still asleep. Give her a Martini, Jack," said Priscilla nervously, and to divert the attention of the company from her friend's quixotic mood she turned to ten Brink. "I believe you're right," she said, "I believe they're detonating depth bombs. Why on Sunday? I thought sailors got a day of rest like everybody else."

A deep, rumbling subterranean thunder rolled, it seemed, beneath the chairs they sat on.

"It sounds like ninepins in the Catskills," said Priscilla.

"I never could abide that story," said Mary Herbert. "Or the Ichabod Crane one, either."

Jack Onslager, his back toward the others as he poured a drink for Beatrice, observed to himself that the trying thing about these weekends was not the late hours, not the overeating and the overdrinking and the excessive batting of tennis balls and shuttlecocks; it was, instead, this kind of aimless prattle that never ceased. There seemed to exist, on weekends in the country, a universal terror of pauses in conversation, so that it was imperative for Mary Herbert to drag in Washington Irving by the hair of his irrelevant head. Beatrice Trueblood, however, was not addicted to prattle, and he silently congratulated her on the way, in the last few minutes, she had risen above their fatuous questions and compliments. That woman was as peaceful as a pool in the heart of a forest. He turned to her, handing her the drink and looking directly into her eyes (blue and green, like an elegant tropic sea), and he said, "I have never seen you looking prettier."

For just a second, a look of alarm usurped her native and perpetual calm, but then she said, "So you're playing it, too. I don't think it's fair not to tell me—unless this is a joke on me. Am I 'it'?"

At last, Jack was unsettled; Priscilla was really scared; ten Brink was angry, and, getting up again to stand over her like a prosecuting attorney interrogating a witness of bad character, he said, "You're not being droll, Beatrice, you're being tiresome."

Mrs. Onslager said, "Did you go swimming this morning, lamb? Perhaps you got water in your ears. Lean over—see, like this," and she bent her head low to the left and then to the right while Beatrice, to whom these calisthenics were inexplicable, watched her, baffled.

Beatrice put her drink on the coffee table, and she ran her forefingers around the shells of her ears. What was the look that came into her face, spreading over it as tangibly as a blush? Onslager afterward could not be sure. At the time he had thought it was terror; he had thought this because, in the confusion that ensued, he had followed, sheeplike with the others, in his wife's lead. But later, when he recaptured it for long reflection, he thought that it had not been terror, but rather that Priscilla in naming it that later was actually speaking of the high color of her own state of mind, and that the look in Beatrice's eyes and on her mouth had been one of revelation, as if she had opened a door and had found behind it a new world so strange, so foreign to all her knowledge and her experience and the history of her senses, that she had spoken only approximately when, in a far, soft, modest voice, she said, "I am deaf. That explains it."

*   *   *

[Onslager visits Beatrice at her apartment months later and communicates by writing notes.]

"Tell me about it," he wrote, and again he felt like a fool.

It was not the deafness itself that scared her, she said—not the fear of being run down by an automobile she had not heard or violated by an intruder whose footfall had escaped her. These anxieties, which beset Priscilla, did not touch Beatrice. Nor had she yet begun so very much to miss voices or other sounds she liked; it was a little unnerving, she said, never to know if the telephone was ringing, and it was strange to go into the streets and see the fast commotion and hear not a sound, but it had its comic side and it had its compensations—it amused her to see the peevish snapping of a dog whose bark her deafness had forever silenced, she was happy to be spared her neighbors' vociferous television sets. But she was scared all the same. What had begun to harry her was that her wish to be deaf had been granted. This was exactly how she put it, and Onslager received her secret uneasily. She had not bargained for banishment, she said; she had only wanted a holiday. Now, though, she felt that the Devil lived with her, eternally wearing a self-congratulatory smile.

"You are being fanciful," Onslager wrote, although he did not think she was at all fanciful. "You can't wish yourself deaf."

But Beatrice insisted that she *had* done just that.

She emphasized that she had *elected* to hear no more, would not permit of accident, and ridiculed the doting Priscilla's sentimental fate. She had done it suddenly and out of despair, and she was sorry now. "I am ashamed. It was an act of cowardice," she said.

"How cowardice?" wrote Onslager.

"I could have broken with Marten in a franker way. I could simply have told him I had changed my mind. I didn't have to make him mute by making myself deaf."

"Was there a quarrel?" he wrote, knowing already the question was superfluous.

"Not *a* quarrel. An incessant wrangle. Marten is jealous and he is indefatigably vocal. I wanted terribly to marry him—I don't suppose I loved him much but he seemed good, seemed safe. But all of a sudden I thought, I cannot and I will not listen to another word. And now I'm sorry because I'm so lonely here, inside my skull. Not hearing makes one helplessly egocentric."

She hated any kind of quarrel, she said—she shuddered at raised voices and quailed before looks of hate—but she could better endure a howling brawl amongst vicious hoodlums, a shrill squabble of shrews, a degrading jangle between servant and mistress, than she could the least altercation between a man and a woman whose conjunction had had as its origin tenderness and a concord of desire. A relationship that was predicated upon love was far too delicate of composition to be threatened by cross-purposes. There were houses where she would never visit again because she had seen a husband and wife in ugly battle dress; there were restaurants she went to unwillingly because in them she had seen lovers in harsh dispute. How could things ever be the same between them again? How could two people possibly continue to associate with each other after such humiliating, disrobing displays?

As Beatrice talked in discreet and general terms and candidly met Jack Onslager's eyes, in another part of her mind she was looking down the shadowy avenue of all the years of her life. As a girl and, before that, as a child, in the rambling, shambling house in St. Louis, Beatrice in her bedroom doing her lessons would hear a rocking chair on a squeaking board two flights down; this was the chair in which her tipsy mother seesawed, dressed for the street and wearing a hat, drinking gin and humming a Venetian barcarole to which she had forgotten the words. Her mother drank from noon, when, with lamentations, she got up, till midnight, when, the bottle dry, she fell into a groaning, nightmare-ridden unconsciousness that resembled the condition immediately preceding death. This mortal sickness was terrifying; her removal from reality was an ordeal for everyone, but not even the frequent and flamboyant threats of suicide, the sobbed proclamations that she was the chief of sinners, not all the excruciating embarrassments that were created by that interminable and joyless spree, were a fraction as painful as the daily quarrels that commenced as soon as her father came home, just before six, and continued, unmitigated, until he—a methodical man, despite his unfathomable spleen—went to bed, at ten. Dinner, nightly, was a hideous experience for a child, since the parents were not inhibited by their children or the maid and went on heaping atrocious abuse upon each other, using sarcasm, threats, lies—every imaginable expression of loathing and contempt. They swam in their own blood, but it was an ocean that seemed to foster and nourish them; their awful wounds were their necessities. Freshly appalled each evening, unforgiving, disgraced, Beatrice miserably pushed her food about on her plate, never hungry, and often she imagined herself alone on a desert, far away from any human voice. The moment the meal was finished, she fled to her schoolbooks, but even when she put her fingers in her ears, she could hear her parents raving, whining, bullying, laughing horrible, malign laughs. Sometimes, in counterpoint to this vendetta, another would start in the kitchen, where the impudent and slatternly maid and one of her lovers would ask *their* cross questions and give crooked answers.

In spite of all this hatefulness, Beatrice did not mistrust marriage, and, moreover, she had faith in her own even temper. She was certain that sweetness could put an end to strife; she believed that her tolerance was limitless, and she vowed that when she married there would be no quarrels.

But there were. The dew in her eyes as a bride gave way nearly at once to a glaze when she was a wife. She left home at twenty, and at twenty-one married Tom Trueblood, who scolded her for seven years. Since she maintained that it took two to make a quarrel, she tried in the beginning, with all the cleverness and fortitude she had, to refuse to be a party to the storms that rocked her house and left it a squalid shambles, but her silence only made her husband more passionately angry, and at last, ripped and raw, she had to defend herself. Her dignity trampled to death, her honor mutilated, she fought back, and felt estranged from the very principles of her being. Like her parents, Tom Trueblood was sustained by rancor and contentiousness; he really seemed to love these malevolent collisions which made her faint and hot and ill, and he seemed, moreover, to regard them as essential to the married state, and so, needing them, he would not let Beatrice go but tricked and snared her and strewed her path with obstacles, until finally she had been obliged to run away and melodramatically leave behind a note.

Beatrice was a reticent woman and had too much taste to bare all these grubby secret details, but she limned a general picture for him and, when she had finished, she said, "Was it any wonder, then, that when the first blush wore off and Marten showed himself to be cantankerous my heart sank?"

Onslager had listened to her with dismay. He and Priscilla were not blameless of the sin she so deplored—no married people were—but their differences were minor and rare and guarded, their sulks were short-lived. Poor, poor Beatrice, he thought. Poor lamb led to the slaughter.

He wrote, "Have you heard from Marten?"

She nodded, and closed her eyes in a dragging weariness. "He has written me volumes," she said. "In the first place, he doesn't believe that I am deaf but thinks it's an act. He says I am indulging myself, but he is willing to forgive me if I will only come to my senses. Coming to my senses involves, among other things, obliterating the seven years I lived with Tom—I told you he was madly jealous? But how do you amputate experience? How do you eliminate what intransigently *was?*"

"If that's Marten's line," wrote Onslager, revolted by such childishness, "obviously you can't give him a second thought. The question is what's to be done about *you?*"

"Oh, I don't know, I *do* not know!" There were tears in her voice, and she clasped her hands to hide their trembling. "I am afraid that I am too afraid ever to hear again. And you see how I speak as if I had a choice?"

Now she was frankly wringing her hands, and the terror in her face was sheer. "My God, the mind is diabolical!" she cried. "Even in someone as simple as I."

The stifling day was advancing into the stifling evening, and Jack Onslager, wilted by heat and unmanned by his futile pity, wanted, though he admired and loved her, to leave her. There was nothing he could do.

She saw this, and said, "You must go. Tomorrow I am starting with an analyst. Reassure Priscilla. Tell her I know that everything is going to be all right. I know it not because I am naïve but because I *still* have faith in the kindness of life." He could not help thinking that it was will instead of faith that put these words in her mouth.

And, exteriorly, everything was all right for Beatrice. Almost at once, when she began treatment with a celebrated man, her friends began to worry less, and to marvel more at her strength and the wholeness of her worthy soul and the diligence with which she and the remarkable doctor hunted down her troublesome quarry. During this time, she went about socially, lent herself to conversation by reading lips, grew even prettier. Her analysis was a dramatic success, and after a little more than a year she regained her hearing. Some months later, she married a man, Arthur Talbot, who was far gayer than Marten ten Brink and far less rich; indeed, a research chemist, he was poor. Priscilla deplored this aspect of him, but she was carried away by the romance (he looked like a poet, he adored Beatrice) and at last found it in her heart to forgive him for being penniless.

When the Talbots came to Newport for a long weekend not long after they had married, Jack Onslager watched them both with care. No mention had ever been made by either Jack or Beatrice of their conversation on that summer afternoon, and when his wife, who had now become a fervent supporter of psychiatry, exclaimed after the second evening that she had never seen Beatrice so radiant, Onslager agreed with her. Why not? There would be no sense in quarrelling with his happy wife. He himself had never seen a face so drained of joy, or even of the memory of joy; he had not been able to meet Bea's eyes.

That Sunday—it was again a summer day beside the sea—Jack Onslager came to join his two guests, who were sitting alone on the lawn. Their backs were to him and they did not hear his approach, so Talbot did not lower his voice when he said to his wife, "I have told you a thousand times that my life has to be exactly as I want it. So stop these hints. *Any* dedicated scientist worth his salt is bad-tempered."

Beatrice saw that her host had heard him; she and Onslager travailed in the brief look they exchanged. It was again an enrapturing day. The weather overhead was fair and bland, but the water was a mass of little wrathful whitecaps.

Character Disorder: The Compromise with Reality

III. The last major category of diagnosis centers around the concept of character. During the course of their lives, the affected persons, rather than developing some symptom such as an hallucination or a paralysis, develop an alteration in their character structure that systematically modifies their modes of interaction with reality. The types of character disorder represent an attempt at classification based on styles of behavior or styles of thought. These types or styles of thinking, feeling, and acting are considered sick or pathological when measured against the customs or norms of the society in which they occur. Often the affected person does not see these qualities as a symptom, as something foreign or strange, appropriate to bring to some helping person's attention as he might, for example, react to a conversion symptom.

For example, the sociopath does not ordinarily regard his antisocial acts as symptoms; if anything, he probably sees them as pranks or crimes to be hidden from the authorities. The paranoid personality doesn't consider his suspicious nature inappropriate; ordinarily he believes himself wiser and more careful, more sensitive to the dangers of life than his neighbors. The schizoid person is not apt to realize that his withdrawal into the world of imagination and his aloofness are dangerous to his well-being. Nonetheless, these special types of thinking and behavior pervade the affected person's life and act as an organizing force and quality, compromising his responses to and interactions with the world of reality.

One of the most typical disorders of character is the compulsive. This special ritualized behavior and way of thinking affects every aspect of life, monitoring relationships to people, to work, and to ideas. Gogol's justly famous story "The Overcoat" illustrates with moving skill the remarkable manner in which this disorder of character can make of a man's life a blind alley. However, Gogol's allegorical genius has not stopped at a psychopathological portrait; his hero, Akaky Akakyevitch, rises to the level of integrity, if not to nobility, within the confines of his disorder. Here we catch an unusual glimpse of a certain positive value, an adaptive value to a pathetic life style.

THE OVERCOAT

Nicolai Gogol   (1809–1852)

In the department of . . . but I had better not mention in what department. There is nothing in the world more readily moved to wrath than a department, a regiment, a government office, and in fact any sort of official body. Nowadays every private individual considers all society insulted in his person. I have been told that very lately a petition

"The Overcoat," by Nicolai Gogol. Translated by Constance Garnett. Reprinted by permission of David Garnett. Published by Chatto & Windus, Ltd., London.

was handed in from a police-captain of what town I don't recollect, and that in this petition he set forth clearly that the institutions of the State were in danger and that its sacred name was being taken in vain; and, in proof thereof, he appended to his petition an enormously long volume of some work of romance in which a police-captain appeared on every tenth page, occasionally, indeed, in an intoxicated condition. And so, to avoid any unpleasantness, we had better call the department of which we are speaking a certain department.

And so, in a certain department there was a government clerk; a clerk of whom it cannot be said that he was very remarkable; he was short, somewhat pock-marked, with rather reddish hair and rather dim, bleary eyes, with a small bald patch on the top of his head, with wrinkles on both sides of his cheeks and the sort of complexion which is usually associated with hemorrhoids . . . no help for that, it is the Petersburg climate. As for his grade in the service (for among us the grade is what must be put first), he was what is called a perpetual titular councillor, a class at which, as we all know, various writers who indulge in the praiseworthy habit of attacking those who cannot defend themselves jeer and jibe to their hearts content. This clerk's surname was Bashmatchkin. From the very name it is clear that it must have been derived from a shoe (*bashmak*); but when and under what circumstances it was derived from a shoe, it is impossible to say. Both his father and his grandfather and even his brother-in-law, and all the Bashmatchkins without exception wore boots, which they simply re-soled two or three times a year. His name was Akaky Akakyevitch. Perhaps it may strike the reader as a rather strange and far-fetched name, but I can assure him that it was not far-fetched at all, that the circumstances were such that it was quite out of the question to give him any other name. Akaky Akakyevitch was born towards nightfall, if my memory does not deceive me, on the twenty-third of March. His mother, the wife of a government clerk, a very good woman, made arrangements in due course to christen the child. She was still lying in bed, facing the door, while on her right hand stood the godfather, an excellent man called Ivan Ivanovitch Yeroshkin, one of the head clerks in the Senate, and the godmother, the wife of a police official, and a woman of rare qualities, Arina Semyonovna Byelobryushkov. Three names were offered to the happy mother for selection—Moky, Sossy, or the name of the martyr Hozdazat. "No," thought the poor lady, "they are all such names!" To satisfy her, they opened the calendar at another place, and the names which turned up were: Trifily, Dula, Varahasy. "What an infliction!" said the mother. "What names they all are! I really never heard such names. Varadat or Varuh would be bad enough, but Trifily and Varahasy!" They turned over another page and the names were: Pavsikahy and Vahtisy. "Well, I see," said the mother, "it is clear that it is his fate. Since that is how it is, he had better be called after his father, his father is Akaky, let the son be Akaky, too." This was how he came to be Akaky Akakyevitch. The baby was christened and cried and made wry faces during the ceremony, as though he foresaw that he would be a titular councillor. So that was how it all came to pass. We have recalled it here so that the reader may see for himself that it happened quite inevitably and that to give him any other name was out of the question. No one has been able to remember when and how long ago he entered the department, nor who gave him the job. However many directors and higher officials of all sorts came and went, he was always seen in the same place, in the same position, at the very same duty, precisely the same copying clerk, so that they used to declare that he must have been born a copying clerk in uniform all complete and with a bald patch on his head. No respect at all was shown him in the department. The porters, far from getting up from their seats when he came in, took no more notice of him than if a simple fly had flown across the vestibule. His superiors treated him with a sort of domineering chilliness. The head clerk's assistant used to throw papers under his nose without even saying: "Copy this" or "Here is an interesting, nice little case" or some agreeable remark of the sort, as is usually done in well-behaved offices. And he would take it, gazing only at the paper without looking to see who had put it there and whether he had the right to do so: he would take it and at once set to work to copy it. The young clerks jeered and made jokes at him to the best of their clerkly wit, and told before his face all sorts of stories of their own invention about him; they would say of his landlady, an old woman of seventy, that she beat him, would enquire when the wedding was to take place, and would scatter bits of paper on his head, calling them snow. Akaky Akakyevitch never answered a word, however, but behaved as though there were no one there. It had no influence on his work even; in the midst of all this teasing, he never made a single mistake in his copying. Only when the jokes were too unbearable, when they jolted his arm and prevented him from going on with his work, he would bring out: "Leave me alone! Why do you insult me?" and there was something strange in the words and in the voice in which they were uttered. There was a note in it of something that aroused compassion, so that one young man, new to the office, who, following the example of the rest, had allowed himself to mock at him, suddenly stopped as though cut to the heart, and from that time forth, everything was, as it were, changed and appeared in a different light to him. Some unnatural force seemed to thrust him away from the companions with whom he had become acquainted, accepting them as well-bred, polished people. And long afterwards, at moments of the greatest gaiety, the figure of the humble little clerk with a bald patch on his head rose before him with his heart-rending words: "Leave me alone! Why do you insult me?" and in those heart-rending words he heard others: "I am your brother." And the poor young man hid his face in his hands, and many times afterwards in his life he shuddered, seeing how much inhumanity there is in man, how much savage brutality lies hidden under refined, cultured politeness, and, my God! even in a man whom the world accepts as a gentleman and a man of honor. . . .

It would be hard to find a man who lived in his work as did Akaky Akakyevitch. To say that he was zealous in his work is not enough; no, he loved his work. In it, in that copying, he found a varied and agreeable world of his own. There was a look of enjoyment on his face; certain letters were favorites with him, and when he came to them he was delighted; he chuckled to himself and winked and moved his lips, so that it seemed as though every letter his pen was forming could be read in his face. If rewards had been given according to the measure of zeal in the service, he might to his amazement have even found himself a civil councillor; but all he gained in the service, as the wits, his fellow-clerks expressed it, was a buckle in his button-hole and a pain in his back. It cannot be said, however, that no notice had ever been taken of him. One director, being a good-natured man and anxious to reward him for his long service, sent him something a little more important than his ordinary copying; he was instructed from a finished document to make some sort of report for another office; the work consisted only of altering the headings and in places changing the first person into the third. This cost him such an effort that it threw him into a regular perspiration: he mopped his brow and said at last, "No, better let me copy something."

From that time forth they left him to go on copying for ever. It seemed as though nothing in the world existed for him outside his copying. He gave no thought at all to his clothes; his uniform was—well, not green but some sort of rusty, muddy color. His collar was very short and narrow, so that, although his neck was not particularly long, yet, standing out of the collar, it looked as immensely long as those of the plaster kittens that wag their heads and are carried about on trays on the heads of dozens of foreigners living in Russia. And there were always things sticking to his uniform, either bits of hay or threads; moreover, he had a special art of passing under a window at the very moment when various rubbish was being flung out into the street, and so was continually carrying off bits of melon rind and similar litter on his hat. He had never once in his life noticed what was being done and going on in the street, all those things at which, as we all know, his colleagues, the young clerks, always stare, carrying their sharp sight so far even as to notice anyone on the other side of the pavement with a trouser strap hanging loose—a detail which always calls forth a sly grin. Whatever Akaky Akakyevitch looked at, he saw nothing anywhere but his clear, evenly written lines, and only perhaps when a horse's head suddenly appeared from nowhere just on his shoulder, and its nostrils blew a perfect gale upon his cheek, did he notice that he was not in the middle of his writing, but rather in the middle of the street.

On reaching home, he would sit down at once to the table, hurriedly sup his soup and eat a piece of beef with an onion; he did not notice the taste at all, but ate it all up together with the flies and anything else that Providence chanced to send him. When he felt that his stomach was beginning to be full, he would rise up from the table, get out a bottle of ink and set to copying the papers he had brought home with him. When he had none to do, he would make a copy expressly for his own pleasure, particularly if the document were remarkable not for the beauty of its style but for the fact of its being addressed to some new or important personage.

Even at those hours when the grey Petersburg sky is completely overcast and the whole population of clerks have dined and eaten their fill, each as best he can, according to the salary he receives and his personal tastes; when they are all resting after the scratching of pens and bustle of the office, their own necessary work and other people's, and all the tasks that an over-zealous man voluntarily sets himself even beyond what is necessary; when the clerks are hastening to devote what is left of their time to pleasure; some more enterprising are flying to the theatre, others to the street to spend their leisure, staring at women's hats, some to spend the evening paying compliments to some attractive girl, the star of a little official circle, while some—and this is the most frequent of all— go simply to a fellow-clerk's flat on the third or fourth storey, two little rooms with an entry or a kitchen, with some pretensions to style, with a lamp or some such article that has cost many sacrifices of dinners and excursions—at the time when all the clerks are scattered about the little flats of their friends, playing a tempestuous game of whist, sipping tea out of glasses to the accompaniment of farthing rusks, sucking in smoke from long pipes, telling, as the cards are dealt, some scandal that has floated down from higher circles, a pleasure which the Russian can never by any possibility deny himself, or, when there is nothing better to talk about, repeating the everlasting anecdote of the commanding officer who was told that the tail had been cut off his horse on the Falconet monument— in short, even when every one was eagerly seeking entertainment, Akaky Akakyevitch did not give himself up to any amusement. No one could say that they had ever seen him at an evening party. After working to his heart's content, he would go to bed, smiling at the thought of the next day and wondering what God would send him to copy. So flowed on the peaceful life of a man who knew how to be content with his fate on a salary of four hundred rubles, and so perhaps it would have flowed on to extreme old age, had it not been for the various calamities that bestrew the path through life, not only of titular, but even of privy, actual court and all other councillors, even those who neither give counsel to others nor accept it themselves.

There is in Petersburg a mighty foe of all who receive a salary of four hundred rubles or about that sum. That foe is none other than our northern frost, although it is said to be very good for the health. Between eight and nine in the morning, precisely at the hour when the streets are full of clerks going to their departments, the frost begins giving such sharp and stinging flips at all their noses indiscriminately that the poor fellows don't know what to do with them. At that time, when even those in the higher grade have a pain in their brows and tears in their eyes from the frost, the poor titular councillors are sometimes almost defenceless. Their only protection lies in running as fast as they can through five or six streets in a wretched, thin little overcoat and then warming their feet thoroughly in the porter's room, till all their faculties and qualifications for their various duties thaw again after being frozen on the way. Akaky Akakyevitch had for some time been feeling that his back and shoulders were particularly nipped by the cold, although he did try to run the regular distance as fast as he could. He wondered at last whether there were any defects in his overcoat. After examining it thoroughly in the privacy of his home, he discovered that in two or three places, to wit on the back and the shoulders, it had become a regular sieve; the cloth was so worn that you could see through it and the lining was coming out. I must observe that Akaky Akakyevitch's overcoat had also served as a butt for the jibes of the clerks. It had even been deprived of the honorable name of overcoat and had been referred to as the "dressing jacket." It was indeed of rather a strange make. Its collar had been growing smaller year by year as it served to patch the other parts. The patches were not good specimens of the tailor's art, and they certainly looked clumsy and ugly. On seeing what was wrong, Akaky Akakyevitch decided that he would have to take the overcoat to Petrovitch, a tailor who lived on a fourth storey up a back staircase, and, in spite of having only one eye and being pock-marked all over his face, was rather successful in repairing the trousers and coats of clerks and others—that is, when he was sober, be it understood, and had no other enterprise in his mind. Of this tailor I ought not, of course, to say much, but since it is now the rule that the character of every person in a novel must be completely drawn, well, there is no help for it, here is Petrovitch too. At first he was called simply Grigory, and was a serf belonging to some gentleman or other. He began to be called Petrovitch from the time that he got his freedom and began to drink rather heavily on every holiday, at first only on the chief holidays, but afterwards on all church holidays indiscriminately, wherever there is a cross in the calendar. On that side he was true to the customs of his forefathers, and when he quarreled with his wife used to call her "a worldly woman and a German." Since we have now mentioned the wife, it will be necessary to say a few words about her too, but unfortunately not much is known about her, except indeed that Petrovitch had a wife and that she wore a cap and not a kerchief, but apparently she could not boast of beauty; anyway, none but soldiers of the Guards peeped under her cap when they met her, and they twitched their moustaches and gave vent to a rather peculiar sound.

As he climbed the stairs leading to Petrovitch's—which, to do them justice, were all soaked with water and slops and saturated through and through with that smell of spirits which makes the eyes smart, and is, as we all know, inseparable from the backstairs of Petersburg houses—Akaky Akakyevitch was already wondering how much Petrovitch would ask for the job, and inwardly resolving not to give more than two rubles. The door was open, for Petrovitch's wife was frying some fish and had so filled the kitchen with smoke that you could not even see the black-beetles. Akaky Akakyevitch crossed the kitchen unnoticed by the good woman, and walked at last into a room where he saw Petrovitch sitting on a big, wooden, unpainted table with his legs tucked under him like a Turkish Pasha. The feet, as is usual with tailors when they sit at work, were bare; and the first object that caught Akaky Akakyvitch's eye was the big toe, with which he was already familiar, with a misshapen nail as thick and strong as the shell of a tortoise. Round Petrovitch's neck hung a skein of silk and another of thread and on his knees was a rag of some sort. He had for the last three minutes been trying to thread his needle, but could not get the thread into the eye and so was very angry with the dark-ness and indeed with the thread itself, muttering in an undertone: "It won't go in, the savage! You wear me out, you rascal." Akaky Akakye-vitch was vexed that he had come just at the minute when Petrovitch was in a bad humor; he liked to give him an order when he was a little "elevated," or, as his wife expressed it, "had fortified himself with fizz, the one-eyed devil." In such circumstances Petrovitch was as a rule very ready to give way and agree, and invariably bowed and thanked him, in-deed. Afterwards, it is true, his wife would come wailing that her hus-band had been drunk and so had asked too little, but adding a single ten-kopeck piece would settle that. But on this occasion Petrovitch was apparently sober and consequently curt, unwilling to bargain, and the devil knows what price he would be ready to lay on. Akaky Akakyevitch perceived this, and was, as the saying is, beating a retreat, but things had gone too far, for Petrovitch was screwing up his solitary eye very atten-tively at him and Akaky Akakyevitch involuntarily brought out: "Good day, Petrovitch!" "I wish you a good day, sir," said Petrovitch, and squinted at Akaky Akakyevitch's hands, trying to discover what sort of goods he had brought.

"Here I have come to you, Petrovitch, do you see . . . !"

It must be noticed that Akaky Akakyevitch for the most part explained himself by apologies, vague phrases, and particles which have absolutely no significance whatever. If the subject were a very difficult one, it was his habit indeed to leave his sentences quite unfinished, so that very often after a sentence had begun with the words, "It really is, don't you know . . ." nothing at all would follow and he himself would be quite oblivious, supposing he had said all that was necessary.

"What is it?" said Petrovitch, and at the same time with his solitary eye he scrutinized his whole uniform from the collar to the sleeves, the back, the skirts, the button-holes—with all of which he was very familiar, they were all his own work. Such scrutiny is habitual with tailors, it is the first thing they do on meeting one.

"It's like this, Petrovitch . . . the overcoat, the cloth . . . you see everywhere else it is quite strong; it's a little dusty and looks as though it were old, but it is new and it is only in one place just a little . . . on the back, and just a little worn on one shoulder and on this shoulder, too, a little . . . do you see? that's all, and it's not much work. . . ."

Petrovitch took the "dressing jacket," first spread it out over the table, examined it for a long time, shook his head and put his hand out to the window for a round snuff-box with a portrait on the lid of some general—which precisely I can't say, for a finger had been thrust through the spot where a face should have been, and the hole had been pasted up with a square bit of paper. After taking a pinch of snuff, Petrovitch held the "dressing jacket" up in his hands and looked at it against the light, and again he shook his head; then he turned it with the lining upwards and once more shook his head; again he took off the lid with the general pasted up with paper and stuffed a pinch into his nose, shut the box, put it away and at last said: "No, it can't be repaired; a wretched garment!" Akaky Akakyevitch's heart sank at those words.

"Why can't it, Petrovitch?" he said, almost in the imploring voice of a child. "Why, the only thing is it is a bit worn on the shoulders; why, you have got some little pieces. . . ."

"Yes, the pieces will be found all right," said Petrovitch, "but it can't be patched, the stuff is quite rotten; if you put a needle in it, it would give way."

"Let it give way, but you just put a patch on it."

"There is nothing to put a patch on. There is nothing for it to hold on to; there is a great strain on it, it is not worth calling cloth, it would fly away at a breath of wind."

"Well, then, strengthen it with something—upon my word, really, this is . . . !"

"No," said Petrovitch resolutely, "there is nothing to be done, the thing is no good at all. You had far better, when the cold winter weather comes, make yourself leg wrappings out of it, for there is no warmth in stockings, the Germans invented them just to make money." (Petrovitch was fond of a dig at the Germans occasionally.) "And as for the overcoat, it is clear that you will have to have a new one."

At the word "new" there was a mist before Akaky Akakyevitch's eyes, and everything in the room seemed blurred. He could see nothing clearly but the general with the piece of paper over his face on the lid of Petrovitch's snuff-box.

"A new one?" he said, still feeling as though he were in a dream; "why, I haven't the money for it."

"Yes, a new one," Petrovitch repeated with barbarous composure.

"Well, and if I did have a new one, how much would it . . . ?"

"You mean what will it cost?"

"Yes."

"Well, three fifty-ruble notes or more," said Petrovitch, and he compressed his lips significantly. He was very fond of making an effect, he was fond of suddenly disconcerting a man completely and then squinting sideways to see what sort of a face he made.

"A hundred and fifty rubles for an overcoat," screamed poor Akaky Akakyevitch—it was perhaps the first time he had screamed in his life, for he was always distinguished by the softness of his voice.

"Yes," said Petrovitch, "and even then it's according to the coat. If I were to put marten on the collar, and add a hood with silk linings, it would come to two hundred."

"Petrovitch, please," said Akaky Akakyevitch in an imploring voice, not hearing and not trying to hear what Petrovitch said, and missing all his effects, "do repair it somehow, so that it will serve a little longer."

"No, that would be wasting work and spending money for nothing," said Petrovitch, and after that Akaky Akakyevitch went away completely crushed, and when he had gone Petrovitch remained standing for a long time with his lips pursed up significantly before he took up his work again, feeling pleased that he had not demeaned himself nor lowered the dignity of the tailor's art.

When he got into the street, Akaky Akakyevitch was as though in a dream. "So that is how it is," he said to himself. "I really did not think it would be so . . ." and then after a pause he added, "So there it is! so that's how it is at last! and I really could never have supposed it would have been so. And there. . . ." There followed another long silence, after which he brought out: "So there it is! well, it really is so utterly unexpected . . . who would have thought . . . what a circumstance. . . ." Saying this, instead of going home he walked off in quite the opposite direction without suspecting what he was doing. On the way a clumsy sweep brushed the whole of his sooty side against him and blackened all his shoulder; a regular hatful of plaster scattered upon him from the top of a house that was being built. He noticed nothing of this, and only after he had jostled against a sentry who had set his halberd down beside him and was shaking some snuff out of his horn into his rough fist, he came to himself a little and then only because the sentry said: "Why are you poking yourself right in one's face, haven't you the pavement to yourself?" This made him look round and turn homeward; only there he began to collect his thoughts, to see his position in a clear and true light and began talking to himself no longer incoherently but reasonably and openly as with a sensible friend with whom one can discuss the most intimate and vital matters. "No, indeed," said Akaky Akakyevitch, "it is no use talking to Petrovitch now; just now he really is . . . his wife must have been giving it to him. I had better go to him on Sunday morning; after the Saturday evening he will be squinting and sleepy, so he'll want a little drink to carry it off and his wife won't give him a penny. I'll slip ten kopecks into his hand and then he will be more accommodating and maybe take the overcoat. . . ."

So reasoning with himself, Akaky Akakyevitch cheered up and waited until the next Sunday; then, seeing from a distance Petrovitch's wife leaving the house, he went straight in. Petrovitch certainly was very tipsy after the Saturday. He could hardly hold his head up and was very drowsy: but, for all that, as soon as he heard what he was speaking about, it seemed as though the devil had nudged him. "I can't," he said, "you must kindly order a new one." Akaky Akakyevitch at once slipped a ten-kopeck piece into his hand. "I thank you, sir, I will have just a drop to your health, but don't trouble yourself about the overcoat; it is not a bit of good for anything. I'll make you a fine new coat, you can trust me for that."

Akaky Akakyevitch would have said more about repairs, but Petrovitch, without listening, said: "A new one now I'll make you without fail; you can rely upon that, I'll do my best. It could even be like the fashion that has come in with the collar to button with silver claws under appliqué."

Then Akaky Akakyevitch saw that there was no escape from a new overcoat and he was utterly depressed. How indeed, for what, with what money could he get it? Of course he could to some extent rely on the bonus for the coming holiday, but that money had long ago been appropriated and its use determined beforehand. It was needed for new trousers and to pay the cobbler an old debt for putting some new tops to some old boot-legs, and he had to order three shirts from a seamstress as well as two specimens of an under-garment which it is improper to mention in print; in short, all that money absolutely must be spent, and even if the director were to be so gracious as to assign him a gratuity of forty-five or even fifty, instead of forty rubles, there would be still left a mere trifle, which would be but as a drop in the ocean beside the fortune needed for an overcoat. Though, of course, he knew that Petrovitch had a strange craze for suddenly putting on the devil knows what enormous price, so

that at times his own wife could not help crying out: "Why, you are
out of your wits, you idiot! Another time he'll undertake a job for nothing, and here the devil has bewitched him to ask more than he is worth
himself." Though, of course, he knew that Petrovitch would undertake
to make it for eighty rubles, still where would he get those eighty rubles?
He might manage half of that sum; half of it could be found, perhaps
even a little more; but where could he get the other half? . . . But, first
of all, the reader ought to know where that first half was to be found.
Akaky Akakyevitch had the habit every time he spent a ruble of putting
aside two kopecks in a little locked-up box with a slit in the lid for slipping the money in. At the end of every half-year he would inspect the
pile of coppers there and change them for small silver. He had done this
for a long time, and in the course of many years the sum had mounted
up to forty rubles and so he had half the money in his hands, but where
was he to get the other half, where was he to get another forty rubles?
Akaky Akakyevitch pondered and pondered and decided at last that he
would have to diminish his ordinary expenses, at least for a year; give up
burning candles in the evening, and if he had to do anything he must go
into the landlady's room and work by her candle; that as he walked along
the streets he must walk as lightly and carefully as possible, almost on
tiptoe, on the cobbles and flagstones, so that his soles might last a little
longer than usual; that he must send his linen to the wash less frequently,
and that, to preserve it from being worn, he must take it off every day
when he came home and sit in a thin cotton-shoddy dressing-gown, a very
ancient garment which Time itself had spared. To tell the truth, he found
it at first rather hard to get used to these privations, but after a while it
became a habit and went smoothly enough—he even became quite accustomed to being hungry in the evening; on the other hand, he had spiritual
nourishment, for he carried ever in his thoughts the idea of his future
overcoat. His whole existence had in a sense become fuller, as though he
had married, as though some other person were present with him, as
though he were no longer alone, but an agreeable companion had consented to walk the path of life hand in hand with him, and that companion
was no other than the new overcoat with its thick wadding and its strong,
durable lining. He became, as it were, more alive, even more strong-
willed, like a man who has set before himself a definite aim. Uncertainty,
indecision, in fact all the hesitating and vague characteristics vanished from
his face and his manners. At times there was a gleam in his eyes, indeed,
the most bold and audacious ideas flashed through his mind. Why not
really have marten on the collar? Meditation on the subject always made
him absent-minded. On one occasion when he was copying a document,
he very nearly made a mistake, so that he almost cried out "ough" aloud
and crossed himself. At least once every month he went to Petrovitch to
talk about the overcoat, where it would be best to buy the cloth, and

what color it should be, and what price, and, though he returned home a little anxious, he was always pleased at the thought that at last the time was at hand when everything would be bought and the overcoat would be made. Things moved even faster than he had anticipated. Contrary to all expectations, the director bestowed on Akaky Akakyevitch a gratuity of no less than sixty rubles. Whether it was that he had an inkling that Akaky Akakyevitch needed a greatcoat, or whether it happened so by chance, owing to this he found he had twenty rubles extra. This circumstance hastened the course of affairs. Another two or three months of partial fasting and Akaky Akakyevitch had actually saved up nearly eighty rubles. His heart, as a rule very tranquil, began to throb. The very first day he set off in company with Petrovitch to the shops. They bought some very good cloth, and no wonder, since they had been thinking of it for more than six months before, and scarcely a month had passed without their going to the shop to compare prices; now Petrovitch himself declared that there was no better cloth to be had. For the lining they chose calico, but of a stout quality, which in Petrovitch's words was even better than silk, and actually as strong and handsome to look at. Marten they did not buy, because it certainly was dear, but instead they chose cat fur, the best to be found in the shop—cat which in the distance might almost be taken for marten. Petrovitch was busy over the coat for a whole fortnight, because there were a great many buttonholes, otherwise it would have been ready sooner. Petrovitch asked twelve rubles for the work; less than that it hardly could have been, everything was sewn with silk, with fine double seams, and Petrovitch went over every seam afterwards with his own teeth imprinting various figures with them. It was . . . it is hard to say precisely on what day, but probably on the most triumphant day of the life of Akaky Akakyevitch that Petrovitch at last brought the overcoat. . . .

CHAPTER two

The Struggle
with Impulse

The three major descriptive categories outlined and illustrated
in Chapter 1 are the foundations for differential diagnosis of
abnormal personality. Before erecting the rest of the complex
superstructure, a brief postponement is in order so as to consider
in a general way the factors that shape pathology. The etiology
or cause of psychological abnormality is not the principal focus
of this book, and only one aspect will be presented briefly
in the hope that it will alert the reader to some of the deeper
insights available in the literary selections.

Modern dynamic theories of personality suggest that
vital forces propel man's actions, and that his struggle for
control and expression of these "dynamisms" helps forge his
personality and character. These theories attempt to explain
man's thought and behavior as in part arising from interacting
forces which emanate from different biological, inter-personal,
conscious, and unconscious sources. There are many names
given to these "dynamisms": e.g., *instincts, drives, impulses,
motives, needs, tendencies, instinctual drives*. What the terms
have in common is that they all suggest some force within man
that drives him in some direction toward some goal. Behavior
in part reflects man's adaptation and adjustment to these forces
in terms of the opportunities and the restraints in his
environment. Society and its internalized representative,
conscience, may prevent certain forces from having free
expression while opening the floodgates to others. Personality
and behavioral disturbances are considered the resultant of
distorted attempts to deal with these drives.

Psychopathology, then, is an abnormal adaptation to the

dynamisms within, and the restraints and opportunities
without. The following examples illustrate the dominating
importance of the struggle with impulse.

a. Victor Hugo's abbe of *The Hunchback of Notre
Dame* has renounced the ordinary passions of life and is a
renowned priest and church scholar. Suddenly his ascetic
existence is threatened as the abbe is trapped between his
rekindled sexual wishes and all of his religious and moral
standards. His first effort to solve the conflict is to develop an
attitude of hatred and vengeance. The more he is aroused
sexually, the greater his need for vengeance becomes, and the
more he invokes the devil. Clearly his vengeful spirit in part
protects him from acknowledging his own frightening sexual
impulses. At last he succumbs and confronts Esmeralda, the
gypsy girl, in a last desperate confession of his lust.

The Hunchback of Notre Dame
Victor Hugo   (1802–1885)

. . . "Ah!" she cried, trembling convulsively and putting
her hands over her eyes: "It's the priest!" Then she dropped her arms
listlessly and sat down, staring at the floor, mute and still trembling. The
priest looked at her like a hawk which has circled for a long time high in
the sky over a poor lark cowering in the grass, silently narrowed the
circles of its flight, then suddenly pounced on its prey like a bolt of
lightning and gripped it panting in its claws.

She began to murmur softly, "Finish! Finish! Strike the last blow!"
She thrust her head down between her shoulders in terror, like a lamb
waiting for the butcher's cudgel to descend.

"Do I horrify you?" he asked finally. She did not answer. He repeated the question. Her lips contracted as if she were smiling. "The
executioner is mocking the condemned," she said. "The months he's
pursued me, threatened me, terrified me! If it weren't for him, oh, God,
how happy I'd be! He's the one who cast me into this abyss! He's the one
who killed . . . who killed him! My Phoebus!" She burst out sobbing,
raised her eyes to the priest and said, "Who are you? What have I done to
you? Why do you hate me so?"

"I love you!" cried the priest.

From *The Hunchback of Notre Dame* by Victor Hugo.

Her tears stopped abruptly. She stared at him, stupefied. He fell to his knees and looked at her with fiery eyes.

"Do you understand? I love you!" he cried once again.

"What love!" she exclaimed, shuddering.

"It's the love of the damned."

They both remained silent for several moments, crushed by the weight of their emotions, he frantic, she dazed. "Listen," he said at length, with a strange calmness which had come back to him, "I'll tell you everything. I'll tell you what until now I have hardly dared tell myself when I furtively questioned my conscience in those deep hours of the night when there are so many shadows that it seems as if God Himself no longer sees us. Listen: before I saw you I was happy."

"So was I!" she sighed weakly.

"Don't interrupt me. Yes, I was happy, or at least I thought I was. I was pure and my soul was full of limpid clarity. No one held his head more proudly than I. Priests consulted me on chastity and theologians on doctrine. Yes, knowledge was everything for me. More than once my flesh was aroused by the passing of a female form. The force of a man's sex and blood which, as a foolish adolescent, I thought I had smothered for life, had more than once convulsively shaken the chain of iron vows which attach me to the cold stones of the altar. But then fasting, prayer, study and the austerity of the cloister would make my soul once again master of my body. I shunned women. Also, I had only to open a book and all the impure vapors of my brain vanished before the splendor of science. After a few minutes I would feel the heavy things of the earth flying far away and I was calm again, dazzled and serene in the presence of the tranquil radiance of eternal truth. As long as the devil sent to attack me only vague shadows of women who passed before my eyes in the church or in the streets and who hardly ever entered my thoughts, I was able to overcome him easily. Alas, if I haven't maintained the victory it's God's fault for not making men and the devil of equal strength. Listen: one day. . . ." He stopped and she heard him heave a deep, painful sigh. He continued:

"One day I was looking out of the window of my cell. . . . What book was I reading then? Oh! All that's a whirl in my head. I was reading. The window overlooked the square. I heard the sound of a tambourine and music. Annoyed at being disturbed in my meditation, I looked down into the square. There were others looking at what I saw, yet it wasn't a sight made for human eyes. There, in the middle of the square—it was noon, bright sunlight—a creature was dancing. Such a beautiful creature that God would have preferred her to the Virgin Mary, would have chosen her for His mother and wanted to be born of her if she had existed when He made Himself a man! Her eyes were black and splendid; some of her black hair shone in the sunlight like threads of gold. Her feet vanished in their movement like the spokes of a rapidly turning wheel. Around her head, in her black tresses, there were pieces of metal which sparkled in the sunlight and formed a crown of stars on her forehead. Her arms, lithe and brown, clasped and unclasped themselves around her waist like two scarves. The form of her body was amazingly beautiful. Oh, that resplendent form, which stood out like something luminous in the light of the sun itself! Alas, dear girl, it was you. . . . Surprised, intoxicated, fascinated, I stood there looking at you. I watched you so intently that suddenly I shivered with fright, for I felt that fate had seized me."

Overcome, the priest stopped again for a moment. Then he went on: "Half spellbound already, I clutched for something to break my fall, I reminded myself of the traps which Satan had set for me before. The creature before my eyes had that superhuman beauty which can come only from either heaven or hell. She was not simply a girl made from our common clay and poorly illuminated inside by the flickering light of a woman's soul. She was an angel! But an angel of flame, not of light. Just as I was thinking this, I saw a goat beside you, an animal of the witches' sabbath, looking at me and laughing. The noonday sun tipped its horns with fire. Then I saw the devil's trap and I no longer had any doubt that you had come from hell to bring about my perdition. I believed it."

He looked her coldly in the eye and added, "I still believe it. . . . Meanwhile the charm was beginning to operate; your dancing whirled in my brain; I felt the mysterious spell at work inside me. Everything in my soul that should have been awake was asleep and, like those who die in the snow, I found pleasure in letting this sleep steal over me. Suddenly you began to sing. What could I do, wretch that I was? Your singing was even more charming than your dancing. I tried to flee but it was impossible. I was nailed, rooted in place. It seemed to me that I had sunk up to my knees in the stone floor. I had to stay there till the end. My feet were like ice and my head was boiling. Finally—perhaps you took pity on me—you stopped singing and went away. The reflection of the dazzling vision and the echo of the enchanting music gradually died away in my eyes and ears. Then I leaned against the window, stiffer and more helpless than a statue. The vesper bells awakened me. I stood up and fled but, alas, something in me had fallen which could not be raised up again, something had arrived from which I could not escape.

"Yes, from that day onward there was in me a man whom I did not know. I had recourse to all my remedies: the cloister, the altar, work and books—but all in vain. Oh, how hollow science rings when you desperately dash a head filled with passions against it! Do you know what I always saw between me and my books from then on? It was you, your shadow, the image of the luminous apparition which had one day passed before me. But that image was no longer the same color: it was dark, sinister and shadowy, like the black circle that remains before the eyes of a man who has been rash enough to look directly at the sun.

"Constantly hearing your voice in my head, constantly seeing your feet dancing on my breviary, constantly feeling your form brushing against my flesh at night, I wanted to see you again, touch you, know who you were, see if I would find you identical with the ideal image of you which had remained with me and perhaps shatter my dream with the aid of reality. In any case, I hoped that a new impression would obliterate the first one, which had become intolerable for me. I sought you out. I saw you again. But alas, when I had seen you twice I wanted to see you a thousand times! I wanted to see you forever. I no longer belonged to myself—how can a man stop on that downward path to hell? The devil had attached one end of his thread to my wings and the other to your foot. I became a wanderer like you. I waited for you in doorways and on street corners, I watched you from the top of my tower. Every night I found myself more charmed, more desperate, more bewitched and more lost!

"I found out who you were—a gypsy. How could I doubt your magic then? I hoped that a trial would break the spell. A witch once cast a spell on Bruno d'Ast; he had her burned at the stake and he was cured. I knew that. I wanted to try that remedy. At first I tried to have you prohibited from entering the square before the cathedral, hoping I might forget you if I never saw you again, but you ignored the prohibition. You came back. Then I conceived the idea of carrying you off. One night I tried it. There were two of us. We had you in our hands when that cursed officer appeared on the scene. He saved you, which was the beginning of your misfortune, along with mine and his. Finally, no longer knowing what else to do, I denounced you to the Ecclesiastical Court. I thought I'd be cured, like Bruno d'Ast. I also thought that a trial would somehow bring us together, that in a prison I could hold you, have you, that you'd be unable to escape from me, that you'd possessed me so long that it was now my turn to possess you. When one does evil, one must do it thoroughly; it's madness to stop halfway! The extremity of crime has a certain delirium of joy. A priest and a witch can mingle in its ecstasy on the straw of a dungeon floor!

"I therefore denounced you. It was then that I frightened you so whenever you saw me. The plot I was weaving against you and the storm I was gathering over your head escaped from me in threats and flashes of lightning. But I still hesitated. My plan had certain frightful aspects which made me shrink back in terror.

"Perhaps I might have renounced it, perhaps my hideous thoughts might have withered in my brain without bearing fruit. I still believed that I had the choice of continuing or stopping the process which I had begun. But an evil thought is inexorable and strives to become an action; where I thought myself all-powerful, fate proved to be more powerful than I. Alas! Alas! It was fate that took you and thrust you into the terrible workings of the mechanism I had constructed. . . . Listen; I'm about to finish.

"One day—also a sunny day—there passed before me a man who pronounced your name and laughed and had lust in his eyes. I followed him. You know the rest."

He was silent. The girl found only one word to say: "Phoebus!"

"Not that name!" cried the priest, seizing her arm violently. "Don't pronounce that name! It was that name that ruined both of us, wretched creatures that we are! Or rather we all ruined one another through the inexplicable workings of fate! . . . You're suffering, aren't you? You're cold, the darkness blinds you, the dungeon presses in on you; but perhaps you still have a glimmer of light within you, be it only your childish love for that hollow man who was playing with your heart. But as for me, I bear the dungeon inside myself; inside me there is winter, ice and despair; my soul is plunged in darkness. Do you know everything I have suffered? I attended your trial. I was seated on the bench of the Ecclesiastical Court. Yes, beneath one of those hoods were the writhings of the damned. When they took you away, I was there; when they questioned you, I was there. It was my crime, it was my gallows which I saw slowly rising above your head. At each testimony, each proof, each plea, I was there. I was there when that ferocious beast—oh! I didn't forsee the torture! Listen: I followed you into the torture chamber. I saw you undressed and handled half-naked by the infamous hands of the torturer. I saw your foot, which I would have given an empire to kiss only once and then die, I saw that foot crushed by the horrible boot which transforms the members of a living being into bloody jelly. While I was watching that, I slashed my chest with a dagger which I held beneath my cloak. When you shrieked, I plunged it into my flesh; if you had shrieked a second time I would have plunged it into my heart! Look, I think it's still bleeding."

He threw open his cassock. His chest was torn as if by the claws of a tiger and there was a rather wide and badly healed wound in his side. La Esmeralda recoiled in horror.

"Have pity on me!" said the priest. "You think yourself miserable but, alas, you don't know what misery is! Oh! To love a woman! To be a priest! To be hated! To love her with all the fury of your soul to feel that for the least of her smiles you'd gladly give your blood, your entrails, your fame, your salvation, your life in this world and in the next! To regret not being a king, an emperor, an archangel, a god, in order to place a greater slave at her feet! To press her to you night and day in your dreams and thoughts, then see her in love with a soldier's uniform! And to have nothing to offer her except a wretched cassock which would only frighten and disgust her! To be present, with your jealousy and rage, while she lavishes treasures of love and beauty on a stupid braggart!

To see that body, whose form burns into you, those sweet, delicate breasts and that flesh palpitating under the kisses of another! To love her feet, her arms, her shoulders, to think of her blue veins, of her brown skin until you writhe on the floor of your cell for nights on end, then see all caresses you've dreamed of giving her end in torture! To have succeeded only in making her lie down on a leather bed! Oh! Those are the real pincers heated in the fire of hell! Oh, happy is the man who is sawn in two or pulled apart by horses! Do you know what torture it is when for long nights your blood boils, your heart breaks, your head bursts and your teeth bite into your hands? Have mercy on me! Throw a few ashes on these burning coals! I beg you, wipe away the sweat that streams down my forehead! Torture me with one hand but caress me with the other!"

He rolled in the water on the floor and hammered his head against the stone steps. She listened to him and watched him. When he stopped speaking, exhausted and panting, she repeated softly, "Oh, my Phoebus!"

The priest crawled toward her on his knees. "I beg you," he cried, "if you have any pity at all, don't repulse me! I love you! I'm a wretched man! When you pronounce that name it's as though you were grinding all the fibers of my heart between your teeth! Mercy! If you've been sent from hell, I'll go there with you! I've done everything for that. Hell with you in it would be heaven for me; the sight of you is more charming than that of God! Will you take me? I would have thought the day a woman rejected a love like mine the mountains would move. Oh, if you wanted to. . . . We could be so happy! We'd run away—I'd get you out of here—we'd go to the place that has the most sunlight, the most trees, the most blue sky. We'd love each other, we'd mingle our souls together and we'd have an undying thirst for each other which we'd constantly quench together from the inexhaustible well of love!"

She interrupted him with a terrible burst of laughter. "Just look at you, Father," she said, "you have blood under your fingernails!"

The priest remained for several instants as if petrified, staring at his hand. "Yes, that's right," he said finally, with strange gentleness, "abuse me, mock me, cover me with ignominy, but come with me! Hurry! You have only till tomorrow! The scaffold of the Place de Grève is always ready. It's horrible! To see you going there in that cart! Have mercy on me! I never really felt how much I love you till now. Come with me! You'll have time to learn to love me after I've saved you. You can hate me as long as you like. But come with me. Tomorrow! Tomorrow! The scaffold! Oh, save yourself! Save me!"

He seized her arm frantically and tried to pull her toward him. She stared at him steadfastly and said, "What has become of my Phoebus?"

"Oh!" cried the priest, releasing her arm. "Have you no pity?"

"What has become of Phoebus?" she repeated coldly.

"He's dead!"

"Dead!" she said, still cold and motionless. "Then why are you speaking to me of living?"

He was not listening to her. "Yes, yes," he said, as if talking to himself, "he must be quite dead. The blade went in very far. I think I touched his heart with the point."

She sprang at him like an enraged tigress and shoved him against the steps with supernatural strength. "Go away, monster!" she cried. "Go away, murderer! Let me die! May my blood and Phoebus' make an everlasting stain on your forehead! Be yours, priest? Never! Never! Nothing will bring us together, not even hell!"

The priest stumbled on the staircase. He silently disengaged his feet from the skirt of his cassock, picked up his lantern and began to climb slowly up the steps leading to the trap door. He opened it and went out. Suddenly La Esmeralda saw his head reappear. His face wore a hideous expression as he cried out to her in a voice full of rage and despair. "I tell you he's dead!"

She fell face downward. Nothing more was heard in the dungeon except the dripping of the water which rippled the pool in the darkness. . . .

b. Thomas Mann's story "The Way to the Churchyard" is a brilliant portrayal of hate unleashed. The protagonist, Praisegod Piepsam, is a passive, weak, depressed, and inadequate man. Behind this facade all the hate lies buried only to be uncovered by a trivial incident. Mann's portrayal of the havoc wreaked by this man's loss of control is typical of what is called a "dissociative reaction." An intense emotional response suddenly overthrows the preexisting personality. Hate is perhaps the most dangerous and frightening impulse with which men must live. Mann here shows the dangers that accrue when hatred that has previously been completely denied suddenly breaks through the floodgates.

THE WAY TO THE CHURCHYARD

Thomas Mann (*1875–1955*)

The way to the churchyard ran along beside the highroad, ran beside it all the way to the end; that is to say, to the churchyard. On the other side of it were houses, new suburban houses, some of them still unfinished; after the houses came fields. The highroad was flanked by trees, gnarled beeches of considerable age, and half of it was paved and half not. But the way to the churchyard had a sprinking of gravel, which made it seem like a pleasant foot-path. Between highroad and path ran a narrow dry ditch, filled with grass and wild flowers.

It was spring, it was nearly summer. The world was smiling, God's blue sky was filled with nothing but small, round, dense little morsels of cloud, tufted all over with funny little dabs of snowy white. The birds were twittering in the beeches, and a soft wind blew across the fields.

A wagon from the next village was going along the highroad towards the town, half on the paved, half on the unpaved part of the road. The driver's legs were hanging down both sides of the shaft, he was whistling out of tune. At the end of the wagon, with its back to the driver, sat a little yellow dog. It had a pointed muzzle and it gazed with an unspeakably solemn and collected air back over the way by which it had come. It was a most admirable little dog, good as gold, a pleasure to contemplate. But no, it does not belong to the matter in hand, we must pass it by.—A troop of soldiers came along, from the barracks close at hand; they marched in their own dust and sang. Another wagon passed, coming from the town and going to the next village. The driver was asleep and there was no dog; hence this wagon is devoid of interest. Two journeymen followed after it, one of them a giant, the other a hunchback. They walked barefoot, because they were carrying their boots on their backs; they shouted a good-natured greeting to the sleeping driver and went their way. Yes, this was but a moderate traffic, which pursued its ends without complications or incidents.

On the path to the churchyard walked a single figure, going slowly, with bent head, and leaning on a black stick. This man was named Piepsam, Praisegod Piepsam and no other name. I mention it expressly because of his ensuing most singular behaviour.

He wore black, for he was on his way to visit the graves of his loved ones. He had on a furry top hat with a wide brim, a frock-coat shiny with age, trousers both too tight and too short, and black kid gloves with all the shine rubbed off. His neck, a long, shrivelled neck with a huge Adam's apple, rose out of a frayed turn-over collar—yes, this turn-over collar was already rough at the corners. Sometimes the man raised his head to see how far away the churchyard still was; and then you got a glimpse of a strange face, a face, unquestionably, which you would not easily forget.

It was smooth-shaven and pallid. But a knobbly nose stuck out between the sunken cheeks, and this nose glowed with immoderate and unnatural redness and swarmed with little pimples, unhealthy excrescences which gave it an uneven and fantastic outline. The deep glow of the nose stood out against the dead paleness of the face; there was something artificial and improbable about it, as though he had put it on, like a

carnival nose, and was wearing it as a sort of funereal joke. But it was no
joke.—His mouth was big, with drooping corners, and he held it tightly
compressed. His eyebrows were black, strewn with little white hairs, and
when he glanced up from the ground he lifted them till they disappeared
under the brim of his hat and you got a good view of the pathetically in-
flamed and red-rimmed eyes. In short, this was a face bound in the end
to evoke one's pity.

Praisegod Piepsam's appearance was not enlivening, it fitted ill into
the lovely afternoon; even for a man who was visiting the graves of his
dear departed he looked much too depressed. His inner man, however,
could one have seen within him, amply explained and justified the outward state. Yes, he was a bit depressed, a bit unhappy, a little hardly
treated—is it so hard for happy people like yourselves to enter into his
feelings? But the fact was, things were not going just a little badly with
him, they were bad in a very high degree.

In the first place, he drank. We shall come on to that later. And he
was a widower, bereft and forsaken of all the world, there was not a soul
on earth to love him. His wife, born Lebzelt, had been taken from him
six months before, when she had presented him with a child. It was the
third child, and it was born dead. The others were dead too, one of
diphtheria, the other of nothing in particular, save general insufficiency.
And as though that were not enough, he had lost his job, been deprived
with contumely of his position and his daily bread—naturally on account
of his vice, which was stronger than Piepsam.

Once he had been able to resist it, to some extent, though yielding to
it by bouts. But when his wife and child were snatched from him, when
he had no work and no position, nothing to support him, when he stood
alone on this earth, then his weakness took more and more the upper hand.
He had been a clerk in the office of a benefit society, a sort of superior
copyist who got ninety marks a month. But he had been drunken and
negligent and after repeated warnings had finally been discharged.

Certainly this did not improve Piepsam's morale. Indeed he declined
more and more to his fall. Wretchedness, in fact, is destructive to our
human dignity and self-respect—it does us no harm to get a little understanding of these matters. For there is much that is strange about them,
not to say thrilling. It does the man no good to keep on protesting that
he is not guilty, for in most cases he despises himself for his own unhappiness. And self-contempt and bad conduct stand in the most frightful
mutual relation: they feed each other, they play into each other's hands,
in a way shocking to behold. Thus was it with Piepsam. He drank because he had no self-respect, and he had no self-respect because the continual breakdown of his good intentions ate it away. At home in his
wardrobe he kept a bottle with a poisonous-coloured liquor in it, the
name of which I will refrain from mentioning. Before this wardrobe

Praisegod Piepsam had before now gone literally on his knees, and in his wrestlings had bitten his tongue—and still in the end capitulated. I do not like even to mention such things—but after all they are very instructive.

Now he was taking his way to the churchyard, striking his black stick before him as he went. The gentle breeze played about his nose too, but he felt it not. A lost and most miserable human being, he stared straight ahead of him with lifted brows.—Suddenly he heard a noise behind him and listened; it was a little rustling sound coming on swiftly from the distance. He turned round and stopped.—A bicycle was approaching at full tilt, its pneumatic tires crunching the gravel; it slowed down because Piepsam stood directly in the way.

A young man perched on the saddle, a youth, a blithe and carefree cyclist. He made no claims to belong to the great and mighty of this earth —oh, dear me, not at all! He rode a cheapish machine, of no matter what make, worth perhaps two hundred marks, at a guess. On it he rode abroad, he came out from the city and the sun glittered on his pedals as he rode straight into God's great out-of-doors—hurrah, hurrah! He wore a coloured shirt with a grey jacket, gaiters, and the sauciest cap in the world, a perfect joke of a cap, brown checks and a button on top. Underneath it a thick sheaf of blond hair stuck out on his forehead. His eyes were blue lightnings. He came on, like life itself, ringing his bell. But Piepsam did not budge a hair's breadth out of the way. He stood there and looked at Life—unbudgeably.

Life flung him an angry glance and went past—whereupon Piepsam too began to move forwards. When Life got abreast of him he said slowly, with dour emphasis:

"Number nine thousand seven hundred and seven." He clipped his lips together and looked unflinchingly at the ground, feeling Life's angry eye upon him.

Life had turned round, grasping the saddle behind it with one hand and slowly pedaling.

"What did you say?" asked Life.

"Number nine thousand seven hundred and seven," Piepsam reiterated. "Oh, nothing. I am going to report you."

"You are going to report me?" asked Life; turned round still further and rode still slower, so that it had to keep its balance by straightening the handle-bars.

"Certainly," said Piepsam, some five or six paces away.

"Why?" asked Life, getting off. It stood there in an expectant attitude.

"You know very well yourself."

"No, I do not know."

"You must know."

"No, I do not know," said Life, "and besides it interests me very little, I must say." It turned to its bicycle as though to mount. Life certainly had a tongue in its head.

"I am going to report you for riding here on the path to the church-yard instead of out on the highroad," said Piepsam.

"But, my dear sir," said Life with a short impatient laugh, turning round again, "look at the marks of bicycles all the way along. Everybody uses this path."

"It makes no difference to me," replied Piepsam. "I am going to report you all the same."

"Just as you please," said Life, and mounted its machine. It really mounted at one go, with a single push of the foot, secured its seat in the saddle, and bent to the task of getting up as much speed as its temperament required.

"Well, if you go on riding here on the foot-path I will certainly report you," said Piepsam again, his voice rising and trembling. But Life paid no attention at all; it went on gathering speed.

If you could have seen Praisegod Piepsam's face at that moment, it would have shocked you deeply. He compressed his lips so tightly that his cheeks and even his red-hot nose were drawn out of shape. His eyebrows were lifted as high as they would go and he stared after the departing bicycle with a maniac expression. Suddenly he gave a forwards rush and covered running the small space between him and Life. He laid hold on the little leather pocket behind the saddle and held fast with both hands. He clung to it with lips drawn out of human semblance, and tugged wildeyed and speechless, with all his strength, at the moving and wobbling machine. It seemed from the appearances in doubt whether he was seeking with malice aforethought to stop it or whether he had been struck with the idea of mounting behind Life and riding with glittering pedals into God's great out-of-doors, hurrah, hurrah! No bicycle could stand the weight; it stopped, it leaned over, it fell.

But now Life became violent. It had come to a stop with one leg on the ground; it stretched out its right arm and gave Herr Piepsam such a push in the chest that he staggered several steps backwards. Then it said, its voice swelling to a threat:

"You are probably drunk, fellow! But if you continue to try to stop me, my fine lad, I'll just chop you into little bits—do you understand? I'll tear you limb from limb. Kindly get that through your head." Then Life turned its back on Herr Piepsam, pulled its cap furiously down on its brow, and once more mounted its bicycle. Yes, Life certainly had a tongue in its head. And it mounted as neatly as before, in one go, settled into the saddle, and had the machine at once under control. Piepsam saw its back retreating faster and faster.

He stood there gasping, staring after Life. And Life did not fall over, no mishap occurred, no tire burst, no stone lay in the way. It moved off on its rubber wheels. Then Piepsam began to shriek and rail; his voice was no longer melancholy at all, you might call it a roar.

"You are not to go on!" he shouted. "You shall not go on. You are to ride out on the road and not here on the way to the churchyard—do you hear? Get off, get off at once! I will report you, I will enter an action against you. Oh, Lord, oh, God, if you were to fall off, if you would only fall off, you rascally windbag, I would stamp on you, I would stamp on your face with my boots, you damned villain, you—"

Never was seen such a sight. A man raving mad on the way to the churchyard, a man with his face swollen with roaring, a man dancing with rage, capering, flinging his arms about, quite out of control. The bicycle was out of sight by this time, but still Piepsam stood where he was and raved.

"Stop him, stop him! Ride on the path to the churchyard, will he? You blackguard! You outrageous puppy, you! You damned monkey, I'd like to skin you alive, you with the blue eyes, you silly cur, you windbag, you blockhead, you ignorant ninny! You get off! Get off this very minute! Won't anybody pitch him off in the dirt? Riding, eh? On the way to the churchyard! Pull him down, damned puppy. . . . Oh, if I had hold of you, eh? What wouldn't I do? Devil scratch your eyes out, you ignorant, ignorant, ignorant fool!"

Piepsam went on from this to expressions which cannot be set down. Foaming at the mouth, he uttered the most shameless objurgations, while his voice cracked in his throat and his writhings grew more fantastic. A few children with a fox-terrier and a basket crossed over from the road; they climbed the ditch, surrounded the shrieking man and peered into his distorted face. Some labourers at work on the new houses, just about to take their midday rest, saw that something was going on and joined the group—there were both men and women among them. But Piepsam went on, his frenzy grew worse and worse. Blind with rage, he shook his fist at all four quarters of the heavens, whirled round on himself, bounded and bent his knees and bobbed up again in the extremity of his effort to shriek even louder. He did not stop for breath and where all his words came from was the greatest wonder. His face was frightfully puffed out, his top hat sat on the back of his neck, and his shirt hung out of his waistcoat. By now he had passed on from the particular to the general and was making remarks which had nothing at all to do with the situation: references to his own vicious mode of life, and religious allusions which certainly sounded strange in such a voice, mingled as they were with his dissolute curses.

"Come on, come on, all of you!" he bellowed. "Not only you and you and you but all the rest of you, with your blue-lightning eyes and your little caps with buttons. I will shriek the truth in your ears and it will fill you with everlasting horror. . . . So you are grinning, so you are shrugging your shoulders? I drink . . . well, yes, of course I drink. I am even a drunkard, if you want to know. What does that signify? It is not yet the last day of all. The day will come, you good-for-nothing vermin, when God shall weigh us all in the balance . . . ah, the Son of Man shall come in the clouds, you filth, and His justice is not of this world. He will hurl you into outer darkness, all you light-headed breed, and there shall be wailing and. . . ."

He was now surrounded by a crowd of some size. People were laughing at him, some were frowning. More hod-carriers and labourers, men and women, came over from the unfinished buildings. A driver got down from his wagon and jumped the ditch, whip in hand. One man shook Piepsam by the arm, but nothing came of it. A troop of soldiers marched by, turning to look at the scene and laughing. The fox-terrier could no longer contain itself; it braced its forefeet and howled into Piepsam's face with its tail between its legs.

Then Praisegod Piepsam screamed once more with all his strength: "Get off, get off at once, you ignorant fool!" He described with one arm a wide half-circle—and collapsed. He lay there, his voice abruptly silenced, a black heap surrounded by the curious throng. His wide-brimmed hat flew off, bounced once, and then lay on the ground.

Two masons bent over the motionless Piepsam and considered his case in the moderate and reasonable tone that working-people have. One of them then got on his legs and went off at a run. The other made experiments with the unconscious man. He sprinkled him with water from a tub, he poured out brandy in the hollow of his hand and rubbed Piepsam's temples with it. None of these efforts were crowned with success.

Some little time passed. Then the sound of wheels was heard and a wagon came along the road. It was an ambulance with a great red cross on each side, drawn by two charming little horses. Two men in neat uniforms got down from the box; one went to the back of the wagon, opened it, and drew out a stretcher; the other ran over to the path, pushed away the yokels standing round Piepsam, and with the help of one of them got Herr Piepsam out of the crowd and into the road. He was laid out on the stretcher and shoved into the wagon as one shoves a loaf of bread into the oven. The door clicked shut and the two men climbed back onto the box. All that went off very efficiently, with but few and practised motions, as though in a theatre. And then they drove Praisegod Piepsam away.

C.   One of the most common restraints in human culture is the incest taboo. The expression of sexual impulses towards a family member is looked on with horror by most societies. Yet the familiar loved family figures surround the adolescent as he begins to feel the press of his sexual impulses. Furthermore, unconscious attachments may draw him towards the taboo figures. The adolescent is caught between the dynamism of his incestuous impulses and the restraining forces of the cultural taboo. James T. Farrell has captured a poignant moment as brother and sister struggle with their incestuous impulses.

Studs Lonigan

James T. Farrell   (1904–   )

. . . Frances came in. She wore a thin nightgown. He could almost see right through it. He tried to keep looking away, but he had to turn his head back to look at her. She stood before him, and didn't seem to know that he was looking at her. She seemed kind of queer; he thought maybe she was sick.

"Do you like Lucy?"

"Oh, a little," he said.

He was excited, and couldn't talk much, because he didn't want her to notice it.

"Do you like to kiss girls?"

"Not so much," he said.

"You did tonight."

"It was all in the game."

"Helen must like Weary."

"I hate her."

"I don't like her either, but . . . do you think they did anything in the post office?"

She wasn't going to pump him and get anything out of him.

She seemed to be looking at him, awful queer, all right.

"You know. Do you think they did anything that was fun . . . or that the sisters wouldn't want them to do . . . or that's bad?"

"I don't know."

Dirty thoughts rushed to his head like hot blood. He told himself he was a bastard because . . . she was his sister.

"I don't know," he said, confused.

"You think maybe they did something bad, and it was fun?"

He shrugged his shoulders and looked out the window so she couldn't see his face.

"I feel funny," she said.

He hadn't better say anything to her, because she'd snitch and give him away.

"I want to do something. . . . They're all in bed. Let's us play leap frog, you know that game that boys play where one bends down, and the others jump over him?" she said.

"We'll make too much noise."

"Do you really think that Weary and Helen did anything that might be fun?" she asked.

She got up, and walked nervously around the room. She plunked down on the piano stool, and part of her leg showed.

He looked out the window. He looked back. They sat. She fidgeted and couldn't sit still. She got up and ran out of the room. He sat there. He must be a bastard . . . she was his sister.

He looked out the window. He wondered what it was like; he was getting old enough to find out.

He got up. He looked at himself in the mirror. He shadow-boxed, and thought of Lucy. He thought of Fran. He squinted at himself in the mirror.

He turned the light out and started down the hallway. Fran called him. She was lying in bed without the sheets over her.

"It's hot here. Awful hot. Please put the window up higher."

"It's as high as it'll go."

"I thought it wasn't."

He looked at Fran. He couldn't help it.

"And please get some real cold water."

He got the water. It wasn't cold enough. She asked him to let the water run more. He did. He handed the water to her. As she rose to drink, she bumped her small breast against him.

She drank the water. He started out of the room. She called him to get her handkerchief.

"I'm not at all tired," she said.

He left, thinking what a bastard he must be.

He went to the bathroom.

Kneeling down at his bedside, he tried to make a perfect act of contrition to wash his soul from sin.

He heard the wind, and was afraid that God might punish him, make him die in the night. He had found out he was old enough, but . . . his soul was black with sin. He lay in bed worried, suffering, and he tossed into a slow, troubled sleep. . . .

CHAPTER three

Psychosis:
The Break with Reality

Psychosis, as described in the first chapter, is one of the three basic categories of mental illness. It is generally considered the most severe psychological disorder, and is characterized by a major break with reality. Those types which have no known organic cause are called functional psychoses. There are two major subdivisions: the schizophrenias and the affective psychoses. The former can be roughly characterized as primarily disorders of thought and mental function; the latter as primarily disorders of feeling and mood.

Schizophrenia

I. Approximately half the hospital beds in the United States are occupied by mental patients, and half of these suffer from some form of schizophrenia. Consequently, one out of every four hospital beds in the United States is taken up by a schizophrenic. Although other countries may have fewer of their afflicted patients in hospitals, the incidence of schizophrenia seems to be approximately the same in all countries. One out of every one hundred human beings can be expected to develop this condition. Obviously an incapacitating disease of such high frequency and of unexplained etiology has been the subject of research by scientists from many different disciplines. However, the crucial questions remain unanswered; no one knows the cause or causes of schizophrenia.

The history of the concept schizophrenia begins under a

different name: dementia praecox. First introduced by the
Belgian, Morel, in 1860, it was Kraepelin in 1898 who organized
a number of different syndromes under this one category,
based on what he thought was the common outcome, dementia.
He included in this group three major types: the hebephrenic,
the catatonic, and the paranoid.

Besides the outcome of dementia, there were a number of
characteristic symptoms, namely: hallucinations, delusions,
inappropriate emotions, stereotyped behavior.

Eugen Bleuler in 1911 achieved a more detailed
classification. He recognized that dementia was not a universal
outcome, and therefore proposed the term schizophrenia in
use today. Bleuler, armed with an understanding of dynamic
psychiatry, attempted to study the thinking processes of these
patients. He was impressed with the loose nature of thought
sequences. Rather than ideas following one another in logical
order, there seemed to be a chain of associations linked in some
unrealistic or obscure fashion. Bleuler called this "loose
association" and made it the hallmark of a disease which he
now called schizophrenia. Schizophrenia literally means a
split mind and frequently is understood as a split personality;
this is incorrect. Split personality is an uncommon type of
neurotic disorder where elements of the personality are
separately lived out in a Dr. Jekyll and Mr. Hyde fashion.
Bleuler meant to indicate a splitting of the basic
functions of the personality; e.g., feeling and thought. Bleuler
also emphasized another important feature of schizophrenic
thinking, the turn away from external reality towards the self,
towards fantasy, and imagination. This he called autism.
(Autism and other major symptoms of psychosis will be
illustrated in a later chapter.)

Descriptive psychiatry in the 20th century has added little
to the work of Kraepelin and Bleuler, although dynamic
psychiatry has enriched our understanding of the disease.

The major subcategories of schizophrenia are discussed
in the following sections.

Simple Schizophrenia

1. Bleuler, among his many contributions, identified a
fourth type of schizophrenia in addition to paranoia,
catatonia, and hebephrenia; this he called simple schizophrenia.

The simple schizophrenic begins early in life to withdraw, becoming reclusive with increasingly constricted interests. There is an impairment of abstract thinking, and the patient eventually becomes a passive burden to his family. The condition is marked by apathy, failure of human relationships, and deterioration over a long period of time—without obvious delusions or hallucinations. This type of schizophrenia is rarely seen in pure form today, and its diagnostic significance is limited.

Catatonia

2.   Catatonia is a relatively common form of schizophrenia; its onset is typically in late adolescence or early adulthood. The catatonic schizophrenic is characterized by exaggerations of activity patterns; either hyperactive agitated posturing and gesturing, or inactive withdrawal into a fetal position with neglect of personal habits and with a complete cessation of overt purposeful activity. Such patients may eventually have to be tube fed and cared for like helpless infants, a condition called catatonic stupor. Mutism is common in this condition; waxy flexibility of the limbs and the maintenance of awkward postures is apt to be seen. The catatonic, although difficult to communicate with, is often found to have active hallucinations and delusions when rapport is established. The general impression is that whatever their overt activity level may be, inwardly they are consumed by fantasies, hallucinations, and world destruction delusions. Balzac has brilliantly illustrated this condition in the form of "Louis Lambert." His story is of particular interest because it illustrates all of the following typical features of the schizophrenic process: the early capacity for visual imagery and the autistic trends in thinking, the isolation from peers, the preoccupation with mysticism, the onset of catatonia (here called cataplexy) at the brink of a meaningful heterosexual relationship, the fear of sexual inadequacy. Balzac's genius also penetrates the phenomenon of loose association, and we learn that much of it can in fact be understood. Through empathy we see that his speech is only a fragmentary record of his thoughts and that this is at least partly attributable to his loss of interest in communicating.

Louis Lambert
Honoré de Balzac   (*1799–1850*)

Louis Lambert was born in 1797, at Montoire, a little
town in the Vendômois, where his father carried on a tannery of no great
importance, expecting to make him his successor. But the boy's inclinations for study, which early showed themselves, changed in a measure
the father's plans. Moreover, the tanner and his wife cherished Louis as
parents cherish an only son, and never thwarted him. The Old and New
Testament fell into the child's hands before he was five years old, and that
book, which contains so many books, decided his destiny. Did his infantile imagination comprehend the deep mysteries of Scripture? could
it already follow the Holy Spirit in its path through the universe? or, was
it merely fascinated by the romantic charms which abound in those poems
of the Orient? did the child's soul in its first innocence sympathize with
the sublime piety which hands divine have shed within the book? To
some readers the following narrative will answer these questions.

One circumstance resulted from the boy's first study of the Bible:
Louis begged and borrowed books throughout the little town, obtaining
them by that persuasive charm whose secret belongs to childhood and
which no one is able to resist. Spending his whole time in reading, which
was neither directed nor interfered with, he reached his tenth year. In
those days substitutes for the conscription were difficult to obtain, and
wealthy parents were in the habit of engaging them in advance, so as not
to be without them when the draft was made. The poor tanners were unable, through poverty, to buy a substitute for their son, and to put him in
the Church was the only other means the law allowed them by which to
save him from the draft. They therefore sent him, in 1807, to his maternal
uncle, the curate of Mer, another little town on the Loire, near Bois. This
course satisfied both Louis' passion for knowledge and his parents' desire
to save him from the frightful uncertainties of a soldier's life; moreover,
his studious tastes and his precocious intellect gave promise of future high
distinction in the Church. After remaining three years with his uncle, an
old and somewhat learned Oratorian, Louis left Mer early in 1811 to enter
the college of Vendôme where he was maintained and educated at the
expense of Madame de Staël.

Louis Lambert owed the protection of this celebrated woman to
chance, a means by which Providence often smooths the way for neglected
genius. To us, whose eyes seldom look below the surface of human events,
such vicissitudes, so frequent in the lives of great men, seem the result of
mere material phenomena; to most biographers the head of a man of

From "Louis Lambert" by Honoré de Balzac.

genius shows above the masses as a fine flower attracts by its brilliancy the eye of a naturalist. The comparison applies to this event in the life of Louis Lambert, who, as a usual thing, spent the time his uncle allowed him for his holidays with his parents at Montoire. Instead of enjoying, as most school-boys do, the sweets of the *far niente*, so enticing at any age, he carried his books and a slice of bread into the woods where he could read and meditate, free from the remonstrances of his mother, to whom such persevering study was beginning to seem dangerous. True mother's instinct! From this time, reading became a species of hunger in Louis' soul which nothing appeased; he devoured books of all sorts—feeding indiscriminately on history, philosophy, physics, and religious works. He once told me that he had found unspeakable delight in reading dictionaries in default of other books, and I readily believe it. What scholar has not again and again found pleasure in searching out the meaning of some obscure substantive? The analysis of a word, its conformation, its history, were to Lambert a text for revery—but not the instinctive revery with which a child accustoms itself to the phenomena of life and strengthens its perceptions both moral and physical (an involuntary culture which, later on, bears fruit in the understanding and in the character); no, Louis seized upon facts and explained them to himself, after searching out their cause and their effect with the perspicacity of a savage. By one of those startling gifts which Nature sometimes delights in bestowing, and which proved the idiosyncrasy of his own being, Louis, at the age of fourteen, was able to give fluent expression to ideas whose real depth and meaning were revealed to me only in after years.

"Often," he once said to me in speaking of his reading, "I have made delightful journeys embarked on a single word which bore me through the abysses of the past as an insect alighting on a blade of grass floats at the will of a current. Starting from Greece I have reached Rome, and traversed the extent of modern eras. What a glorious book might be written on the life and adventures of a word! No doubt it receives many impressions from the events in whose service it is used; it awakens different ideas, according to its surroundings; but its real greatness appears when we consider it under the triple aspect of soul, body, and motion. The mere consideration of a word, even if we abstract its functions, its effects, its performances, is sufficient to launch us on a wide expanse of meditation. Are not most words dyed with the ideas they externally represent? To what originating genius do we owe them? If a vast intellect was needed for the creation of a single word, how old is human speech? The assembling of letters, their form, the countenance, as it were, which they give to a word, present an accurate image (according to the character of each nation) of the unknown beings whose memory survives in us. Who shall explain to us philosophically the transition from sensation to thought, from thought to word, from the word to its hieroglyphical ex-

pression, from hieroglyphs to alphabet, from the alphabet to written
eloquence, whose beauty lies in a train of images classed by rhetoricians,
which are, as it were, the hieroglyphs of thought? May not the ancient
picturing of human ideas configured by zoölogical forms have determined
the earliest signs used in the East for the writing of language? May it not
also have left, traditionally, certain vestiges to our modern tongues, all of
which have caught up fragments of the primitive language of departed
nations—majestic and solemn language, whose majesty and solemnity de-
crease as societies grow older; whose sonorous echoes in the Hebrew Bible,
still so beautiful in Greece, grow feebler through the progress of our successive civilizations. Is it to that first essence that we owe the mysterious
spirit hidden in human speech? Is there not a species of visible rectitude
in the word TRUTH? The terse sound of the word calls up an image of
chaste nudity, of the simplicity of the True in all things. The very syllable
breathes freshness. I take the formula of an abstract idea for my example,
not wishing to express the problem by a word which might make it too
easy to comprehend—such, for instance, as the word *float,* which speaks
clearly of the senses. So it is with other words; all are instinct with a
living power derived from the soul which they send back to its source by
the mysterious force of a marvellous action and reaction between word
and thought—like, as it were, a lover drawing from the lips of his mistress
as much love as he presses into them. Words, by their mere aspect to the
eye, vivify in our brain the creations to which they serve as garments. Like
other things, they have their own place where alone their qualities can
fully work and develop. But the subject is a science in itself." He paused
and shrugged his shoulders as if to say, "We are too great, and yet too
little."

Louis' passion for reading had been well nourished. His uncle owned
from two to three thousand volumes. These treasures came from the
pillage of abbeys and castles during the Revolution. The worthy man had
been able as *prêtre assermenté* to cull the choicest works from the precious
collections which were sold in those days by the weight. In three years
Louis Lambert had assimiliated the substance of all the books in his uncle's
library that deserved study. The absorption of ideas through reading became in him a curious phenomenon; his eye took in seven or eight lines at
a glance; his mind caught and appreciated their meaning with a swiftness
equal to the action of the eye; often one word in a sentence was enough to
give him the meaning of the whole. His memory was amazing, retaining
with equal fidelity the thoughts acquired by reading and those which
reflection or conversation suggested to him. In fact, he possessed all forms
of memory—for names, words, places, things, and faces. Not only could
he recall objects at will, but he could see them again in his own mind,
precisely the same in situation, vividness, and coloring as they were when
he first beheld them. This power he applied equally to the intangible acts

of the understanding. He recollected, to use his own saying, not only the position of thoughts on the page of the books from which he took them, but also the workings of his own mind at distant periods. By an almost unheard-of privilege his memory was able to retrace the entire life and progress of his mind, from the earliest idea that dawned upon it to the last fruition of his thought; through dimness to lucidity. His brain, early subjected to the difficult mechanism of the concentration of human powers, drew from its own rich stores a crowd of images, wonderful for their reality and their vigor, with which he fed his mind during the process of his limpid contemplations.

"When it pleases me to do so," he said in his peculiar language, to which the treasures of memory imparted a precocious originality, "I draw a veil before my eyes. I retire within myself and find a darkened chamber, where the events of nature reproduce themselves in purer forms than those under which they first appeared to my exterior senses."

At twelve years of age his imagination, stimulated by the perpetual exercise of his faculties, was developed to a degree which enabled him to obtain such exact notions of things which he knew through reading only that the image imprinted on his mind could not have been more vivid had he seen them in reality—whether he reached the result by analogy, or whether he were gifted with a species of second-sight by which he was enabled to embrace all nature.

"When I read of the battle of Austerlitz," he one day said to me, "I saw all the incidents. The volleys of cannon, the shouts of the combatants sounded in my ears and stirred my very entrails. I smelt the powder; I heard the tramp of horses and the cries of men; I saw the plain where the armed nations clashed together as though I stood on the heights of the Santon. The sight was awful to me, like a page of the Apocalypse."

When he thus put all his forces into reading he lost, to a certain extent, the consciousness of physical life; existing only through all-powerful action of his inward organs, the compass of which was then immeasurably extended—to use his own expression, he "left space behind him." But I will not anticipate the history of the intellectual phases of his life. I have been led, in spite of myself, to invert the order in which I ought to unfold the history of a man who carried all his action into thought, just as others put all their being into action.

A strong inclination led him toward the study of mysticism. "*Abyssus abyssum,*" he said to me, "our mind is an abyss which delights in depths profound. As children, men, and dotards, we love mystery, under whatever form it comes." The predilection was fatal to him—if indeed we may judge his life by ordinary standards, and measure his joys by our own or by the theories of social prejudice. This taste for "the things of heaven" (another of his phrases), this *mens divinior*, was due perhaps to the influence of the first books which he read in his uncle's library. Saint-

Theresa and Madame Guyon were to him a continuation of the Bible, the first food of his adult intelligence, and they accustomed him to those ardent reactions of the soul in which ecstasy is both a means and a result. This study, this taste, uplifted his heart, ennobled and purified it, gave him a thirst for the Divine nature, inspired him with delicate emotions that were almost feminine and which are instinctive in the souls of great men; possibly the sublimity of such men comes from the need of self-devotion which distinguishes womanhood—carried by them into higher things. Thanks to his early impressions, Louis continued pure through his college life. This noble virginity of the senses had the effect, necessarily, of enriching the warmth of his blood and increasing the faculties of his mind.

*   *   *

To me, the life of his mind is divided into three phases.

Urged from his infancy to precocious activity, caused no doubt by some malady or some perfection of his organs, his forces concentrated themselves on the working of his inward faculties and on the superabundant production of the nervous fluid. A creature of ideas, he sought to quench the thirst of a brain which longed to assimilate all ideas. Hence, his reading, and from his reading his reflections, which gave him power to reduce things to their simplest expressions, to absorb them within himself that he might study them in their essence. The benefits of this magnificent period of his mind's training, which come to other men only as the result of long study, fell to Louis during his bodily childhood—a happy childhood, colored with the studious felicities of a poem. The limit which most brains attain was the point of departure from which his was one day to start in search of new regions of intelligence. He thus created for himself, without as yet knowing what he did, the most exacting of lives, and the most insatiable. Merely to exist, he was forced to throw incessant nourishment into the gulf he had opened within him. Like certain beings of the mundane regions, he was liable to perish for want of nutriment to intemperate and balked appetites. Was it not, in fact, a debauchery of the soul, which might bring it, like certain bodies saturated with alcohol, to spontaneous combustion?

This earliest mental phase I knew nothing of. Not until the present day have I explained to myself its amazing fructifications and results. Lambert was then thirteen years old.

I was fortunate enough to be with him in the first years of the second stage, during which Lambert (and it may have been this that saved him) endured all the wretchedness of school life and expended the superabundance of his thought. After passing from things to their simplest terms, from words to their ideal substance, from that substance to principles—in short, after abstracting all, he still aspired, as a necessity of life, to other intellectual creations. Subdued by his college sufferings and by the crises of his physical life, he continued meditative, divined feelings, foresaw new sciences and vast masses of ideas. Checked in his course, and too feeble as yet to contemplate the upper spheres, his eyes turned inward in self-contemplation. He showed me then the struggle of thought reacting against itself, and seeking to discover the secrets of its own nature, as a doctor studies the progress of his own malady. In this state of strength and weakness, childlike grace and superhuman power, Louis Lambert gave me the most poetic and the truest idea of the being whom we call *angel*—excepting always one woman whose name, person, and life it is my wish to withhold from the world, so that I alone may know the secret of her existence and bury it forever in my heart.

The third phase of Lambert's mental life escaped me. It must have begun after I parted from him; perhaps when he left college in 1815—being then eighteen years old. He had lost his father and mother during the preceding six months. Finding no one in his family with whom his soul—naturally expansive, but since our separation always repressed—could sympathize, he took refuge with his uncle, now his guardian, who, deposed from his parish for having taken the oath, now lived in obscurity at Blois. There Louis stayed for some time, until, driven by the desire to pursue his studies, which he felt were incomplete, he went to Paris to seek Madame de Staël, and to drink in science at the fountain-head. The old priest, having a great affection for his nephew, allowed Louis to spend his patrimony on a three years' sojourn in Paris—though even so the young man lived in the utmost poverty, for his inheritance was small. Lambert returned to Blois at the beginning of the year 1820, driven from Paris by sufferings which all persons without means are compelled to endure there. During his stay, he must often have been a prey to inward storms, to those horrible tempests of thought which shake the artistic soul, if we may judge by the only fact his uncle could remember, and the only letter the good man had preserved of the many Louis wrote him at that period—a letter which probably owed its preservation to the fact that it was the last and longest of all.

Here, in the first place, is the fact. Louis was sitting one evening on a bench in the second gallery of the Théâtre-Français, near one of the columns between which in those days were the third tier of boxes. Rising during the first intermission, he saw a young lady who had just entered the adjoining box. The sight of this woman, young, beautiful, and well-dressed, possibly with bare neck and arms, accompanied by a lover on whom she smiled with all the grace of happy love, produced so cruel an effect upon the soul and senses of Louis Lambert that he was obliged to leave the theatre. If he had not used the last gleams of his reason, which, in the first moment of this fiery passion, did not entirely desert him, he might have succumbed to an almost unconquerable desire to kill the young man at whom the woman looked. It was, in the midst of our world of Paris, a flash of the love of a savage darting on woman as on a prey, the effect of a bestial instinct joined to the rapid and ever luminous outburst of a soul hitherto held down under the weight of thought.

*   *   *

In 1823 I was travelling from Paris to Touraine in the diligence. When we reached Mer the conductor took a passenger for Blois. As he opened the door of the division of the coach in which I was he said to this person, laughing, "You will not be squeezed, Monsieur Lefebre." I was, in fact, alone. Hearing the name, and seeing an old gentleman with white hair who appeared to be an octogenarian, I naturally thought of Lambert's uncle. After a few indirect questions, I found I was not mistaken. The old priest had sold his vintages at Mer and was returning to Blois. I at once asked for news of my school friend. At the first mention of Lambert's name, the face of the old Oratorian, already grave and severe as that of a soldier who has suffered, grew darker and sadder; the lines of his forehead contracted, he pressed his lips together, gave me a doubtful look, and said:

"You have not seen him since your schooldays?"

"No," I answered. "But we are equally guilty of neglect, if neglect it be. You know the eager and adventurous life that young men lead after they leave college; they must meet again before they know if their attachment continues. However, a youthful sentiment sometimes survives, and then it is impossible to forget altogether, especially in the case of such friends as Lambert and I. In college they used to call us the "Poet-and-Pythagoras.' "

I told him my name; but when he heard it his face grew darker still.

"Then you do not know his history?" he said. "My poor nephew was to have married the richest heiress in Blois, but he went mad the evening before his marriage."

"Lambert mad!" I exclaimed, bewildered. "From what cause? His was the richest memory, the best organized mind, the most sagacious judgment I have ever met. Glorious genius! too much inclined, perhaps, to mysticism, but the noblest heart in the world! Some most extraordinary thing must have happened to him."

"I see that you knew him well," said the old man.

From Mer to Blois we talked of my poor comrade with many digressions, through which I learned the particulars of his story which I have already related, in order to give sequence to these facts and render them interesting. I told his uncle of our secret studies and the nature of his nephew's cherished occupations; in return he related to me the chief events of Lambert's life after our separation. According to Monsieur Lefebre's account Lambert must have shown signs of madness before his marriage. But as these symptoms were like those of other men passionately in love, I thought them less characteristic of insanity after I knew Mademoiselle de Villenoix and the ardor of his feeling for her. In the provinces, where ideas have a tendency to rarefy, a man full of novel thoughts and possessed by theories, like Louis, would naturally be considered an original. His very language was surprising—all the more because he seldom talked. He would say of this or that man, "He does not belong to my heaven," just as others might say, "We are not on visiting terms." Every man of genius has his semi-insane points. The greater his genius, the more salient are the peculiarities which constitute the different degrees of his originality. In the provinces an original man is rated as half-insane.

The first words Monsieur Lefebre said made me doubt my comrade's madness; while I listened to the old man I mentally criticised his statements. The most important symptom showed itself several days before the marriage was to take place. Louis had a well-defined attack of catalepsy. He remained standing for fifty-nine hours, motionless, his eyes fixed, without speaking or eating—a purely nervous state into which persons are liable to fall when a prey to violent passions, a phenomenon rare to be sure but whose effects are perfectly well known to physicians. If there were anything extraordinary about this seizure it was that Louis had not already had several attacks of the same malady, to which his habit of ecstasy and the nature of his ideas predisposed him. But his constitution, both external and internal, was so perfect that it had hitherto resisted this strain on his powers. The exaltation to which he was brought by the expectation of his marriage, increased, in him, by the chastity of his body and the power of his soul, might very likely have brought on this nervous crisis, whose results are no better understood than their cause. The foregoing letters, accidentally preserved, show plainly enough his transition from the pure idealism in which he lived to the most acute physical emotions. In our college days we were filled with admiration for that human phenomenon in which Lambert was able to see the temporary separation of our two natures, and the symptoms of a total absence of the inward being using its mysterious faculties under the rule of some cause as yet undiscovered. Catalepsy, a mystery as deep as sleep itself, formed part of the collection of proof which Louis had annexed to his "Treatise on the Will." While Monsieur Lefebre was telling me of Lambert's first attack, I suddenly remembered a conversation we had had on this subject after reading a medical book.

"Deep meditation or glorious ecstasy," he said, "may be catalepsy in the bud."

The day when he expressed this thought thus concisely he had been trying to link all moral phenomena together by a chain of effects—following step by step all actions of the intellect, beginning with the simple stirrings of purely animal instinct, which suffice for so many human beings, especially for certain men whose strength excels in purely mechanical labor; and then passing to the aggregation of thoughts, until he reached comparison, meditation, and finally ecstasy, and thus catalepsy. Undoubtedly Lambert believed, with the artless consciousness of early youth, that he had planned a noble book in thus marshalling the different degrees of mental power in man. I remember that by one of those fatalities which force us to believe in predestination, we happened upon the "Book of the Martyrs," which relates very curious facts as to the complete abolition of corporeal life to which man can attain during the paroxysms of his inward faculties. Reflecting on the effects of fanaticism, Lambert was led to think that the collection of ideas to which we give the name of sentiments might be the material effluence of some fluid which men produce in more or less abundance according to the manner in which their organs absorb the generating substances in the centers where they live. We grew eager in the study of catalepsy, and, with the ardor which lads put into their undertakings, we tried to endure pain by *thinking of other things*. We fatigued ourselves terribly by trying certain experiments analogous to those of the Spasmodics of the last century—a religious fanaticism which will some day be of use to human science. I stood on Lambert's stomach for several minutes without causing him the least pain; but in spite of such foolish experiments, neither of us were attacked with catalepsy.

I have felt it necesary to give the foregoing explanation of my doubts as to Louis' madness, which Monsieur Lefebre's further statement fully confirmed.

"When the attack was over," he said, "my nephew was seized with terror and fell into a state of the profoundest melancholy. He believed himself impotent. I watched him with the solicitude of a mother for her child, and prevented him one day from performing on himself the operation to which Origen supposed he owed his gifts. I took him at once to Paris and placed him under the care of Monsieur Esquirol. During the journey Louis remained in a state of almost continual somnolence, and did not recognize me. The physicians in Paris thought him incurable, and unanimously advised his being left in complete solitude, care being taken that nothing should disturb the quiet necessary for his very improbable recovery; they also advised my keeping him in a cool room, somewhat darkened. Mademoiselle de Villenoix, from whom I concealed his actual condition, followed us to Paris and there learned the decision of the doctors. She asked to see my nephew, who scarcely recognized her; she then determined, after the fashion of noble souls, to consecrate her life to his service and give him the care that was necessary for his recovery. 'I should have been obliged to do so,' she said, 'were he my husband; why should I do less for my lover?' She took Louis to Villenoix, where they have been living for the last two years."

Instead of continuing my journey I stopped at Blois, intending to go and see Louis. The worthy old priest would not let me stay at an inn, but took me to his own house, where he showed me his nephew's room, with the books and articles that belonged to him. As he glanced round it a sad exclamation rose to the old man's lips, revealing the hopes which Lambert's precocious genius had excited in his mind, and the dreary desolation of his irreparable loss.

"That young man knew all things," he said, taking down a volume which contained the writings of Spinoza. "How could a mind so well organized become unhinged?"

"But, Monsieur," I replied, "may it not have been an effect of his vigorous organization? If he is really the victim of that crisis, so insufficiently observed in its manifestations, which we call *insanity*, I am tempted to ascribe the cause to his passion. His studies, his ways of life, had brought his faculties to a degree of power at which the slightest overexcitement of them compelled nature to give way. Love either destroyed them or raised them to some other mode of expression, which, perhaps, we calumniate as madness, without comprehending its true quality. In short, may he not have foreseen in the pleasures of his marriage an obstacle to the perfectibility of his interior senses and to his flight through the spiritual worlds?"

"My dear sir," said the old priest, after listening to me very attentively, "your reasoning is no doubt logical; but even if I agreed with it, the melancholy knowledge it imparts would not comfort me for the loss of my nephew."

Lambert's uncle was one of the men who live only through the heart.

The next day I started for Villenoix. Monsieur Lefebre accompanied me to the gate of Blois. When he had put me into the road which leads to Villenoix he stopped, and said:

"You can easily understand that I never go there. Do not forget what I have said to you. In the presence of Mademoiselle de Villenoix be careful not to appear to see that Louis is mad."

The old priest remained where I left him, looking after me until I was out of sight. It was not without deep emotion that I continued my way to Villenoix. Reflections crowded upon me at every step of the way which Louis had so often traversed with a heart full of hope and a soul elated by the promptings of love. The shrubs, the trees, the caprices of the winding way whose borders were rent here and there by tiny ravines, all had the deepest interest for me; I tried to revive from and through them the thoughts and impressions of my poor comrade. No doubt the evening conversations of which his letters tell, beside the hedge where his mistress met him, had initiated Mademoiselle de Villenoix into the secrets of that vast and noble soul, as in my own case a few years earlier. But the fact which most preoccupied me, and which gave to my pilgrimage a deep interest of curiosity in addition to the half-religious emotions which guided me, was that splendid belief of Mademoiselle de Villenoix in her lover's sanity, of which the old priest had warned me. Had she, as time went on, contracted his madness; or was she able to enter the portals of that soul and comprehend its thoughts, even the most perplexing? I lost myself in meditation over this problem of a sentiment higher than the highest inspirations of love and its noblest devotions. To die for another is a common sacrifice. To live faithful to a single love is a heroism that made Mademoiselle Dupuis immortal. If Napoleon the Great and Lord Byron had successors in the hearts that once loved them, we may be allowed to reverence this widow of Bolingbroke; but Mademoiselle Dupuis possessed the memory of many years of happiness on which to live, while Mademoiselle de Villenoix, knowing nothing of love but its earliest sentiments, seemed to my eyes the type of self-devotion in its broadest expression. If she had become half-mad, she was sublime; but if, on the other hand, she comprehended and interpreted the madness of him she loved, she added to the beauty of a great heart a master-gift of passion worthy of being studied.

When I saw the high towers of the château, a sight that so often had made poor Lambert quiver, my heart beat violently. I had associated myself, so to speak, with his present life and situation by recalling to mind the events of our boyhood. Before long, I entered a deserted courtyard and even entered the vestibule of the château without meeting any one. The noise of my steps brought out an old woman, to whom I gave a letter which Monsieur Lefebre had written to Mademoiselle de Villenoix. Presently the same woman returned to fetch me, and showed me into a lower room, paved with black and white marble and darkened by closed blinds, at the further end of which I saw, very indistinctly, Louis Lambert.

"Will you take this chair, Monsieur?" said a sweet voice which went to my heart.

Mademoiselle de Villenoix was beside me, though I had not perceived her, and now offered me a chair which at first I did not take. The obscurity of the room was so great that until I grew accustomed to it Mademoiselle de Villenoix and Louis seemed two black masses projected from the depths of the murky atmosphere. I sat down, a prey to the feelings which overcome us, almost in spite of ourselves, under the sombre arches of a church: My eyes, still influenced by the sunlight, only gradually grew accustomed to the artificial night.

"This gentleman," she said to him, "is your college friend."

Louis made no reply. I could now see him, and the sight was one that stamped itself upon my memory everlastingly. He stood, both elbows resting on a projection of the wood-work, so that his chest seemed to bend under the weight of his bowed head. His hair, which was long like that of a woman, fell over his shoulders and round his face in a manner that gave him some resemblance to the busts of great men of the time of Louis XIV. His face was perfectly white. He rubbed one leg against the other habitually, with a mechanical movement that nothing could check, and the continual friction of the two bones produced a distressing noise. Near him was a mattress made of moss, lying on a plank.

"He seldom lies down," Mademoiselle de Villenoix said to me. "When he does, he sleeps for several days."

Louis stood, just as I now saw him, day and night, with fixed eyes, never raising or lowering the lids, as others do. Having asked Mademoiselle de Villenoix whether a little more light would pain him, I slightly opened one blind, and could then see the expression of my friend's countenance. Alas! already wrinkled, already blanched! no longer any light in the eyes, which were glassy like those of the blind. All his features seemed drawn by some convulsion toward the top of his head. I tried to speak to him from time to time; but he did not hear me. He was a corpse snatched from a tomb, a sort of conquest won by life over death, or by death over life. I was there nearly an hour, lost in undefinable revery, harrowed by afflicting thoughts. I listened to Mademoiselle de Villenoix who told me all the details of this, as it were, infant life. Suddenly Louis ceased to rub his legs one against the other, and said slowly, "*The angels are white.*"

I cannot explain the effect produced upon me by these words, by the sound of that loved voice, by the tones I was painfully awaiting, which now seemed to take him forever away from me. In spite of myself, tears filled my eyes. An involuntary consciousness passed rapidly through my soul, and made me doubt more strongly than ever if Louis' reason had left him. I was very certain that he neither saw nor heard me, but the harmonics of that voice, which seemed to speak a joy divine, communicated to the words he had uttered an irresistible power. Incomplete revelation of an unknown world, that saying echoed in our souls like some glorious chime of bells heard in the silence of a darksome night. I no longer wondered why Mademoiselle de Villenoix thought him sane. Perhaps the life of the soul had annihilated the life of the body. Perhaps his companion had had, as I had then, vague intuitions of that melodious and flowering Nature which we call, in its highest development, HEAVEN. This woman, this angel, was ever there, sitting at her tapestry frame, and looking up to him with a sad and tender expression as she drew the needle through her work. Unable to bear the dreadful sight, for I could not, like Mademoiselle de Villenoix, divine its secrets, I left the room; she followed me and we walked up and down for some time while she spoke of herself and of Lambert.

"No doubt Louis appears to be insane," she said, "but he is not so, if the word insanity is applied only to those whose brain, from unknown causes, becomes vitiated, and who are, therefore, unable to give a reason for their acts. The equilibrium of my husband's mind is perfect. If he does not recognize you corporeally, do not think that he has not seen you. He is able to disengage his body and to see us under another form, I know not of what nature. When he speaks, he says marvellous things. Only, in fact often, he completes in speech an idea begun in the silence of his mind, or else he begins a proposition in words and finishes it mentally. To other men he must appear insane; to me, who live in his thought, all his ideas are lucid. I follow the path of his mind; and though I cannot understand many of its turnings and digressions, I, nevertheless, reach the end with him. Does it not often happen that while thinking of some trifling matter, we are drawn into serious thought by the gradual unfolding of ideas and recollections? Often, after speaking of some frivolous thing, the accidental point of departure for rapid meditation, a thinker forgets, or neglects to mention the abstract links which have led him to his conclusions, and takes up in speech only the last rings in the chain of reflections. Common minds to whom this quickness of mental vision is unknown, and who are ignorant of the inward travail of the soul, laugh at dreamers and call them madmen if they are given to such forgetfulness of connecting thoughts. Louis is always so; he wings his way through the spaces of thought with the agility of a swallow; yet I can follow him in all his circlings. That is the history of his so-called madness. Perhaps he will one day return to this world in which we vegetate; but if now he breathes the air of heaven before the time appointed for us to live there, why should we wish him back among us? I am content to hear the beating of his heart; it is happiness enough for me to live beside him. Is he not all mine? Twice in the last two years and at separate times, I have regained him for several days—once in Switzerland, and again in Brittany, where I took him for sea-bathing. I can live on those memories."

*   *   *

Hebephrenia

3. The diagnosis hebephrenia is applied to schizophrenics whose most typical symptom is silly, inappropriate behavior with unpredictable giggling and bizarre mannerisms. The characteristic clinical picture is most common in women, and the figure of Ophelia in Shakespeare's *Hamlet* demonstrates these aspects of this condition. After her father is killed by the man she loves, she is confronted with insurmountable emotional hurdles and regresses to bizarre and inappropriate behavior.

Many psychiatrists today consider hebephrenia a result of chronic deterioration frequently produced by poor or inadequate care. It is a condition which some psychiatrists believe is produced by the social isolation that can occur in large, overcrowded hospitals where many patients go for weeks and months without meaningful personal interaction.

These patients demonstrate profound regression with neglect of personal habits; bizarre language; inappropriate, rapidly fluctuating emotions; poorly formed delusions; and hallucinations. They may be denudative or wear bizarre costumes and carry bundles filled with a strange assortment of mementoes. A feature frequently noted is delusions of body disintegration.

It is, however, the inappropriate emotional responses of this type of schizophrenia which somehow most dramatically illustrate madness. Shakespeare utilizes it in the tragic figure of Ophelia.

HAMLET

William Shakespeare   (1564–1616)

Enter OPHELIA *distracted.*

OPHELIA. Where is the beauteous Majesty of Denmark?
QUEEN. How now, Ophelia?

OPHELIA (*sings*). How should I your true-love know
> From another one?
> By his cockle hat and staff
> And his sandal shoon.

QUEEN. Alas, sweet lady, what imports this song?
OPHELIA. Say you? Nay, pray you mark.

[*Sings*] He is dead and gone, lady,
> He is dead and gone;
> At his head a grass-green turf,
> At his heels a stone.

O, ho!
QUEEN. Nay, but Ophelia—
OPHELIA. Pray you mark.

[*Sings*] White his shroud as the mountain snow—

Enter KING.

QUEEN. Alas, look here, my lord!

From *Hamlet* by William Shakespeare. Act IV, Scenes V and VII (excerpts).

OPHELIA (*sings*). Larded all with sweet flowers;
    Which bewept to the grave did not go
    With true-love showers.

KING. How do you, pretty lady?

OPHELIA. Well, God dild you! They say the owl was a baker's daughter. Lord, we know what we are, but know not what we may be. God be at your table!

KING. Conceit upon her father.

OPHELIA. Pray let's have no words of this; but when they ask you what it means, say you this:

[*Sings*]   To-morrow is Saint Valentine's day,
       All in the morning betime,
    And I a maid at your window,
       To be your Valentine.

    Then up he rose and donn'd his clo'es
       And dupp'd the chamber door,
    Let in the maid, that out a maid
       Never departed more.

KING. Pretty Ophelia!

OPHELIA. Indeed, la, without an oath, I'll make an end on't!

[*Sings*]   By Gis and by Saint Charity,
       Alack, and fie for shame!
    Young men will do't if they come to't.
       By Cock, they are to blame.

    Quoth she, 'Before you tumbled me,
       You promis'd me to wed.'

He answers:

    'So would I 'a' done, by yonder sun,
       An thou hadst not come to my bed.'

KING. How long hath she been thus?

OPHELIA. I hope all will be well. We must be patient; but I cannot choose but weep to think they would lay him i' th' cold ground. My brother shall know of it; and so I thank you for your good counsel. Come, my coach! Good night, ladies. Good night, sweet ladies. Good night, good night.   *Exit.*

KING. Follow her close; give her good watch, I pray you.

[*Exit* HORATIO.]

O, this is the poison of deep grief; it springs
All from her father's death. O Gertrude, Gertrude,
When sorrows come, they come not single spies,
But in battalions! First, her father slain;

Next, your son gone, and he most violent author
Of his own just remove; the people muddied,
Thick and unwholesome in their thoughts and whispers
For good Polonius' death, and we have done but greenly
In hugger-mugger to inter him; poor Ophelia
Divided from herself and her fair judgment,
Without the which we are pictures or mere beasts.

*   *   *

A noise within: 'Let her come in.'

LAERTES. How now? What noise is that?

Enter OPHELIA.

O heat, dry up my brains! Tears seven times salt
Burn out the sense and virtue of mine eye!
By heaven, thy madness shall be paid by weight
Till our scale turn the beam. O rose of May!
Dear maid, kind sister, sweet Ophelia!
O heavens! is't possible a young maid's wits
Should be as mortal as an old man's life?
Nature is fine in love, and where 'tis fine,
It sends some precious instance of itself
After the thing it loves.

OPHELIA (*sings*).
> They bore him barefac'd on the bier
> (Hey non nony, nony, hey nony)
> And in his grave rain'd many a tear.

Fare you well, my dove!

LAERTES. Hadst thou thy wits, and didst persuade revenge,
It could not move thus.

OPHELIA. You must sing 'A-down a-down, and you call him a-down-a.'
O, how the wheel becomes it! It is the false steward, that stole his master's
daughter.

LAERTES. This nothing's more than matter.

OPHELIA. There's rosemary, that's for remembrance. Pray you, love,
remember: And there is pansies, that's for thoughts.

LAERTES. A document in madness! Thoughts and remembrance fitted.

OPHELIA. There's fennel for you, and columbines. There's rue for you,
and here's some for me. We may call it herb of grace o' Sundays. O, you
must wear your rue with a difference! There's a daisy. I would give you
some violets, but they wither'd all when my father died. They say he
made a good end.

[*Sings*]   For bonny sweet Robin is all my joy.

LAERTES. Thought and affliction, passion, hell itself,
She turns to favour and to prettiness.

OPHELIA (*sings*).
> And will he not come again?
> And will he not come again?
>   No, no, he is dead;
>   Go to thy deathbed;
> He never will come again.

> His beard was as white as snow,
> All flaxen was his poll.
>   He is gone, he is gone,
>   And we cast away moan.
> God 'a' mercy on his soul!

And of all Christian souls, I pray God. God b' wi' you.

*   *   *

Enter QUEEN.

KING. How now, sweet queen?
QUEEN. One woe doth tread upon another's heel,
So fast they follow. Your sister's drown'd, Laertes.
LAERTES. Drown'd! O, where?
QUEEN. There is a willow grows aslant a brook,
That shows his hoar leaves in the glassy stream.
There with fantastic garlands did she come
Of crowflowers, nettles, daisies, and long purples,
That liberal shepherds give a grosser name,
But our cold maids do dead men's fingers call them.
There on the pendent boughs her coronet weeds
Clamb'ring to hang, an envious sliver broke,
When down her weedy trophies and herself
Fell in the weeping brook. Her clothes spread wide
And, mermaid-like, awhile they bore her up;
Which time she chaunted snatches of old tunes,
As one incapable of her own distress,
Or like a creature native and indued
Unto that element; but long it could not be
Till that her garments, heavy with their drink,
Pull'd the poor wretch from her melodious lay
To muddy death.

Paranoid Schizophrenia

4. Today paranoia is the most commonly diagnosed
form of schizophrenia. Although paranoid thinking may
develop as early as adolescence, the peak incidence is around the

third to fourth decade. These patients typically are delusional, believing that they are being plotted against or persecuted; they are often grandiose; and frequently there are auditory hallucinations. They have the idea that everything that occurs around them is in some way related to them. Such misinterpretation of reality is quite common, and has been called "ideas of reference." Sexual anxiety and concerns about homosexuality are common in this condition.

Paranoid schizophrenia has already been illustrated in Chapter 1, using an example from Chekhov. There, feelings of persecution are the prominent feature. This example from Gogol illustrates a type of paranoia that strangely enough is common in European psychoses, but less so in American experience; in these cases grandiosity is the major feature. Grandiosity has fascinated psychiatrists familiar with the symptoms of schizophrenia. It is an issue in every schizophrenic, and in the analysis of most delusions a secret kernel of grandiosity is uncovered. Where it originates and why is still unclear, and yet for those who work intensively with schizophrenics it always emerges as an important factor. Even behind the persecutory delusions there stands the question why one is so important that he has been selected for such an extensive and complicated attack by so many powerful organizations.

"The Diary of a Madman" carefully records the development of grandiosity paralleled by the break with reality. The last tragi-comic note in the story suggests the beginning of a deterioration into hebephrenia.

THE DIARY OF A MADMAN

Nicolai Gogol   (1809–1852)

Year 2000, April 43

This is a day of great jubilation. Spain has a king. They've found him. *I* am the King. I discovered it today. It all came to me in a flash. It's incredible to me now that I could have imagined that I was a civil-service

From *The Diary of a Madman and Other Stories* by Nicolai Gogol, translated by Andrew R. MacAndrew. Copyright © 1961 by Andrew R. MacAndrew. Published by arrangement with The New American Library of World Literature, Inc., New York.

clerk. How could such a crazy idea ever have entered my head? Thank
God no one thought of slapping me into a lunatic asylum. Now I see
everything clearly, as clearly as if it lay in the palm of my hand. But what
was happening to me before? Then things loomed at me out of a fog.
Now, I believe that all troubles stem from the misconception that human
brains are located in the head. They are not: human brains are blown in
by the winds from somewhere around the Caspian Sea.

Marva was the first to whom I revealed my identity. When she heard
that she was facing the King of Spain, she flung up her hands in awe. She
almost died of terror. The silly woman had never seen a King of Spain
before. However, I tried to calm her and, speaking graciously, did my
best to assure her of my royal favor. I was not going to hold against her
all the times she had failed to shine my boots properly. The masses are so
ignorant. One can't talk to them on lofty subjects. Probably she was so
frightened because she thought that all kings of Spain are like Philip II.
But I carefully pointed out that I wasn't like Philip II at all. I didn't go to
the office. The hell with it. No, my friends, you won't entice me there
now; never again shall I copy your dreadful documents.

Martober 86. Between day and night

Today, our Divisional Chief sent someone to make me go to the office. I
hadn't been there for over three weeks. I went, just for a lark. The Divisional Chief expected me to come apologizing to him but I just looked at
him indifferently, with not too much ire, nor too much benevolence
either; then I sat down in my usual place as though unaware of the people
around me. I looked around at all that scribbling rabble and thought: If
only you had an inkling of who's sitting here among you, oh Lord, what
a fuss you'd make. There'd be a terrific to-do and the Divisional Chief
himself would bow deeply to me, as he does to the Director. They put
some papers in front of me which I was supposed to abstract or something.
I didn't even stir. A few minutes later, there was a general commotion.
They said the Director was on his way. Several clerks jumped up, hoping
he'd notice them. But I didn't budge. When word came that the Director
was about to pass through our Division, they all buttoned up their coats.
I did nothing of the sort. What kind of a Director does he think he is?
Who says I should get up for him? Never! He's an old cork, not a
Director. Yes, just an ordinary cork, the kind used for stoppering a bottle.
That's all he is. But the funniest thing of all was when they gave me a
paper to sign. They expected I'd sign it in the corner: head clerk such
and such. Well, let them think again. I wrote in the main space, the one
reserved for the Director's signature: Ferdinand VIII. You should have
witnessed the awed silence that followed; but I merely waved my hand

graciously and said: "Dispense with the manifestation of allegiance!" and walked out of the room. From there, I went straight to the Director's house. He was not at home. The footman tried to stop me from going in but what I said made his arms drop limp at his sides. I went straight to her boudoir. She was sitting in front of her mirror. She jumped up and stepped back, away from me. Still I did not tell her that I was the King of Spain. I simply told her that she couldn't even imagine the happiness awaiting her and that despite all our enemies' intrigues, we would be together. I did not want to say more and left. Oh, women are such perfidious things! Only now did I understand what a woman is like. So far, no one has found out whom Woman is in love with. I was the first to discover it: Woman is in love with the Devil. And I'm not joking either. Physicists write a lot of drivel about her being this, that and the other. She loves only the Devil. Look, do you see over there, in the front tier of the boxes? She raises her lorgnette. You think she's looking at that fat man with the star over there? Nothing of the sort. She's staring at the Devil, the Devil hiding behind the fat man's back. See, now he has hidden himself in the star and he's beckoning to her with his finger! And she'll marry him too. She will for sure. As for all the rest of them, all those who lick boots and proclaim their patriotism, all they really want is annuities and more annuities. Some patriots! They'd sell their mother, their father, and their God for money, the strutting betrayers of Christ! And all this crazy ambition and vanity come from the little bubble under the tongue which has a tiny worm about the size of a pinhead in it, and it's all the work of a barber on Pea Street. I can't recall his name but the moving force behind it all is the Sultan of Turkey who pays the barber to spread Mohammedanism all over the world. They say that in France, already, the majority of the people have embraced the Mohammedan faith.

No date. A day without date

Went along Nevsky Avenue incognito. Saw the Tsar riding past. Everybody was doffing his hat, and so did I. I gave no sign that I was the King of Spain. I thought it would be undignified to reveal my identity there, in front of all those people, that it would be more proper to be presented at Court first. What has prevented me so far is the fact that I haven't got Spanish royal attire. If only I could get hold of a royal mantle of some sort. I thought of having one made but tailors are so stupid. Besides, they don't seem to be interested in their trade nowadays and go in for speculation, so that most of them end up mending roads. I decided to make a mantle out of my best coat, which I had only worn twice. But I didn't want those good-for-nothings to mess it all up—I preferred to do it myself. I locked my door so as not to be seen. I had to cut my coat to ribbons with the scissors since a mantle has a completely different style.

*Can't remember the day. Nor
was there a month. Damned if
I know what's been going on*

The mantle is ready. Marva really let out a yell when I put it on. Even so,
I still don't feel ready to be presented at Court. My retinue hasn't as yet
arrived from Spain. The absence of a retinue would be incompatible with
my dignity. I'm expecting them at any time.

1st Date

I'm puzzled by the unaccountable delay in the arrival of my retinue.
What can be holding them up? I went to the post office and inquired
whether the Spanish delegates had arrived. But the postmaster is an utter
fool and knows nothing: No, he says, there are no Spanish delegates
around here but if you wish to mail a letter, we'll accept it. What the hell
is he talking about? What letter? Letter my foot! Let druggists write
letters. . . .

Madrid, Februarius the thirtieth

So I'm in Spain. It all happened so quickly that I hardly had time to
realize it. This morning the Spanish delegation finally arrived for me and
we all got into a carriage. I was somewhat bewildered by the extraordinary speed at which we traveled. We went so fast that in half an hour
we reached the Spanish border. But then, nowadays there are railroads all
over Europe and the ships go so fast too. Spain is a strange country. When
we entered the first room, I saw a multitude of people with shaven heads.
I soon realized, though, that these must be Dominican or Capuchin monks
because they always shave their heads. I also thought that the manners of
the King's Chancellor, who was leading me by the hand, were rather
strange. He pushed me into a small room and said: "You sit quiet and
don't you call yourself King Ferdinand again or I'll beat the nonsense out
of your head." But I knew that I was just being tested and refused to sub-
mit. For this, the Chancellor hit me across the back with a stick, twice,
so painfully that I almost let out a cry. But I contained myself, remembering that this is customary procedure among knights on initiation into an
exalted order. To this day, they adhere to the chivalric code in Spain.

   Left to myself, I decided to devote some time to affairs of state. I
have discovered that China and Spain are the same thing and it's only
ignorance that makes people take them for two separate countries. I advise anybody who doubts it to take a piece of paper and write the word
"Spain" and they'll see for themselves that it comes out "China." I also
gave much thought to a sad event that must occur tomorrow at seven
o'clock. As foreseen by the famous English chemist Wellington, the
Earth will mount the Moon. I confess I was deeply worried when I
thought of the Moon's extraordinary sensitivity and fragility. The Moon,
of course, is made in Hamburg, and I must say they do a very poor job.

I wonder why England doesn't do something about it. It's a lame cooper that makes the Moon, and it's quite obvious that the fool has no conception of what the Moon should be. He uses tarred rope and olive oil and that's why the stench is so awful all over the Earth and we are forced to plug our noses. And that's why the Moon itself is such a delicate ball that men cannot live there—only noses. And that's why we can't see our own noses: they are all on the Moon. And when I thought what a heavy thing the Earth is and that, sitting down on the Moon, it would crush our noses into a powder, I became so worried that I put on my socks and shoes and rushed into the State Council Room to order my police force to stand by to prevent the Earth from mounting the Moon. The Capuchin monks I found in the State Council Room were very clever people and when I said, "Gentlemen, let's save the Moon, the Earth is preparing to mount it," they all rushed at once to execute my royal wish and many tried to climb the wall to reach the Moon. But at that moment, the Grand Chancellor came in. As soon as they saw him, they scattered. Being the King, I remained there alone. But to my surprise, the Chancellor hit me with his stick and chased me into my room. Such is the power of popular tradition in Spain!

> *January of the same year which*
> *happened after Februarius*

I still can't make out what sort of a place Spain is. The customs and the etiquette at the Court are quite incredible. I don't see, I don't grasp it, I don't understand at all! Today, they shaved my head, although I shouted with all my might that I did not want to become a monk. But then they began to drip cold water on my head and everything went blank. Never have I been through such hell. I just can't understand the point of this peculiar custom, so stupid, so senseless. And the irresponsibility of the kings who never got around to outlawing this custom is quite beyond me.

Some indications make me wonder whether I haven't fallen into the hands of the Inquisition. Maybe the man I took for the Chancellor is really the Grand Inquisitor himself? But then, I can't see how the King can be subjected to the Inquisition. True, this could be the work of France, especially Polignac. That Polignac is an absolute beast. He has sworn to drive me to my death. And so he maneuvers on and on. But I know, my fine fellow, that you in turn are being led by the English. The English are great politicians. They sow the seeds of dissension everywhere. The whole world knows that when England takes snuff, France sneezes.

> *25th Date*

Today, the Grand Inquisitor entered my room. I heard his steps approaching while he was still far off and hid under a chair. He looked around and, not seeing me, he began to call out. First he shouted my name and civil-

service rank. I remained silent. Then, Ferdinand VIII, King of Spain! I
was about to stick my head out but thought to myself: No, they won't
get me that way! They may want to pour cold water on my head again.
But he saw me and chased me out from under the chair with his stick. His
damn stick hurts dreadfully. But my very latest discovery made me feel
better: I had found that every rooster has his own Spain and he has it
under his feathers. The Grand Inquisitor left very angry, threatening me
with some punishment or other. Of course, I completely ignored his helpless fury. I knew he was a puppet. A tool of England.

da 34 te Mnth. Yr. yraurbeF 349

No, I have no strength left. I can't stand any more. My God! What
they're doing to me! They pour cold water on my head. They don't
listen to me, they don't hear me, they don't see me. What have I done to
them? Why do they torture me so? What do they want from me? What
can I give them? I haven't anything to give. I have no strength, I cannot
bear this suffering, my head is on fire, and everything goes around me in
circles. Save me! Take me away from here! Give me a carriage with
horses swift as wind! Drive on, coachman, let the harness bells ring! Soar
upward, my horses, carry me away from this world! Further, further,
where I will see nothing, nothing. There is the sky smoking before me. A
star twinkles far away, the forest rushes past with its dark trees and the
crescent moon. The violet fog is a carpet underfoot. I hear the twanging
of a guitar string through the fog; on one side, the sea, and on the other,
Italy. Then Russian huts come into sight. Perhaps that's my house over
there, looking blue in the distance. And isn't that my mother sitting by
the window? Mother, save your wretched son! Let your tears fall on his
sick head! See how they torture him! Hold me, a poor waif, in your arms.
There's no room for him in this world. They are chasing him. Mother,
take pity on your sick child. . . .

And, by the way, have you heard that the Dey of Algiers has a wart
right under his nose?

Acute Undifferentiated Schizophrenia

5.   A large number of schizophrenic patients have
symptoms representative of two or more subtypes of
schizophrenia. This mixture is particularly common in patients
in their late teens and twenties who frequently have both
paranoid and catatonic elements; less often hebephrenic
features appear as part of the symptoms. Schizophrenia in some
of these cases seems to have a relatively acute onset, although
this impression often melts away on prolonged contact with the
patient and family. Symptoms at the outset are variable; there

may be excitement or depression, confused thinking, emotional turmoil, dreamlike states, and emotional outbursts with intense fear and anxiety. When the onset is acute, some traumatic event may occasionally be discovered which seems to contribute to the sudden breakdown. Sometimes the trauma is found to be sexual in nature, especially in the younger age groups with acute onset.

F. Scott Fitzgerald described such an instance in *Tender Is the Night*. The heroine develops acute schizophrenic symptoms following an incestuous relationship with her father. This dramatic chapter, as the father confesses his involvement, has seemed bizarre and unreal to some literary critics. It is not unreal to psychiatrists who work with young schizophrenics where frequently after prolonged investigation and treatment such a precipitating event will be uncovered and confirmed by patient and family. Fitzgerald's chapter also reveals some of the difficulties involved in obtaining an accurate history of the important events when members of the family hold back out of conscious or unconscious guilt and shame.

TENDER IS THE NIGHT

F. Scott Fitzgerald   (1896–1940)

. . . About a year and a half before, Doctor Dohmler had some vague correspondence with an American gentleman living in Lausanne, a Mr. Devereux Warren, of the Warren family of Chicago. A meeting was arranged and one day Mr. Warren arrived at the clinic with his daughter Nicole, a girl of sixteen. She was obviously not well and the nurse who was with her took her to walk about the grounds while Mr. Warren had his consultation.

Warren was a strikingly handsome man looking less than forty. He was a fine American type in every way, tall, broad, well-made—"un homme très chic," as Doctor Dohmler described him to Franz. His large gray eyes were sun-veined from rowing on Lake Geneva, and he had that special air about him of having known the best of this world. The conversation was in German, for it developed that he had been educated at Göttingen. He was nervous and obviously very moved by his errand.

"Doctor Dohmler, my daughter isn't right in the head. I've had lots of specialists and nurses for her and she's taken a couple of rest cures but the thing has grown too big for me and I've been strongly recommended to come to you."

"Very well," said Doctor Dohmler. "Suppose you start at the beginning and tell me everything."

"There isn't any beginning, at least there isn't any insanity in the family that I know of, on either side. Nicole's mother died when she was eleven and I've sort of been father and mother both to her, with the help of governesses—father and mother both to her."

He was very moved as he said this. Doctor Dohmler saw that there were tears in the corners of his eyes and noticed for the first time that there was whiskey on his breath.

"As a child she was a darling thing—everybody was crazy about her, everybody that came in contact with her. She was smart as a whip and happy as the day is long. She liked to read or draw or dance or play the piano—anything. I used to hear my wife say she was the only one of our children who never cried at night. I've got an older girl, too, and there was a boy that died, but Nicole was—Nicole was—Nicole——"

He broke off and Doctor Dohmler helped him.

"She was a perfectly normal, bright, happy child."

"Perfectly."

Doctor Dohmler waited. Mr. Warren shook his head, blew a long sigh, glanced quickly at Doctor Dohmler and then at the floor again.

"About eight months ago, or maybe it was six months ago or maybe ten—I try to figure but I can't remember exactly where we were when she began to do funny things—crazy things. Her sister was the first one to say anything to me about it—because Nicole was always the same to me," he added rather hastily, as if some one had accused him of being to blame, "—the same loving little girl. The first thing was about a valet."

"Oh, yes," said Doctor Dohmler, nodding his venerable head, as if, like Sherlock Holmes, he had expected a valet and only a valet to be introduced at this point.

"I had a valet—been with me for years—Swiss, by the way." He looked up for Doctor Dohmler's patriotic approval. "And she got some crazy idea about him. She thought he was making up to her—of course, at the time I believed her and I let him go, but I know now it was all nonsense."

"What did she claim he had done?"

"That was the first thing—the doctors couldn't pin her down. She just looked at them as if they ought to know what he'd done. But she certainly meant he'd made some kind of indecent advances to her—she didn't leave us in any doubt of that."

"I see."

"Of course, I've read about women getting lonesome and thinking there's a man under the bed and all that, but why should Nicole get such an idea? She could have all the young men she wanted. We were in Lake Forest—that's a summer place near Chicago where we have a place—and she was out all day playing golf or tennis with boys. And some of them pretty gone on her at that."

All the time Warren was talking to the dried old package of Doctor Dohmler, one section of the latter's mind kept thinking intermittently of Chicago. Once in his youth he could have gone to Chicago as fellow and docent at the university, and perhaps become rich there and owned his own clinic instead of being only a minor shareholder in a clinic. But when he had thought of what he considered his own thin knowledge spread over that whole area, over all those wheat fields, those endless prairies, he had decided against it. But he had read about Chicago in those days, about the great feudal families of Armour, Palmer, Field, Crane, Warren, Swift, and McCormick and many others, and since that time not a few patients had come to him from that stratum of Chicago and New York.

"She got worse," continued Warren. "She had a fit or something—the things she said got crazier and crazier. Her sister wrote some of them down—" He handed a much-folded piece of paper to the doctor. "Almost always about men going to attack her, men she knew or men on the street—anybody——"

He told of their alarm and distress, of the horrors families go through under such circumstances, of the ineffectual efforts they had made in America, finally of the faith in a change of scene that had made him run the submarine blockade and bring his daughter to Switzerland.

"—on a United States cruiser," he specified with a touch of hauteur. "It was possible for me to arrange that, by a stroke of luck. And, may I add," he smiled apologetically, "that as they say: money is no object."

"Certainly not," agreed Dohmler dryly.

He was wondering why and about what the man was lying to him. Or, if he was wrong about that, what was the falsity that pervaded the whole room, the handsome figure in tweeds sprawling in his chair with a sportsman's ease? That was a tragedy out there, in the February day, the young bird with wings crushed somehow, and inside here it was all too thin, thin and wrong.

"I would like—to talk to her—a few minutes now," said Doctor Dohmler, going into English as if it would bring him closer to Warren.

Afterward when Warren had left his daughter and returned to Lausanne, and several days had passed, the doctor and Franz entered upon Nicole's card:

> Diagnostic: Schizophrénie. Phase aiguë en décroissance. La peur des hommes est un symptôme de la maladie, et n'est point constitutionnelle. . . . Le pronostic doit rester réservé.*

Diagnosis: Divided Personality. Acute and down-hill phase of the illness. The fear of men is a symptom of the illness and is not at all constitutional. . . . The prognosis must be reserved.

And then they waited with increasing interest as the days passed for Mr. Warren's promised second visit.

It was slow in coming. After a fortnight Doctor Dohmler wrote. Confronted with further silence he committed what was for those days "une folie," and telephoned to the Grand Hotel at Vevey. He learned from Mr. Warren's valet that he was at the moment packing to sail for America. But reminded that the forty francs Swiss for the call would show up on the clinic books, the blood of the Tuileries Guard rose to Doctor Dohmler's aid and Mr. Warren was got to the phone.

"It is—absolutely necessary—that you come. Your daughter's health—all depends. I can take no responsibility."

"But look here, Doctor, that's just what you're for. I have a hurry call to go home!"

Doctor Dohmler had never yet spoken to any one so far away but he dispatched his ultimatum so firmly into the phone that the agonized American at the other end yielded. Half an hour after this second arrival on the Zurichsee, Warren had broken down, his fine shoulders shaking with awful sobs inside his easyfitting coat, his eyes redder than the very sun on Lake Geneva, and they had the awful story.

"It just happened," he said hoarsely. "I don't know—I don't know.

"After her mother died when she was little she used to come into my bed every morning, sometimes she'd sleep in my bed. I was sorry for the little thing. Oh, after that, whenever we went places in an automobile or a train we used to hold hands. She used to sing to me. We used to say, 'Now let's not pay any attention to anybody else this afternoon—let's just have each other—for this morning you're mine.'" A broken sarcasm came into his voice. "People used to say what a wonderful father and daughter we were—they used to wipe their eyes. We were just like lovers—and then all at once we were lovers—and ten minutes after it happened I could have shot myself—except I guess I'm such a Goddamned degenerate I didn't have the nerve to do it."

"Then what?" said Doctor Dohmler, thinking again of Chicago and of a mild pale gentleman with a pince-nez who had looked him over in Zurich thirty years before. "Did this thing go on?"

"Oh, no! She almost—she seemed to freeze up right away. She'd just say, 'Never mind, never mind, Daddy. It doesn't matter. Never mind.'"

"There were no consequences?"

"No." He gave one short convulsive sob and blew his nose several times. "Except now there're plenty of consequences."

As the story concluded Dohmler sat back in the focal armchair of the middle class and said to himself sharply, "Peasant!"—it was one of the few absolute worldly judgments that he had permitted himself for twenty years. Then he said:

"I would like for you to go to a hotel in Zurich and spend the night and come see me in the morning."

"And then what?"

Doctor Dohmler spread his hands wide enough to carry a young pig. "Chicago," he suggested. . . .

Chronic Undifferentiated Schizophrenia

6. If a mixture of schizophrenic symptoms persists, it is eventually diagnosed as chronic rather than acute. Sartre's example provides a picture of chronic paranoid and catatonic features. Like Balzac's "Louis Lambert," this story also shows the effort of a loving person to maintain emotional contact.

The impact of schizophrenia on a family unit is hard to imagine. Not infrequently a family will attempt to deny or minimize the illness. Rarely, a wife or mother will be so caught up in the symptoms and pathological ideas of her husband or child that she willingly, or because of her own psychological instability, enters into the delusional system rather than lose emotional contact. When such dual participation in the psychopathology results in a break with reality, the condition is called folie à deux. Sartre, in his powerful story "The Room," has brilliantly illustrated a woman hovering at the brink of entering the world of her husband's madness.

The Room

Jean-Paul Sartre   (1905–   )

. . . She opened the door and entered the room.

The heavy odor of incense filled her mouth and nostrils as she opened her eyes and stretched out her hands for a long time the perfume and the gloom had meant nothing more to her than a single element, acrid and heavy, as simple, as familiar as water, air or fire—and she prudently advanced toward a pale stain which seemed to float in the fog. It was Pierre's face: Pierre's clothing (he dressed in black ever since he had been sick) melted in obscurity. Pierre had thrown back his head and closed his eyes. He was handsome. Eve looked at his long, curved lashes, then sat close to him on the low chair. *He seems to be suffering*, she thought. Little by little her eyes grew used to the darkness. The bureau emerged

From *Intimacy* by Jean-Paul Sartre, translated by Lloyd Alexander. Copyright 1948 by New Directions.

first, then the bed, then Pierre's personal things: scissors, the pot of glue, books, the herbarium which shed its leaves onto the rug near the arm-chair.

"Agatha?"

Pierre had opened his eyes. He was watching her, smiling. "You know, that fork?" he said. "I did it to frighten that fellow. There was *almost* nothing the matter with it."

Eve's apprehensions faded and she gave a light laugh. "You suc-ceeded," she said. "You drove him completely out of his mind."

Pierre smiled. "Did you see? He played with it a long time, he held it right in his hands. The trouble is," he said, "they don't know how to take hold of things; they grab them."

"That's right," Eve said.

Pierre tapped the palm of his left hand lightly with the index finger of his right.

"They take with that. They reach out their fingers and when they catch hold of something they crack down on it to knock it out."

He spoke rapidly and hardly moving his lips; he looked puzzled.

"I wonder what they want," he said at last, "that fellow has already been here. Why did they send him to me? If they want to know what I'm doing all they have to do is read it on the screen, they don't even need to leave the house. They make mistakes. They have the power but they make mistakes. I never make any, that's my trump card. *Hoffka!*" he said. He shook his long hands before his forehead. "The bitch Hoffka! Paffka! Suffka! Do you want any more?"

"Is it the bell?" asked Eve.

"Yes. It's gone." He went on severely. "This fellow, he's just a sub-ordinate. You know him, you went into the living room with him."

Eve did not answer.

"What did he want?" asked Pierre. "He must have told you."

She hesitated an instant, then answered brutally. "He wanted you locked up."

When the truth was told quietly to Pierre he distrusted it. He had to be dealt with violently in order to daze and paralyze his suspicions. Eve preferred to brutalize him rather than lie: when she lied and he acted as if he believed it she could not avoid a very slight feeling of superiority which made her horrified at herself.

"Lock me up!" Pierre repeated ironically. "They're crazy. What can walls do to me. Maybe they think that's going to stop me. I sometimes wonder if there aren't two groups. The real one, the Negro—and then a bunch of fools trying to stick their noses in and making mistake after mis-take."

He made his hand jump up from the arm of the chair and looked at it happily.

"I can get through walls. What did you tell them?" he asked, turning to Eve with curiosity.

"Not to lock you up."

He shrugged. "You shouldn't have said that. You made a mistake too . . . unless you did it on purpose. You've got to call their bluff."

He was silent. Eve lowered her head sadly: "*They grab things!*" *How scornfully he said that—and he was right. Do I grab things too? It doesn't do any good to watch myself, I think most of my movements annoy him. But he doesn't say anything.* Suddenly she felt as miserable as when she was fourteen and Mme. Darbedat told her "You don't know what to do with your hands." She didn't dare make a move and just at that time she had an irresistible desire to change her position. Quietly she put her feet under the chair, barely touching the rug. She watched the lamp on the table—the lamp whose base Pierre had painted black—and the chess set. Pierre had left only the black pawns on the board. Sometimes he would get up, go to the table and take the pawns in his hands one by one. He spoke to them, called them Robots and they seemed to stir with a mute life under his fingers. When he set them down, Eve went and touched them in her turn (she always felt somewhat ridiculous about it). They had become little bits of dead wood again but something vague and incomprehensible stayed in them, something like understanding. *These are his things,* she thought. *There is nothing of mine in the room.* She had had a few pieces of furniture before; the mirror and the little inlaid dresser handed down from her grandmother and which Pierre jokingly called "*your* dresser." Pierre had carried them away with him; things showed their true face to Pierre alone. Eve could watch them for hours: they were unflaggingly stubborn and determined to deceive her, offering her nothing but their appearance—as they did to Dr. Franchot and M. Darbedat. *Yet,* she told herself with anguish, *I don't see them quite like my father. It isn't possible for me to see them exactly like him.*

She moved her knees a little: her legs felt as though they were crawling with ants. Her body was stiff and taut and hurt her; she felt it too alive, too demanding. *I would like to be invisible and stay here seeing him without his seeing me. He doesn't need me; I am useless in this room.* She turned her head slightly and looked at the wall above Pierre. Threats were written on the wall. Eve knew it but she could not read them. She often watched the big red roses on the wallpaper until they began to dance before her eyes. The roses flamed in shadow. Most of the time the threat was written near the ceiling, a little to the left of the bed; but sometimes it moved. *I must get up. I can't . . . I can't sit down any longer.* There were also white disks on the wall that looked like slices of onion. The disks spun and Eve's hands began to tremble: *Sometimes I think I'm going mad. But no,* she thought, *I can't go mad. I get nervous, that's all.*

Suddenly she felt Pierre's hand on hers.

"Agatha," Pierre said tenderly.

He smiled at her but he held her hand by the ends of his fingers with a sort of revulsion, as though he had picked up a crab by the back and wanted to avoid its claws.

"Agatha," he said, "I would so much like to have confidence in you."

She closed her eyes and her breast heaved. *I mustn't answer anything, if I do he'll get angry, he won't say anything more.*

Pierre had dropped her hand. "I like you, Agatha," he said, "but I can't understand you. Why do you stay in the room all the time?"

Eve did not answer.

"Tell me why."

"You know I love you," she said dryly.

"I don't believe you," Pierre said. "Why should you love me? I must frighten you: I'm haunted." He smiled but suddenly became serious. "There is a wall between you and me. I see you, I speak to you, but you're on the other side. What keeps us from loving? I think it was easier before. In Hamburg."

"Yes," Eve said sadly. Always Hamburg. He never spoke of their real past. Neither Eve nor he had ever been to Hamburg.

"We used to walk along the canal. There was a barge, remember? The barge was black; there was a dog on the deck."

He made it up as he went along; it sounded false.

"I held your hand. You had another skin. I believed all you told me. Be quiet!" he shouted.

He listened for a moment. "They're coming," he said mournfully.

Eve jumped up. "They're coming? I thought they wouldn't ever come again."

Pierre had been calmer for the past three days; the statues did not come. Pierre was terribly afraid of the statues even though he would never admit it. Eve was not afraid: but when they began to fly, buzzing, around the room, she was afraid of Pierre.

"Give me the ziuthre," Pierre said.

Eve got up and took the ziuthre: it was a collection of pieces of cardboard Pierre had glued together; he used it to conjure the statues. The ziuthre looked like a spider. On one of the cardboards Pierre had written "Power over ambush" and on the other "Black." On a third he had drawn a laughing face with wrinkled eyes: it was Voltaire.

Pierre seized the ziuthre by one end and looked at it darkly.

"I can't use it any more," he said.

"Why?"

"They turned it upside down."

"Will you make another?"

He looked at her for a long while. "You'd like me to, wouldn't you," he said between his teeth.

Eve was angry at Pierre. *He's warned every time they come: how does he do it? He's never wrong.*

The ziuthre dangled pitifully from the ends of Pierre's fingers. *He always finds a good reason not to use it. Sunday when they came he pretended he'd lost it but I saw it behind the paste pot and he couldn't fail to see it. I wonder if he isn't the one who brings them.* One could never tell if he were completely sincere. Sometimes Eve had the impression that despite himself Pierre was surrounded by a swarm of unhealthy thoughts and visions. But at other times Pierre seemed to invent them. *He suffers. But how much does he* believe *in the statues and the Negro. Anyhow, I know he doesn't see the statues, he only hears them: when they pass he turns his head away; but he still says he sees them; he describes them.* She remembered the red face of Dr. Franchot: "But my dear madame, all mentally unbalanced persons are liars; you're wasting your time if you're trying to distinguish between what they really feel and what they pretend to feel." She gave a start. *What is Franchot doing here? I don't want to start thinking like him.*

Pierre had gotten up. He went to throw the ziuthre into the wastebasket: *I want to think like you,* she murmured. He walked with tiny steps, on tiptoe, pressing his elbows against his hips so as to take up the least possible space. He came back and sat down and looked at Eve with a closed expression.

"We'll have to put up black wallpaper," he said. "There isn't enough black in this room."

He was crouched in the armchair. Sadly Eve watched his meager body, always ready to withdraw, to shrink: the arms, legs and head looked like retractable organs. The clock struck six. The piano downstairs was silent. Eve sighed: the statues would not come right away; they had to wait for them.

"Do you want me to turn on the light?"

She would rather not wait for them in darkness.

"Do as you please," Pierre said.

Eve lit the small lamp on the bureau and a red mist filled the room. Pierre was waiting too.

He did not speak but his lips were moving, making two dark stains in the red mist. Eve loved Pierre's lips. Before, they had been moving and sensual; but they had lost their sensuality. They were wide apart, trembling a little, coming together incessantly, crushing against each other only to separate again. They were the only living things in this blank face; they looked like two frightened animals. Pierre could mutter like that for hours without a sound leaving his mouth and Eve often let herself be fascinated by this tiny, obstinate movement. *I love his mouth.* He never kissed her any more; he was horrified at contacts: at night they touched him—the hands of men, hard and dry, pinched him all over; the long-nailed hands of women caressed him. Often he went to bed with his clothes on but the hands slipped under the clothes and tugged at his shirt. Once he heard laughter and puffy lips were placed on his mouth. He never kissed Eve after that night.

"Agatha," Pierre said, "don't look at my mouth."

Eve lowered her eyes.

"I am not unaware that people can learn to read lips," he went on insolently.

His hand trembled on the arm of the chair. The index finger stretched out, tapped three times on the thumb and the other fingers curled: this was a spell. *It's going to start*, she thought. She wanted to take Pierre in her arms.

Pierre began to speak at the top of his voice in a very sophisticated tone.

"Do you remember Sao Paulo?"

No answer. Perhaps it was a trap.

"I met you there," he said, satisfied. "I took you away from a Danish sailor. We almost fought but I paid for a round of drinks and he let me take you away. All that was only a joke."

He's lying, he doesn't believe a word of what he says. He knows my name isn't Agatha. I hate him when he lies. But she saw his staring eyes and her rage melted. *He isn't lying*, she thought, *he can't stand it any more. He feels them coming; he's talking to keep from hearing them.* Pierre dug both hands into the arm of the chair. His face was pale; he was smiling.

"These meetings are often strange," he said, "but I don't believe it's by chance. I'm not asking who sent you. I know you wouldn't answer. Anyhow, you've been smart enough to bluff me."

He spoke with great difficulty, in a sharp, hurried voice. There were words he could not pronounce and which left his mouth like some soft and shapeless substance.

"You dragged me away right in the middle of the party, between the rows of black automobiles, but behind the cars there was an army with red eyes which glowed as soon as I turned my back. I think you made signs to them, all the time hanging on my arm, but I didn't see a thing. I was too absorbed by the great ceremonies of the Coronation."

He looked straight ahead, his eyes wide open. He passed his hand over his forehead very rapidly, in one spare gesture, without stopping his talking. He did not want to stop talking.

"It was the Coronation of the Republic," he said stridently, "an impressive spectacle of its kind because of all the species of animals that the colonies sent for the ceremony. You were afraid to get lost among the monkeys. I said among the monkeys," he repeated arrogantly, looking around him, "I could say *among the Negroes!* The abortions sliding under the tables, trying to pass unseen, are discovered and nailed to the spot by my Look. The password is silence. To be silent. Everything in place and attention for the entrance of the statues, that's the countersign. Tralala . . ." he shrieked and cupped his hands to his mouth. "Tralalala, tralalalala!"

He was silent and Eve knew that the statues had come into the room. He was stiff, pale and distrustful. Eve stiffened too and both waited in silence. Someone was walking in the corridor: it was Marie the housecleaner, she had undoubtedly just arrived. Eve thought, *I have to give her money for the gas.* And then the statues began to fly; they passed between Eve and Pierre.

Pierre went "Ah!" and sank down in the armchair, folding his legs beneath him. He turned his face away; sometimes he grinned, but drops of sweat pearled his forehead. Eve could stand the sight no longer, this pale cheek, this mouth deformed by a trembling grimace; she closed her eyes. Gold threads began to dance on the red background of her eyelids; she felt old and heavy. Not far from her Pierre was breathing violently. *They're flying, they're buzzing, they're bending over him.* She felt a slight tickling, a pain in the shoulder and right side. Instinctively her body bent to the left as if to avoid some disagreeable contact, as if to let a heavy, awkward object pass. Suddenly the floor creaked and she had an insane desire to open her eyes, to look to her right, sweeping the air with her hand.

She did nothing; she kept her eyes closed and a bitter joy made her tremble: *I am afraid too,* she thought. Her entire life had taken refuge in her right side. She leaned toward Pierre without opening her eyes. The slightest effort would be enough and she would enter this tragic world for the first time. *I'm afraid of the statues,* she thought. It was a violent, blind affirmation, an incantation. She wanted to believe in their presence with all her strength. She tried to make a new sense, a sense of touch out of the anguish which paralyzed her right side. She *felt* their passage in her arm, in her side and shoulder.

The statues flew low and gently; they buzzed. Eve knew that they had an evil look and that eyelashes stuck out from the stone around their eyes; but she pictured them badly. She knew, too, that they were not quite alive but that slabs of flesh, warm scales appeared on their great bodies; the stone peeled from the ends of their fingers and their palms were eaten away. Eve could not *see* all that: she simply thought of enormous women sliding against her, solemn and grotesque, with a human look and compact heads of stone. *They are bending over Pierre*—Eve made such a violent effort that her hands began trembling—*they are bending over me.* A horrible cry suddenly chilled her. They had touched him.

She opened her eyes: Pierre's head was in his hands, he was breathing
heavily; Eve felt exhausted: *a game*, she thought with remorse; *it was
only a game. I didn't sincerely believe it for an instant. And all that time
he suffered as if it were real.*

Pierre relaxed and breathed freely. But his pupils were strangely
dilated and he was perspiring.

"Did you see them?" he asked.

"I can't see them."

"Better for you. They'd frighten you," he said. "I am used to them."

Eve's hands were still shaking and the blood had rushed to her head.
Pierre took a cigarette from his pocket and brought it up to his mouth.
But he did not light it.

"I don't care whether I see them or not," he said, "but I don't want
them to touch me: I'm afraid they'll give me pimples."

He thought for an instant, then asked, "Did you hear them?"

"Yes," Eve said, "it's like an airplane engine." (Pierre had told her
this the previous Sunday.)

Pierre smiled with condescension. "You exaggerate," he said. But he
was still pale. He looked at Eve's hands. "Your hands are trembling. That
made quite an impression on you, my poor Agatha. But don't worry.
They won't come back again before tomorrow." Eve could not speak.
Her teeth were chattering and she was afraid Pierre would notice it.
Pierre watched her for a long time.

"You're tremendously beautiful," he said, nodding his head. "It's too
bad, too bad."

He put out his hand quickly and toyed with her ear. "My lovely
devil-woman. You disturb me a little, you are too beautiful: that distracts
me. If it weren't a question of recapitulation. . . ."

He stopped and looked at Eve with surprise.

"That's not the word . . . it came . . . it came," he said, smiling
vaguely. "I had another on the tip of my tongue . . . but this one . . .
came in its place. I forget what I was telling you."

He thought for a moment, then shook his head.

"Come," he said, "I want to sleep." He added in a childish voice,
"You know, Agatha, I'm tired. I can't collect my thoughts any more."

He threw away his cigarette and looked at the rug anxiously. Eve
slipped a pillow under his head.

"You can sleep too," he told her, "they won't be back." . . . *Recapitulation . . .*

Pierre was asleep, a candid, half-smile on his face; his head was turned
to one side: one might have thought he wanted to caress his cheek with
his shoulder. Eve was not sleepy, she was thoughtful: *Recapitulation.* Pierre
had suddenly looked stupid and the word had slipped out of his mouth,
long and whitish. Pierre had stared ahead of him in astonishment, as if

he had seen the word and didn't recognize it; his mouth was open, soft; something seemed broken in it. He stammered. *That's the first time it ever happened to him; he noticed it, too. He said he couldn't collect his thoughts any more.* Pierre gave a voluptuous little whimper and his hand made a vague movement. Eve watched him harshly: *how is he going to wake up.* It gnawed at her. As soon as Pierre was asleep she had to think about it. She was afraid he would wake up wild-eyed and stammering. *I'm stupid,* she thought, *it can't start before a year; Franchot said so.* But the anguish did not leave her; a year: a winter, a springtime, a summer, the beginning of another autumn. One day his features would grow confused, his jaw would hang loose, he would half open his weeping eyes. Eve bent over Pierre's hand and pressed her lips against it: *I'll kill you before that.*

The Affective Psychoses

II. Grief and happiness are emotions natural to man. Ordinarily such emotions occur appropriately at times of sorrow and loss, of joy and satisfaction. Characteristic of these emotions in the normal range of experience is their relationship and responsiveness to reality events, their modulated intensity, and, within reasonable limits, their capacity to be self-contained or altered by adaptive behavior. Occasionally a sustained emotion or mood will last and recur without obvious reason and be inexplicable to the person who experiences it. Such emotional patterns are, for example, quite typical of the moody adolescents and the highly vulnerable individual in middle age. In certain afflicted individuals the grossest caricatures of grief and joy occur. The extreme of grief is depression or melancholia, and the bizarre distortion of joy is mania.

Depression and mania of the most intense variety are classified among the psychoses, the most extreme of mental illnesses. There are two major categories:

Psychotic Depressive Reaction

1. At the time of a great personal tragedy or loss a person will normally enter a period of mourning. This may be related to a life goal, to status, or it may be the loss of a loved person. The loss of a loved person can produce extreme grief, and it is often difficult at first to differentiate this from depression.

a. A brief vignette of normal mourning from Flaubert's
Madame Bovary will provide a frame of reference for comparison
with more pathological depressions.

Madame Bovary

Gustave Flaubert (*1821–1880*)

. . . One morning old Rouault brought Charles the
money for setting his leg—seventy-five francs in forty-sou pieces, and a
turkey. He had heard of his loss, and consoled him as well as he could.

"I know what it is," said he, clapping him on the shoulder; "I've been
through it. When I lost my dear departed, I went into the fields to be
quite alone. I fell at the foot of a tree; I cried; I called on God; I talked
nonsense to Him. I wanted to be like the moles that I saw on the branches,
their insides swarming with worms, dead, and an end of it. And when I
thought that there were others at that very moment with their nice little
wives holding them in their embrace, I struck great blows on the earth
with my stick. I was pretty well mad with not eating; the very idea of
going to a café disgusted me—you wouldn't believe it. Well, quite softly,
one day following another, a spring on a winter, and an autumn after a
summer, this wore away, piece by piece, crumb by crumb; it passed away,
it is gone, I should say it has sunk; for something always remains at the
bottom, as one would say—a weight here, at one's heart. But since it is the
lot of all of us, one must not give way altogether, and, because others have
died, want to die too. You must pull yourself together, Monsieur Bovary.
It will pass away. Come to see us; my daughter thinks of you now and
again, d'ye know, and she says you are forgetting her. Spring will soon be
here. We'll have some rabbit shooting in the warrens to amuse you a
bit." . . .

b. Pathological mourning deepens, lasts, extends, and
begins to affect the capacity to function in the community.
Thoughts of death and suicide, feelings of helplessness and
hopelessness occur. Life seems worthless, and the afflicted
person cannot recover his perspective or his capacity for
enjoyment and pleasure. No gratification seems possible, and
no appetite seems important. Self-esteem is low and
self-derogation is high; occasionally suicide is the outcome,
although generally such depressions are self-limiting and last

From *Madame Bovary* by Gustave Flaubert.

only several months. Daudet's "The Arlesian Girl" is an example of a reactive depression that ends in suicide.

This brief story contains an especially important insight; namely, the fact that suicides frequently occur at a time when the depressed person has to all outward appearance begun an improvement.

This young man might not have been diagnosed as a psychotic depressive since there is no delusional guilt or hypochondriasis and his depression was in response to a real event. His symptoms do include other typical psychotic features: namely, agitation, intractable insomnia, and periodic episodes of profound retardation; and suicidal rumination no doubt preceded his suicide. However, there is sometimes no clear-cut distinction between neurotic and psychotic depressive reactions and in these instances the distinction is apt to be based on a quantitative rather than a qualitative consideration of symptoms.

THE ARLESIAN GIRL

Alphonse Daudet   (1840–1897)

In order to reach the village by way of my mill, I must pass a farmhouse built close to the road, in back of a large courtyard planted with nettle trees. It is a typical Provencal farmhouse with red tiles, a large brown facade with irregular openings, and then, over a tall weathervane on the hayloft, a pulley for raising the bales of hay and some wisps of brown hay which have dropped out.

Why did this house attract me? Why did this closed gate move me? I could not say, and yet the place somehow gave me the chills. There was an unearthly silence about this home; when I was passing the dogs never barked, the hens fled without a sound. Inside the house, not a murmur! Nothing, not even the tinkling of a mule's bell. Without the white curtains in the windows and the smoke which rose above the roof, one would think the place uninhabited.

Yesterday at noon I was returning from the village, and to keep out of the sun I passed beside the walls of the farm in the shade of the nettle trees. On the road in front of the house silent farmhands were loading a cart with hay. The gate was ajar. While passing I glanced in and I saw at the back of the courtyard, leaning his elbows on a large stone table, his

From "The Arlesian Girl" ("L'Arlesienne") by Alphonse Daudet, translated by Janet E. Levy from Lettres de mon moulin.

head in his hands, a large white-haired man wearing a short jacket and tattered pants. I stopped. One of the men said to me quietly:

"*Chut!* That is the master. He has been like this since the misfortune with his son."

At that moment a woman and a small boy dressed in black passed next to us with gilt-edged prayerbooks and entered the farmyard.

The man added: "The mistress and her little boy are returning from Mass. They have gone there every day since the boy was killed. Oh, sir, such sorrow! The father continues to wear the dead boy's clothes. No one can make him take them off. *Dia! hue!* Get along, girl!"

The cart started to leave. Wanting to learn more of the story, I asked one of the hands if I could ride beside him, and it was there, high up in the hay, I learned all of the tragic story.

He was called Jan. He was an admirable peasant of twenty years, quiet as a girl, solid and with an open face. Because he was very handsome, the girls all admired him, but he had only one on his mind—a little Arlesian girl—dressed all in velvet and lace, whom he had met only once at Lice d'Arles. At the house no one viewed this affair with pleasure at first. The girl was thought to be a coquette and her parents were not natives of the country. But Jan wanted his Arlesian girl in the face of all opposition. He said: "I will die if you do not give her to me."

They had no choice. They decided to let them marry after the harvest.

Then, one Sunday evening, in the courtyard of the house, the family was finishing its dinner. It was almost a wedding feast. The fiancée was not there, but everyone drank her health all evening. Then, a man appeared at the door and asked in a trembling voice to speak to Mr. Estève alone. Estève rose and went out to the road.

"Sir," the man said to him, "You are going to allow your son to marry a hussy who has been my mistress for two years. What I am saying can be proved—here are letters! Her parents know everything and have promised her to me, but since your son has been pursuing her, neither they nor the girl would have anything more to do with me. I would have believed, however, that after what has happened she would not become the wife of anyone else."

"So!" said Mr. Estève, when he had looked at the letters; "Come in and have a glass of muscat."

The man replied, "Thank you, but I am too troubled to drink," and so he left.

The father went back into the house, his face expressionless; he took his seat again and the dinner ended gaily.

That evening Mr. Estève and his son went out to the fields together. They remained outside for a long time. When they returned, the mother was waiting from them.

"Wife," said the husband, leading their son to her, "Kiss him, he is unhappy."

Jan never spoke again of the Arlesian girl. He always loved her, however, and now more than ever since they had shown her to him in the arms of another. But he was too proud to say anything, and that's what killed the poor boy. Sometimes he spent whole days alone in a corner, without moving. During other days he threw himself on the land in a rage, and almost killed himself doing the work of ten men. When night fell, he would take the road to Arles and walk straight ahead until he saw the sun rising, framed by the slender steeples of that town. Then he would return. He never traveled the full distance.

To see him thus, always sad and alone, made his family feel helpless. They dreaded a calamity. One time at the table, his mother, watching him with eyes filled with tears, said to him, "All right, listen, Jan, if you want her still, we will give her to you."

The father, red with embarrassment, bowed his head.

Jan shook his head and went out.

From that day he changed his ways and seemed always to be gay in order to reassure his parents. People saw him at dances, at cabarets, and at the *ferrades*. At Fonteville it was he who led the *farandole*.

The father said, "He is cured." The mother, however, was still afraid and watched her son more than ever. Jan slept with his younger brother, and the poor old woman made herself a bed outside their door.

Then came the festival of St. Eloi, the patron saint of householders.

There was great happiness in the household. There was *chateauneuf* for everyone, and wine flowed like rain. Then there were firecrackers, fires on the threshing floor, lanterns of all colors in the trees. Vive St. Eloi! They danced the *farandole* to exhaustion. The little boy scorched his new shirt. Jan seemed to be happy, he wanted to dance with his mother; the poor woman was crying with joy.

At midnight they went to bed. Everyone needed sleep. Jan remained awake. His little brother later told them that he had sobbed all night. Ah, I tell you he was really bitten, that one.

The next day, at dawn, the mother heard someone running through her room. She had something like a premonition.

"Jan, is that you?"

Jan did not answer; he was already on the stairs.

Very quickly the mother got up.

He was climbing to the hayloft; she climbed after him.

"My son, in the name of heaven!"

He closed the door and drew the bolt.

"Jan, my little Jan, answer me! What are you doing?"

Groping, with trembling hands, she searched for the lock. Then a window opened. There was the sound of a body breaking on the tiles of the courtyard, and that was all.

He must have said to himself, the poor child: "I love her too much, I am going away." Oh, miserable souls that we are; it is strange, after all, that scorn cannot kill love.

That morning, the village people had asked each other who was crying down there at the Estève house.

It was the mother, standing naked in the courtyard near the stone table covered with dew and blood, sobbing, with her dead son in her arms.

C.   More of the pathological aspects and psychodynamics of psychotic depression are illustrated in "An Old Man Dies," a story by Luise Rinser. Miss Rinser has intuitively described the strange relationship between a husband and wife. Uncle Gottfried has coped all his married life with a selfish and narcissistic woman. This patient, self-sacrificing, and masochistic man has only one release, alcohol. His wife, insensitive and unfeeling, has a relationship with him based only on his gratifying her needs. Whatever love she has is mixed with dissatisfaction and at the deeper level is probably ambivalent; that is, a mixture of love and hate. It is typically the loss of an ambivalently regarded object by a narcissistic person that produces a depression. At her husband's death a psychotic identification occurs, and the wife in this story, previously contemptuous of alcohol, becomes an alcoholic, as she copes with her depression.

An Old Man Dies

Luise Rinser (1911–   )

Aunt Emily died a year after her husband. They couldn't really tell what she died of. The doctor wrote "old age" on the death certificate, but he shrugged his shoulders as he wrote it, for Aunt Emily was barely sixty. But what else could the doctor have written? He hadn't known her. But I had, and that's how I know what she died of.

Uncle Gottfried was ten years older than she was, and he hadn't been sick a day in his life. So we were more surprised than alarmed when we received Aunt Emily's postcard saying that Uncle Gottfried would like "to see us once more." It was the end of February, cold, dreary, and raw, and I was expecting my first child.

"You can't take a trip like that," said my husband, "and anyhow, you know Aunt Emily. Uncle Gottfried probably has nothing more than a cold and she doesn't know what to do about it." But the note had made me apprehensive; I felt that "to see us once more" might really mean "to see us once more and then never again." And so we went after all.

"You know," said Peter, "I'd like to see Uncle Gottfried outlive her. It wouldn't be right the other way. It wouldn't be fair."

It seemed, indeed, bitterly unfair. Uncle Gottfried had married Aunt Emily when she was only a young girl. They said she was very pretty, and he idolized her and spoiled her. He was the one who would get up first, light the stove, and take breakfast to her in bed. He was the one who bought the vegetables and the meat; he took care of the cleaning woman, drove the nails, and sewed the buttons. In short, he did everything. At first, she thought it was considerate of him; then she began taking it all for granted, and eventually the whole thing began to bore her. They had no children because she didn't want any, and he complied. The years passed, and finally they led separate and parallel lives, like strangers. She stayed in bed for days at a time and read and got fat. He began to drink and got fat, too. They never quarreled; they had grown too indifferent even for that—or so it seemed. Once I said to Uncle Gottfried, "Why don't you get a divorce?" He looked at me, surprised. "A divorce? Why?" I was embarrassed. "Don't you know what I mean? I didn't think that you were ever really happy with Aunt Emily." "Is that right?" he said calmly, "I never thought about that." And after a pause, he added, "All right, what are you driving at?"

"My God," I said, "you can't do penance twenty years just because you once made the wrong choice."

He patted me on the shoulder good-naturedly. "Yes," he said, "yes, you can. Right to the end."

I loved him very much, that fat old man with his flushed and puffy face. I had both pity and respect for him, and my respect was the greater. This seems even stranger, since Uncle Gottfried came home drunk night after night, and during the day scraped the carrots, peeled the potatoes, washed the dishes, and put up with Aunt Emily's moods with a patience which made him seem simple-minded. But the equanimity and dignity and quiet melancholy with which he accepted life impressed me. I remember that when I once heard the phrase "contented servility," I immediately associated it with Uncle Gottfried, and I have ever since.

The two of them together had grown hard of hearing and far-sighted and old, after a life that seemed as morose as a rainy Sunday. And now it appeared that Uncle Gottfried was not to be granted a few peaceful years without the tenacious burden that his wife had become. What kind of justice was this which granted Aunt Emily the final victory?

When Aunt Emily opened the door, her glance fell first on me. She wrung her hands in dismay. "Good Lord," she shrieked, "that, too?"

Peter pushed her aside impatiently. "What's wrong with Uncle Gottfried?"

"Gottfried?" she said absent-mindedly, still staring at my belly. "He's in a bad way. He's going to die."

She said it matter-of-factly, rather as if she were announcing supper. "He's got tuberculosis," she added, and opened the door to the bedroom. "There," she shouted, "you can see for yourself. He's not going to last much longer."

"Quiet!" I whispered, horrified. "For heaven's sake, be quiet!"

She looked at me, surprised. "Whatever for? He's unconscious. He can't hear anything any more."

I stroked Uncle Gottfried's hand. He lay there with his eyes wide open, staring at the ceiling. But I had the feeling that he recognized me, even if for only a second.

"Can't he talk any more?" I asked softly. But I had forgotten Aunt Emily's deafness.

"What did you say?" she shouted, her hand cupped to her ear.

"Please let's go into another room," I said.

"Why another room? There isn't a fire going anywhere else. We'll have a cup of coffee." And in a pitiful voice she added, "But I haven't got a bite to eat in the house. He always did the shopping. I haven't any idea how to do it."

So Peter went to buy a few things and I whipped some evaporated milk which I had brought along. Aunt Emily made the coffee and continued speaking loudly and incessantly.

"Today is the ninth day," she said. "It's the crisis. The doctor thinks he's going to pull through, but the doctor's a fool. You can see for yourself that he has no more resistance. He always drank too much. So that's that."

She poured the coffee through the strainer.

"Did he ask for me?"

"Yes, the first evening he got the fever."

"Why on earth didn't you write me right away!" I was angry.

She shrugged her shoulders, and then asked, in surprise, "What good would that have done?"

"Well, my God, maybe it would have helped him a little."

"Do you think so?" she asked, unmoved. "He has me, you know."

I suppressed what I was about to say and took a saucer full of whipped cream in to Uncle Gottfried. He was lying just as before. I put a little of the cream on his lips, which were as cracked and rough as singed wood. He always had loved whipped cream, nearly as much as his wine; but now he couldn't swallow it. It ran out of the corners of his mouth and over the stubble on his chin.

"What in the world are you doing in there?" Aunt Emily called out as she came in with the coffeepot. "You're just wasting the cream. You can see that he can't get anything down."

But I continued to feed the cool cream into his dry mouth, and little gulping motions told me that some of it was finding its way into the poor, burned throat.

Finally Peter returned with bread and butter. Aunt Emily began to devour it greedily.

"I haven't eaten for two days, you know," she declared as she chewed. "He always used to bring home food for a week. But today is already the tenth day."

"How did he get so sick?" asked Peter.

Again she shrugged her shoulders. "It didn't have to happen at all," she said. "But you know how stubborn he is. He had a little cold. 'Don't go out in weather like this,' I said. But no, he had to go shopping, and when he got back he had the fever."

Peter couldn't restrain himself. "Why the hell did you let him go out when he had a cold? Couldn't you have gone just once?"

She looked at him, hurt. "Me?" she asked with petulant amazement. "Why me all of a sudden, when he's done the shopping for forty years?"

Peter sighed.

"Well, at least you're both here," said Aunt Emily. "You'll be staying right on for the funeral, won't you?"

"Aunt Emily," said Peter angrily, "that's just about enough now. Or do you want us to think that you can hardly wait to have him dead and buried."

She gave him a long, odd look. "You can think what you want," she mumbled finally, and left the room.

She didn't come back until evening. "Is he still breathing?" she asked. Neither of us answered.

Night came. "Go to bed," said Peter. "I'll stay up." But none of us went to bed. The hours passed. Finally, Peter and Aunt Emily fell asleep. I sat down on the edge of Uncle Gottfried's bed.

"Uncle Gottfried," I said close to his ear. He opened his eyes and looked at me. The look he gave me was so clear that I was startled. He tried to smile his old, melancholy smile. Suddenly his eyes began to wander about the room. With an effort, he asked, "Emily?"

"She's over there, asleep."

"Let her be for now," he whispered, "but don't leave her." And very softly and tenderly he added, "She's such a child."

Suddenly he lapsed again into unconsciousness.

Peter, who had awakened, asked, "Who are you talking to?"

"Shh," I said, "go back to sleep."

I was all alone with Uncle Gottfried again, and I had the feeling that he was beginning to slip away.

Even though my throat contracted with fear, I wouldn't have wakened either of the others for anything in the world. His death struggle was hardly a struggle at all. It was more a stubborn hesitancy before his final surrender. The hours came and went. At dawn, Aunt Emily awoke.

"Is he still alive?" she asked loudly. She bent over the dying man, raised the bed covers and felt his legs. "It'll be soon," she muttered. "Soon." She let the blanket fall back on him, then she shuffled from the room. I heard her fussing about in the kitchen with the stove and the pots and pans.

All at once Uncle Gottfried looked me straight in the eyes and said, with astonishing volume and firmness, "Be good to Emily."

Those were his last words; a few moments later, even before I could have called Aunt Emily, he died. The expression of patient melancholy remained on his face. I summoned Peter and Aunt Emily.

"Is he dead?" she asked. And immediately an expression of wild terror was in her eyes, and she began to wail.

She cried uncontrollably, clinging first to Peter and then to me.

But then, just as suddenly, she said, "So now he's just left me all alone. So that was his trick, just to go away like that. Now I can die for all he cares. He's gone, and nothing can bother him any more." Peter led her out of the bedroom and into the kitchen. There he let her cry as long and as loud as she wanted.

Then he went to get the doctor. I remained alone with the dead man.

By noon, everything was taken care of. Uncle Gottfried lay in the mortuary, and Aunt Emily sat in her kitchen, staring into space. We didn't dare to leave her alone.

Rain poured down on the funeral, but even that didn't keep people away. Half the town, it seemed, had come; many of them were weeping, even some of the men. I think that they weren't crying so much about the death of the old man as they were at a fate which seemed so near their own. They all felt cheated by life; and when they buried Uncle Gottfried, each might have thought that he could have been this old man to whom life still owed so much at the end, but on whose casket heavy clumps of wet earth were now falling.

Aunt Emily, in her finest dress and long mourning veil, was not crying. She stared motionless at the casket.

When we were once again at her house, she threw off the veil, looked about her with sparkling eyes and said, "So. Now I'm going to have new wallpaper in this room. Blue, everything's going to be blue. I'm going to have the furniture re-covered, too." Then she went to a cupboard and pulled out a train schedule. "Show me how to read this schedule," she commanded. "I'm going to take a trip."

Peter had hardly begun to explain it to her, when suddenly she exclaimed, "But he won't be going with me!" And she began to cry so passionately and miserably and with such abandon that we were at a complete loss what to do. She cried for hours and hours. It was like an upheaval in nature and there was something about it that was secret and terrifying.

We didn't leave until the next day, when she had calmed down. She seemed eager and enterprising, and had already made an arrangement with the decorator.

A few days after that, we had a son, whom we called Gottfried. A few weeks later we wrote Aunt Emily to see if she might want to come for a visit; but she didn't come. She merely wrote cryptic little postcard notes which never gave any indication of how she was.

Half a year after Uncle Gottfried's death, we visited her. She sat, tiny and emaciated, in a blue armchair at the window. Despite the warm sun, she was wrapped in a heavy shawl. The whole room was a bluish green and looked like an aquarium.

"Well, well!" exclaimed Peter. "So now you've got things just the way you've always wanted them." She threw up her hands in a defensive gesture. "Are you satisfied now?" he continued unmercifully.

"What do you understand about it?" she said wearily.

"But now you can do anything you want to—can't you?"

She didn't answer him.

I nudged Peter to keep him quiet, and said, "Such a lovely blue color!"

"So?" she said. "Lovely?" Her voice grew loud and sharp. "You think it's lovely? Just take a closer look at your lovely blue. Can you see it?"

The fabric was already faded and spotty from the sun.

"Do you understand?" she asked. "He always used to hate blue." She looked at us as sharply as she could with her now dull eyes and cried, "You probably think I'm crazy! I'm just as clear in the head as you are. But you can't understand."

She shrugged her shoulders. "What's the difference anyway?" she muttered. Then she pulled a wine bottle from behind the armchair and held it up to the light. "Empty," she said. "The last one. I've finished them all."

"You? I always thought you hated wine!"

"That's right," she said. "Maybe there's peace between us now. He always wanted me to drink with him." She wrapped herself tighter in her shawl, and withdrew into a world to which we had no access. We were too young.

A few weeks later, she was dead. She hadn't been ill for a moment.

One evening she went to bed as usual, and in the morning the cleaning woman found her.

"Old age" is what the doctor wrote on the death certificate. But I understood what she died of, and I shuddered to realize what weird forms love can assume.

d. Depression is a rather common phenomenon in middle age. Women undergo the changes of the menopause and experience alterations in their endocrine system. Quite often some transient emotional symptoms accompany this physiological transformation. During this phase some women enter a profound depression that is complicated by intense somatic concerns and occasionally has paranoid features. These depressions are apt to be quite severe and are designated by a special term, involutional melancholia.

Men do not undergo such a direct and complete biological change. There is in middle age, however, some waning of physical and sexual stamina, a condition which has been called the male climacteric. This condition, too, is associated with depression. Dostoevsky illustrates this in his portrait of Velchaninov. Velchaninov is somewhat younger and his malady milder than the ordinary case; nonetheless, he has many of the most typical features of a middle-aged depression. In addition, the picture that Dostoevsky presents of his earlier or "pre-morbid" personality is typical. Velchaninov was a self-interested person, attentive to his own pleasure, and unable to make any lasting or complete human attachments. As his illness begins, we see the characteristic patterns of guilt and intensification of the conscience.

The Eternal Husband

Fyodor Dostoevsky (*1821–1881*)

The summer had come and, contrary to expectations, Velchaninov remained in Petersburg. The trip he had planned to the south of Russia had fallen through, and the end of his case was not in sight. This case—a lawsuit concerning an estate—had taken a very unfortunate turn. Three months earlier it had appeared to be quite straight-

From "The Eternal Husband" by Fyodor Dostoevsky.

forward, almost impossible to contest; but suddenly everything was changed. "And, in fact, everything has changed for the worse!" Velchaninov began frequently and resentfully repeating that phrase to himself. He was employing an adroit, expensive, and distinguished lawyer, and was not sparing money; but through impatience and lack of confidence he had been tempted to meddle in the case himself too. He read documents and wrote statements which the lawyer rejected point-blank, ran from one court to another, collected evidence, and probably hindered everything; the lawyer complained, at any rate, and tried to pack him off to a summer villa. But Velchaninov could not even make up his mind to go away. The dust, the stifling heat, the white nights of Petersburg, that always fret the nerves were what he was enjoying in town. His flat was near the Grand Theatre; he had only recently taken it, and it, too, was a failure. "Everything is a failure!" he thought. His nervousness increased every day; but he had for a long time past been subject to nervousness and hypochondria.

He was a man whose life had been full and varied, he was by no means young, thirty-eight or even thirty-nine, and his "old age," as he expressed it himself, had come upon him "quite unexpectedly"; but he realized himself that he had grown older less by the number than by the quality, so to say, of his years, and that if he had begun to be aware of waning powers, the change was rather from within than from without. In appearance he was still strong and hearty. He was a tall, sturdily-built fellow, with thick flaxen hair without a sign of greyness and a long fair beard almost half-way down his chest; at first sight he seemed somewhat slack and clumsy, but if you looked more attentively, you would detect at once that he was a man of excellent breeding, who had at some time received the education of an aristocrat. Velchaninov's manners were still free, assured and even gracious, in spite of his acquired grumpiness and slackness. And he was still, even now, full of the most unhesitating, the most snobbishly insolent self-confidence, the depth of which he did not himself suspect, although he was a man not merely intelligent, but even sometimes sensible, almost cultured and unmistakably gifted. His open and ruddy face had been in old days marked by a feminine softness of complexion which attracted the notice of women; and even now some people, looking at him, would say: "What a picture of health! What a complexion!" And yet this picture of health was cruelly subject to nervous depression. His eyes were large and blue, ten years earlier they had possessed great fascination; they were so bright, so gay, so careless that they could not but attract everyone who came in contact with him. Now that he was verging on the forties, the brightness and good-humor were almost extinguished. Those eyes, which were already surrounded by tiny wrinkles, had begun to betray the cynicism of a worn-out man of doubtful morals, a duplicity, an ever-increasing irony and another shade of feeling, which was new: a shade of sadness and of pain—a sort of absent-minded sadness as though about nothing in particular and yet acute. This sadness was especially marked when he was alone. And, strange to say, this man who had been only a couple of years before fond of noisy gaiety, careless and good-humored, who had been so capital a teller of funny stories, liked nothing now so well as being absolutely alone. He purposely gave up a great number of acquaintances whom he need not have given up even now, in spite of his financial difficulties. It is true that his vanity counted for something in this. With his vanity and mistrustfulness he could not have endured the society of his old acquaintances. But, by degrees, in solitude even his vanity began to change its character. It grew no less, quite the contrary, indeed; but it began to develop into a special sort of vanity which was new in him; it began at times to suffer from different causes—from unexpected causes which would have formerly been quite inconceivable, from causes of a "higher order" than ever before—"if one may use such an expression, if there really are higher or lower causes. . . ." This he added on his own account.

Yes, he had even come to that; he was worrying about some sort of *higher* ideas of which he would never have thought twice in earlier days. In his own mind and in his conscience he called "higher" all "ideas" at which (he found to his surprise) he could not laugh in his heart—there had never been such hitherto—in his secret heart only, of course; oh, in company it was a different matter! He knew very well, indeed, that—if only the occasion were to arise—he would the very next day, in spite of all the mysterious and reverent resolutions of his conscience, with perfect composure disavow all these "higher ideas" and be the first to turn them into ridicule, without, of course, admitting anything. And this was really the case, in spite of a certain and, indeed, considerable independence of thought, which he had of late gained at the expense of the "lower ideas" that had mastered him till then. And how often, when he got up in the morning, he began to be ashamed of the thoughts and feelings he had passed through during a sleepless night! And he had suffered continually of late from sleeplessness. He had noticed for some time past that he had become excessively sensitive about everything, trifles as well as matters of importance, and so he made up his mind to trust his feelings as little as possible. But he could not overlook some facts, the reality of which he was forced to admit. Of late his thoughts and sensations were sometimes at night completely transformed, and for the most part utterly unlike those which came to him in the early part of the day. This struck him— and he even consulted a distinguished doctor who was, however, an acquaintance; he spoke to him about it jocosely, of course. The answer he received was that the transformation of ideas and sensations, and even the possession of two distinct sets of thoughts and sensations, was a universal fact among persons "who think and feel," that the convictions of a whole lifetime were sometimes transformed under the melancholy influences of night and sleeplessness; without rhyme or reason most momentous decisions were taken; but all this, of course, was only true up to a certain point—and, in fact, if the subject were too conscious of the double nature of his feelings, so that it began to be a source of suffering to him, it was certainly a symptom of approaching illness; and then steps must be taken at once. The best thing of all was to make a radical change in the mode of life, to alter one's diet, or even to travel. Relaxing medicine was beneficial, of course.

Velchaninov did not care to hear more; but to his mind it was conclusively shown to be illness.

"And so all this is only illness, all these 'higher ideas' are mere illness and nothing more!" he sometimes exclaimed to himself resentfully. He was very loth to admit this.

Soon, however, what had happened exclusively in the hours of the night began to be repeated in the morning, only with more bitterness than at night, with anger instead of remorse, with irony instead of emotion. What really happened was that certain incidents in his past, even in his distant past, began suddenly, and God knows why, to come more and more frequently back to his mind, but they came back in quite a peculiar way. Velchaninov had, for instance, complained for a long time past of loss of memory: he would forget the faces of acquaintances, who were offended by his cutting them when they met; he sometimes completely forgot a book he had read months before; and yet in spite of this loss of memory, evident every day (and a source of great uneasiness to him), everything concerning the remote past, things that had been quite forgotten for ten or fifteen years, would sometimes come suddenly into his mind now with such amazing exactitude of details and impressions that he felt as though he were living through them again. Some of the facts he remembered had been so completely forgotten that it seemed to him a miracle that they could be recalled. But this was not all, and, indeed, what man of wide experience has not some memory of a peculiar sort? But the point was that all that was recalled came back now with a quite fresh, surprising and, till then, inconceivable point of view, and seemed as though some one were leading up to it on purpose. Why did some things he remembered strike him now as positive crimes? And it was not a question of the judgment of his mind only: he would have put little faith in his gloomy, solitary and sick mind; but it reached the point of curses and almost of tears, of inward tears. Why, two years before, he would not have believed it if he had been told that he would ever shed tears! At first, however, what he remembered was rather of a mortifying than of a sentimental character: he recalled certain failures and humiliations in society; he remembered, for instance, how he had been slandered by an intriguing fellow, and in consequence refused admittance to a certain house; how, for instance, and not so long ago, he had been publicly and unmistakably insulted, and had not challenged the offender to a duel; how in a circle of very pretty women he had been made the subject of an extremely witty epigram and had found no suitable answer. He even recollected one or two unpaid debts—trifling ones, it is true, but debts of honor—owing to people whom he had given up visiting and even spoke ill of. He was also worried (but only in his worst moments) by the thought of the two fortunes, both considerable ones, which he had squandered in the stupidest way possible. But soon he began to remember things of a "higher order."

Suddenly, for instance, apropos of nothing, he remembered the forgotten, utterly forgotten, figure of a harmless, grey-headed and absurd old clerk, whom he had once, long, long ago, and with absolute impunity, insulted in public simply to gratify his own conceit, simply for the sake of an amusing and successful jest, which was repeated and increased his prestige. The incident had been so completely forgotten that he could not even recall the old man's surname, though all the surroundings of the incident rose before his mind with incredible clearness. He distinctly remembered that the old man was defending his daughter, who was unmarried, though no longer quite young, and had become the subject of gossip in the town. The old man had begun to answer angrily, but he suddenly burst out crying before the whole company, which made some sensation. They had ended by making him drunk with champagne as a joke and getting a hearty laugh out of it. And now when, apropos of nothing, Velchaninov remembered how the poor old man had sobbed and hidden his face in his hands like a child, it suddenly seemed to him as though he had never forgotten it. And, strange to say, it had all seemed to him very amusing at the time, especially some of the details, such as the way he had covered his face with his hands; but now it was quite the contrary.

Later, he recalled how, simply as a joke, he had slandered the very pretty wife of a schoolmaster, and how the slander had reached the husband's ears. Velchaninov had left the town soon after and never knew what the final consequences of his slander had been, but now he began to imagine how all might have ended—and there is no knowing to what lengths his imagination might not have gone if this memory had not suddenly been succeeded by a much more recent reminiscence of a young girl of the working-class, to whom he had not even felt attracted, and of whom, it must be admitted, he was actually ashamed. Yet, though he could not have said what had induced him, he had got her into trouble and had simply abandoned her and his child without even saying good-bye (it was true, he had no time to spare), when he left Petersburg. He had tried to find that girl for a whole year afterwards, but he had not succeeded in tracing her. He had, it seemed, hundreds of such reminiscences

—and each one of them seemed to bring dozens of others in its train. By degrees his vanity, too, began to suffer.

We have said already that his vanity had degenerated into something peculiar. That was true. At moments (rare moments, however), he even forgot himself to such a degree that he ceased to be ashamed of not keeping his own carriage, that he trudged on foot from one court to another, that he began to be somewhat negligent in his dress. And if someone of his own acquaintance had scanned him with a sarcastic stare in the street or had simply refused to recognize him, he might really have had pride enough to pass him by without a frown. His indifference would have been genuine, not assumed for effect. Of course, this was only at times: these were only the moments of forgetfulness and nervous irritation, yet his vanity had by degrees grown less concerned with the subjects that had once affected it, and was becoming concentrated on one question, which haunted him continually.

"Why, one would think," he began reflecting satirically sometimes (and he almost always began by being satirical when he thought about himself), "why, one would think someone up aloft were anxious for the reformation of my morals, and were sending me these cursed reminiscences and 'tears of repentance'! So be it, but it's all useless! It is all shooting with blank cartridge! As though I did not know for certain, more certainly than certainty, that in spite of these fits of tearful remorse and self-reproach, I haven't a grain of independence for all my foolish middle age! Why, if the same temptation were to turn up tomorrow, if circumstances, for instance, were to make it to my interest to spread a rumor that the schoolmaster's wife had taken presents from me, I should certainly spread it, I shouldn't hesitate—and it would be even worse, more loathsome than the first time, just because it would be the second time and not the first time. Yes, if I were insulted again this minute by that little prince whose leg I shot off eleven years ago, though he was the only son of his mother, I should challenge him at once and condemn him to crutches again. So they are no better than blank cartridges, and there's no sense in them! And what's the good of remembering the past when I've not the slightest power of escaping from myself?"

Manic Depressive Psychosis

2. Manic depressive psychosis is the least prevalent of the major psychoses, constituting approximately five per cent of mental hospital admissions. The diagnosis is applied to patients who demonstrate cycles of manic excited behavior, alternating with depression. In some patients the depressive phase is brief, and passes unnoticed; in others the manic phase is transient. It is the apparent combination of these extremes of

emotion that lead to this particular diagnosis. Since the
depressive symptoms per se are not readily distinguished from
other depressions, this condition is here illustrated by a literary
figure with pronounced manic symptoms.

The manic may become coarsely aggressive, lewd,
verbacious, ceaselessly active, indulging all his appetites in an
unrelenting and sometimes infantile manner. Judgment is
impaired and thoughts flood consciousness, jostling for the
attention of the manic mind. Ignat Gordeyev is such a man.
Gorky not only provides a brilliant description of manic
episodes, but also in his character portrait describes a type that
modern psychiatry has come to associate with this disease;
i.e., an aggressive, ambitious, socially mobile person.

FOMA GORDEYEV

Maxim Gorky (*1868–1936*)

Some sixty years ago, when fortunes mounting to millions
were being made overnight on the Volga, a bailer named Ignat Gordeyev
worked on a barge belonging to the rich merchant Zayev.

Gordeyev was strong and handsome, far from stupid, and one of
those people who are always successful—not because they are talented and
hard-working, but because, endowed with enormous stocks of energy,
they do not spurn—are, in fact, incapable of spurning—any means that
leads to the achieving of their end, and recognize no law save their own
desires. Sometimes these people speak with awe of their consciences, they
may even endure real torture struggling with them. But only a weak man is
unable to conquer his conscience; a strong one easily subdues it and makes
it serve his purpose. He may sacrifice several nights of sleep to the struggle; his conscience may even win out in the end, but if it does, his spirit
is not broken by defeat and he goes on living just as vigorously under its
rule as he did before.

By the time he was forty, Ignat Gordeyev himself was the owner of
three steamboats and a dozen barges. He was respected all along the Volga
as a man of wealth and brains, but was given the nickname of "Freakish,"
for his life did not flow smoothly down a main channel as did the lives of
other men like him, but kept seething with rebellion, leaping out of its
bed, tearing away from the pursuit of wealth, which was looked on as the

Reprinted from *Foma Gordeyev* by Maxim Gorky, by permission of Am-Rus
Literary Agency. Copyright 1962 by Dell Publishing Company.

main purpose of existence. It was as if there were three Gordeyevs, three spirits inhabiting Ignat's body. One of them, and the most important one, was acquisitive and nothing else, and when it held the whip handle Ignat was a man possessed by a passion for work. This passion burned in him day and night, consuming him body and soul, and he went about snatching up hundreds and thousands of rubles as if he could never get enough of the sweet rustle and clink of money. He rushed up and down the Volga, setting and tightening the nets he caught his gold in; he bought corn in the villages and took it to Rybinsk in his barges; he cheated— sometimes without being aware of it, sometimes deliberately—always laughing triumphantly in the face of his victims. His craze for money reached poetic intensity. Yet, for all the energy he put into the acquisition of wealth, he was not greedy in the narrow sense of the word. Indeed, he would sometimes display complete indifference to his own wealth.

One day when the ice was breaking on the Volga, he stood on the bank watching the floes crush his new two-hundred-and-fifty-foot barge against a steep embankment.

"That's right . . . squeeze her again . . . come on," he muttered through clenched teeth. "Again I tell you!"

"Looks as if the ice were squeezing a cool ten thousand out of your pocket, eh, Ignat?" said Mayakin, his best friend and the godfather of his children.

"Let it. I'll make another hundred thousand. But look what the Volga's doing! Lord, what power! She could turn up the earth like batter with a spoon if she had the mind to. Look! There goes my *Boyarina*. And she was only afloat one season. Well, let's have a drink to mark her end, shall we?"

The barge was crushed. Ignat and his friend sat at a window of a tavern on the river bank drinking vodka and watching the river carry away the remains of the *Boyarina* along with the ice.

"Sorry to lose your barge, Ignat?" asked Mayakin.

"No sense being sorry. The Volga gave, the Volga hath taken away. It's not my hands she chopped off."

"Even so . . ."

"Even so—what? At least I've seen with my own eyes how it happened. A good lesson for the future. Too bad I didn't see how my *Volgar* burned that time. What a sight it must have been—a bonfire that size out on the water in the middle of the night! She was a big boat!"

"I suppose you weren't sorry to lose her, either?"

"That steamboat? No, I can't say that. I really was sorry to lose her. But it's silly to be sorry. What's the use? Cry if you like, but tears won't put out a fire. Let the boats burn. I don't give a damn if they all burn, so long as the fires inside of me keep burning too."

"H'm," said Mayakin with a little laugh. "A man who talks like that is rich even if he hasn't a shirt to his back."

Despite his philosophical acceptance of the loss of thousands of rubles, Ignat knew the value of every kopek. He rarely gave money to beggars, and then only to those who were unable to do any work at all. If he saw that a beggar was not hopelessly incapacitated he would say sternly:

"Get along with you! Can't you work? Here, go and help my yard porter clear away that pile of manure and I'll give you two kopeks."

When the obsession for work seized him he became hard and merciless to those about him—but he was just as merciless to himself as he chased the ruble. And then all of a sudden (this would usually occur in the spring, when the world is full of charm and loveliness and the soul is aware of some gentle reproach in the clear gaze of the sky) Ignat Gordeyev seemed to sense that he was not the master of his affairs, but their despicable slave. Then he would grow thoughtful, glance inquiringly out from under shaggy knit brows, and go about morbid and irritable, as though asking himself something he dared not give voice to. And another spirit awoke within him—the fierce, lustful spirit of a hungry beast. He was rude to people and profane in his speech; he drank, indulged his coarse instincts, and got others to drink with him, enjoying a very frenzy of excess, as though a volcano were erupting filth inside of him. He seemed to be tearing at the chains he had forged and clamped onto himself—tearing wildly at them without being able to break them. Dirty, unkempt, his face swollen with drink and lack of sleep, his eyes wild, his voice hoarse and bellowing, he went from one brothel to another, taking no account of the money he squandered; he grew maudlin when soulful songs were sung, he danced, he fought with anybody who came to hand, but none of these things brought him relief.

The townsfolk made up legends about his orgies and severely condemned him for them, but nobody ever refused an invitation to take part in them. He would go on in this way for weeks at a time. And then he would come home unexpectedly, reeking with the smell of the bars, but subdued and depressed. Silently and with downcast eyes, which now expressed nothing but shame, he would accept the reproaches of his wife, meek as a lamb led to slaughter, then go to his room and lock himself in. For hours on end he would kneel before the holy images, his head drooping, his arms hanging limply at his sides, his shoulders sagging. But he did not utter a word, as if he dared not pray. His wife would tiptoe to his door and listen at the keyhole. Great sighs, like those of a sick and weary horse, came from inside the room.

"Dear Lord, Thou seest everything," Ignat would murmur at last, pressing his hands hard against his massive chest.

As long as his penance lasted he lived on bread and water. Every morning his wife would put a large bottle of water, a pound and a half of bread, and some salt outside of his room. He would open the door to take in this monastic fare, then lock himself in again. No one disturbed him at such times; indeed, everyone avoided him.

After a few days of this he would turn up on the stock exchange, laughing and joking and signing contracts for grain deliveries, sharp-eyed as a bird of prey, keen judge of all things having to do with business.

But in all three aspects Ignat was possessed of one great desire—the desire to have a son. The older he grew, the stronger the desire became. He often spoke to his wife about it. At breakfast or the noonday meal he would scowl at his fat, overstuffed Akulina with her rosy cheeks and sleepy eyes, and say:

"Well, don't you feel anything?"

She knew very well what he meant, but she invariably replied:

"How can I help feeling something? You've got fists like ten-pound weights."

"I'm asking about your belly, you fool."

"As if a woman who took such beatings could carry a child!"

"It's not the beatings that matter, it's your guzzling. You cram yourself so full of food there's no room for a baby."

"Why, haven't I had babies?"

"Girls!" said Ignat contemptuously. "It's a son I want, can't you understand that? A son and heir. Who'll I leave my money to when I die? Who'll pray for me after I'm dead? Give it all to a monastery? I've given them enough as it is. Leave it to you? A fine intercessor you'd be! Your mind's full of meat pies even when you're in church. And when I die you'll get married again and all my money will fall into the hands of some fool. Do you think that's what I work for? Bah!"

And he would grow peevish and morose, convinced that his life was meaningless without a son who would carry on after him.

In the nine years of their married life his wife had borne him four daughters, but all of them had died. Although he had eagerly awaited each of the births, he grieved little over the deaths; he did not want girls. He began to beat his wife in the second year of their marriage. At first he beat her only when he was drunk, and did it without malice, merely in accordance with the saying: "Love your wife like your life, but shake her like the apple tree." But as each child she bore him frustrated his hopes, he began to hate her and take pleasure in beating her for not giving him a son.

Once when he was in the Samara Gubernia on business, he got a message saying that his wife had died. He crossed himself, and after some deliberation wrote to his friend Mayakin:

"Bury her without me. Keep an eye on the property."

He went to church and had the funeral service read, and when he had prayed for the repose of her soul, he resolved to marry again as soon as possible.

At that time he was forty-three years old. He was tall and broad-shouldered and had a deep bass voice. The glance of his large eyes, over-shadowed by dark brows, was bold and intelligent. There was much rough and wholesome Russian beauty in his sunburnt face with its thick black beard, and in all of his powerful frame. A consciousness of his own strength was inherent in the easy swing of his walk and the grace of all his movements. Women were attracted to him, and he did not avoid them.

Before his wife had been dead six months he asked for the hand of the daughter of an Old Faith Cossack who lived in the Urals, and with whom he had business connections. The Cossack consented to the marriage even though Ignat's reputation of being "freakish" had reached the Urals. The girl's name was Natalia. Tall, graceful, with enormous blue eyes and a long chestnut plait, she was a worthy mate for the handsome Ignat. He was proud of his new wife, and loved her with the love of a healthy male. But soon he began to study her thoughtfully.

A smile was rarely to be seen on his wife's lovely oval face. She was always pensive, and at times her blue eyes, coldly tranquil, would be disturbed by a look that was dark and forbidding. When free of household duties, she would go into the largest room of the house, sit down at the window, and remain sitting there motionless for two or three hours. Although she gazed out into the street, her expression was at once so detached from all that was going on beyond the window and so full of concentration that she seemed to be searching her own soul. She had a strange walk: she did not move freely about the spacious rooms of the house, but slowly and gingerly. The house was furnished in a heavy style that was coarsely ostentatious. All its glittering appointments shrieked of the owner's wealth, but the Cossack woman sidled past the expensive furniture and the sideboards loaded with silver as if she were afraid they might seize her and crush her. The seething life of this large trading town held no interest for her, and when she went out for a ride with her husband she kept eyes fixed on the coachman's back. If her husband asked her to go visiting with him, she did not refuse, but she was just as quiet in company as she was at home. If guests came to see her, she pressed her food and drink upon them without taking any interest in what they talked about or caring more for one than for another. The only person who could coax the faintest shadow of a smile to her face was Mayakin, a clever, witty man.

"She's not a woman; she's a stick," was what he said of her. "But just wait—life is a bonfire, and this young nun will be kindled by it yet. All she needs is time. Then we'll see what pretty flowers she'll put forth!"

"Well, long-face," said Ignat banteringly to his wife, "what's on your mind? Are you homesick? Come, cheer up!"

She looked at him calmly without answering.

"You spend too much time in church. It's too early for that. You'll have plenty of time to pray away your sins—commit them first. If you don't sin, you won't have anything to repent, and if you don't repent, you won't find salvation. So come, do a little sinning while you're young. Let's go for a ride, shall we?"

"I don't think I will."

He sat down beside her and put his arms round her, but she was cold and unresponsive.

"Natalia," he said, peering into her eyes, "what makes you so moody? Find me a bore, eh?"

"No," she said briefly.

"Then what is it? Miss your own folk?"

"Not particularly."

"What's on your mind?"

"Nothing."

"Then what's the matter?"

"Nothing."

One day he got her to express herself more fully:

"I have a vague feeling inside of me. And everything looks vague . . . and it seems to me that all these things are—not real."

With a wave of her hand she indicated the walls, the furniture, all her surroundings. Ignat did not bother to reflect upon her words, he merely gave a little laugh and said:

"Well, you're wrong. They're all real—all good and solid and expensive. But if you want me to, I'll burn them up, I'll sell them. I'll give them away, and buy everything new. Do you want me to?"

"What for?" she asked impassively.

He marveled that one so young and healthy could live as in a daze, without wanting anything, without going anywhere except to church, without seeing anyone.

"Just wait, you'll bear me a son and then life will be different," he consoled her. "It's not having anything to do that makes you so unhappy; he'll give you plenty to do. You *will* bear me a son, won't you?"

"God willing," she said, dropping her eyes.

Later on her moodiness got on his nerves.

"Well, you nun, you, what are you looking so down-in-the-mouth for? You walk as if you were treading on glass and wear a look as if you had killed somebody. You're a hefty wench, but you've got no spirit. A little fool, that's what you are."

One day he came home slightly tipsy and began to make love to her. She resisted him. This made him angry.

"Natalia!" he cried. "Watch your step!"

She looked him straight in the face and said, unperturbed:

"What will happen if I don't?"

Ignat was infuriated by her words and her fearless glance.

"What?" he cried, making for her.

"Perhaps you would like to strike me?" she said, without retreating a step or blinking an eye.

Ignat was used to having people tremble before his wrath, and he was maddened and insulted by her composure.

"I'll show you!" he shouted, swinging his arm. Unhurriedly, but in good time, she evaded the blow, seized his arm, and thrust it away from her.

"If you touch me, never come near me again," she said without raising her voice.

Her enormous eyes were narrowed, and their piercing glint brought Ignat to his senses. Her face told him that she, too, was a strong animal, and that she would not give in even though he beat her to death.

"Bah, long-face!" he roared, and went out.

He had surrendered to her this time, but he would never do it again. It would be humiliating to have a woman, and that woman his wife, refuse to bow down before him. Yet he sensed she would never yield to him in anything, and that meant a fierce battle would be fought between them.

"Very well, we'll see who will win," he said to himself the next day as he followed her every movement with glum curiosity. Deep down in his heart a storm of impatience was gathering: the sooner he began the fight, the sooner would he enjoy his victory.

But four days later Natalia informed him that she was with child. A thrill of joy passed over him. He threw his arms about his wife and said in a voice thick with feeling:

"Natasha, if it's a son . . . if you give me a son . . . I'll smother you in gold! But that's nothing. I'll be your servant for life! I swear to God I will! I'll lie down at your feet and you can walk all over me!"

"It is not for us, but for God to say what the child will be," she reminded him mildly.

"Ah, yes . . . for God," said Ignat bitterly, hanging his head. From that moment he was as solicitous of his wife as if she were a small child.

"Why are you sitting at the window? You'll catch a chill if you don't watch out," he said with affectionate severity. "What are you running up and down stairs for? You may hurt yourself. Here, eat some more; eat for two, so that he shall have his share."

Natalia grew even more quiet and thoughtful while with child. She receded further into herself, absorbed in thoughts of the new life she was cherishing within her. But the smile on her lips became more distinct, and at times there was a new shine to her eyes as faint and fleeting as the first flush of dawn.

Her birth pangs began early in the morning of an autumn day. Ignat turned pale at his wife's first cry of pain. He wanted to say something to her, but no words would come. With a despondent wave of his hand he left his wife and went downstairs to the little room that had been his mother's prayer room. He had the servant bring him some vodka and sat there miserably, drinking and listening to the bustle in the house. The faces of the holy images, dark and indifferent, were dimly outlined in the corner lighted by the icon lamps. He heard the shuffle of feet upstairs, the sound of something heavy being dragged across the floor, the clatter of basins and vessels. Everything was being done in a hurry, but time dragged on.

"She can't seem to give birth," someone said in a despairing voice. "Maybe we ought to send to the church and have them open the Gates of the Kingdom."

A pious old woman who lived as a hanger-on in the house entered the room next to the one in which Ignat was sitting and began to pray in a loud whisper:

"Dear Lord and Savior . . . descended from heaven to be born of the Holy Virgin . . . knowing the weakness of Thy creatures . . . forgive this, Thy faithful servant. . . ."

From time to time a heart-rending shriek would drown out all other sounds, or a long-drawn moan would float through the rooms of the house, fading away in corners darkened by the shadows of evening. Ignat threw anguished glances at the icons, sighed deeply, and thought: can it be that it will be a girl again?

He would interrupt his waiting by getting up, crossing himself, and bowing low to the icons; then he would sit down at the table again, go on drinking vodka (which did not make him drunk now) and doze off. In this way he spent the evening, the night, and the next morning.

At noon the midwife came running down the stairs and cried in a thin, happy voice:

"Congratulations on the birth of a son, Ignat Matveyevich!"

"Do you—you aren't fooling, are you?"

"Oh, dear no, why should I?"

He drew in a breath that filled his whole massive chest, then dropped to his knees.

"Praise be to Thee, oh God," he muttered in a shaking voice, his hands pressed to his breast. "It is clear Thou didst not wish to see my line cut off. My offspring shall make amends for the sins I have committed against Thee. Thank Thee, dear Lord!" The next moment he was on his feet and giving orders in a loud voice: "Hullo! Have someone go to St.

Nicholas's for the priest! Say Ignat Matveyevich sent for him! Say he is to read a prayer for a woman delivered of child!"

The serving maid came in and said in an anxious voice:

"Ignat Matveyevich! Natalia Fominishna is asking for you. She's in a bad way."

"Bad? She'll get over it," he roared, his eyes flashing with joy. "Tell her I'll be right up! Tell her I'm proud of her. Tell her I'll come with a fine present! Wait! Get some food ready for the priest and send for Mayakin, the godfather."

The intoxication of joy seemed to make his big form even bigger. He flung about the room, rubbing his hands together, casting grateful glances at the icons, crossing himself and waving his arms. In the end, he went up to his wife.

The first thing that caught his eye was a little red body that the midwife was washing in a tub. The minute he saw it he clasped his hands behind his back and tiptoed towards it, pursing up his lips comically. It was squealing and twisting in the water—naked, helpless, pitiful.

"Be careful how you handle it. He hasn't got any bones yet," whispered Ignat to the midwife in pleading tones.

She gave a toothless laugh and tossed the baby lightly from one hand to the other.

"Go to your wife."

He turned obediently.

"Well, Natalia?" he said as he walked over.

On reaching the bed he pulled back the curtain.

"I'll never get over it," came a faint voice.

Ignat stared at the face of his wife, sunk deep in a white pillow over which, like dead snakes, were scattered her dark locks. He had difficulty in recognizing this yellow, lifeless face with dark rings round the enormous wide-open eyes. Nor did he recognize those dreadful eyes, fixed motionless on some point beyond the wall. A premonition of disaster retarded the joyful beating of his heart.

"That's all right . . . it's always like this . . ." he said, bending down to kiss her. But she repeated, looking him straight in the eye:

"I'll never get over it."

Her lips were white and cold, and as soon as his own lips touched them he knew that death already dwelt within her.

"Dear God!" he murmured, fear clutching his heart and cutting off his breath. "Natalia, you can't! He . . . he needs you. What are you thinking of?"

He all but shouted at his wife. The midwife was dancing about him, waving the crying baby in the air and trying to make him understand what she was saying, but he heard nothing and was unable to tear his eyes off the fearful face of his wife. Her lips were moving and he could catch

occasional words, but he did not understand them. He sat down on the
edge of the bed and said in a hollow, groping voice:

"But . . . he can't get on without you . . . he's just been born.
Come take yourself in hand . . . don't let yourself think such a thing
. . . drive the thought out of your head . . . drive it away. . . ."

He spoke—and knew that his words were useless. Tears welled up
within him, and he felt something as heavy as lead, as cold as ice, in his
chest.

"Forgive me. Farewell. Look after him. Don't drink," murmured
Natalia soundlessly.

The priest came and put something over her face. With many sighs
he began to chant suppliant words:

"Great God and Father of the Universe, who curest all ills, cure
your humble servant Natalia, just delivered of child . . . raise her up
from the bed on which she lieth . . . mindful of the words of the prophet
David: 'They indulge in lawlessness and are wicked in Thine eyes.' "

The old man's voice broke, his thin face was stern, a smell of incense
came from his clothes.

". . . and save the child she has borne from all evil . . . from all
violence . . . from all storms . . . and from the evil spirits that fly by
day and by night. . . ."

Ignat wept quietly. His tears, large and warm, fell upon his wife's
bare arm. But she could not have felt them, for she did not move her arm
or shudder when the tears struck her. When the prayer was over, she fell
into a coma and died two days later without uttering another word to
anyone—died as silently as she had lived. Ignat gave her an elaborate burial,
had his son christened Foma, and then, with a stab of regret, placed him
in the family of his godfather, Mayakin, whose wife had just had a baby
herself. The death of his wife left many a gray hair in Ignat's dark beard,
but it also added something new—something soft and tender—to the shine
of his eyes.

Senility

III. As science discovers new ways to sustain and
extend life, the problem of senility becomes increasingly
important. A large part of the mental-hospital population
now consists of senile patients. Senility has increased because,
although "medicine" has been able to prolong the life span, it
has not been able to protect the brain from the effects of
hardening of the arteries and deterioration of brain cells. Thus
the number of patients whose bodies remain viable, but whose

higher mental functions are impeded or nonexistent, has
increased enormously. These patients suffer from a clouding of
consciousness, their capacity for memory of recent events
fades, concentration is impaired, and general deterioration of
cognitive ability occurs. Emotional lability is sometimes a
prominent feature.

Senility, however, involves much more than deterioration
of the brain. Old age is a time of loss: loved ones die, one's
vocation ends, physical capacities become limited, the past has
more to offer than the future, and death is imminent. Each of
these factors is a stress of the highest order, and each occurs
at a time when the personality has become hardened and rigid.
Theodore Dreiser captures the spirit of this time of life in his
moving story of an elderly man who cannot accept the present
and prefers to live in the past. His hallucinations are the
fulfillment of a wish that leads him at last to a reunion in
happier times.

The Lost Phoebe

Theodore Dreiser   (1871–1945)

. . . Old Henry Reifsneider and his wife Phoebe were
a loving couple. You perhaps know how it is with simple natures that
fasten themselves like lichens on the stones of circumstance and weather
their days to a crumbling conclusion. The great world sounds widely, but
it has no call for them. They have no soaring intellect. The orchard, the
meadow, the cornfield, the pig-pen, and the chicken-lot measure the
range of their human activities. When the wheat is headed it is reaped
and threshed; when the corn is browned and frosted it is cut and shocked;
when the timothy is in full head it is cut, and the hay-cock erected. After
that comes winter, with the hauling of grain to market, the sawing and
splitting of wood, the simple chores of fire-building, meal-getting, occasional repairing, and visiting. Beyond these and the changes of weather—
the snows, the rains, and the fair days—there are no immediate, significant
things. All the rest of life is a far-off, clamorous phantasmagoria, flickering like Northern lights in the night, and sounding as faintly as cow-bells
tinkling in the distance.

Old Henry and his wife Phoebe were as fond of each other as it is possible for two old people to be who have nothing else in this life to be fond of. He was a thin old man, seventy when she died, a queer, crotchety person with coarse gray-black hair and beard, quite straggly and unkempt. He looked at you out of dull, fishy, watery eyes that had deep-brown crow's-feet at the sides. His clothes, like the clothes of many farmers, were aged and angular and baggy, standing out at the pockets, not fitting about the neck, protuberant and worn at elbow and knee. Phoebe Ann was thin and shapeless, a very umbrella of a woman, clad in shabby black, and with a black bonnet for her best wear. As time had passed, and they had only themselves to look after, their movements had become slower and slower, their activities fewer and fewer. The annual keep of pigs had been reduced from five to one grunting porker, and the single horse which Henry now retained was a sleepy animal, not over-nourished and not very clean. The chickens, of which formerly there was a large flock, had almost disappeared, owing to ferrets, foxes, and the lack of proper care, which produces disease. The former healthy garden was now a straggling memory of itself, and the vines and flower-beds that formerly ornamented the windows and dooryard had now become choking thickets. A will had been made which divided the small tax-eaten property equally among the remaining four, so that it was really of no interest to any of them. Yet these two lived together in peace and sympathy, only that now and then old Henry would become unduly cranky, complaining almost invariably that something had been neglected or mislaid which was of no importance at all.

"Phoebe, where's my corn-knife? You ain't never minded to let my things alone no more."

"Now you hush, Henry," his wife would caution him in a cracked and squeaky voice. "If you don't, I'll leave yuh. I'll git up and walk out of here some day, and then where would y' be? Y' ain't got anybody but me to look after yuh, so yuh just behave yourself. Your corn-knife's on the mantel where it's allus been unless you've gone an' put it summers else."

Old Henry, who knew his wife would never leave him in any circumstances, used to speculate at times as to what he would do if she were to die. That was the one leaving that he really feared. As he climbed on the chair at night to wind the old, long-pendulumed, double-weighted clock, or went finally to the front and the back door to see that they were safely shut in, it was a comfort to know that Phoebe was there, properly ensconced on her side of the bed, and that if he stirred restlessly in the night, she would be there to ask what he wanted.

"Now, Henry, do lie still! You're as restless as a chicken."

"Well, I can't sleep, Phoebe."

"Well, yuh needn't roll so, anyhow. Yuh kin let me sleep."

This usually reduced him to a state of somnolent ease. If she wanted a pail of water, it was a grumbling pleasure for him to get it; and if she did rise first to build the fires, he saw that the wood was cut and placed within easy reach. They divided this simple world nicely between them.

As the years had gone on, however, fewer and fewer people had called. They were well-known for a distance of as much as ten square miles as old Mr. and Mrs. Reifsneider, honest, moderately Christian, but too old to be really interesting any longer. The writing of letters had become an almost impossible burden too difficult to continue or even negotiate via others, although an occasional letter still did arrive from the daughter in Pemberton County. Now and then some old friend stopped with a pie or cake or a roasted chicken or duck, or merely to see that they were well; but even these kindly minded visits were no longer frequent.

One day in the early spring of her sixty-fourth year Mrs. Reifsneider took sick, and from a low fever passed into some indefinable ailment which, because of her age, was no longer curable. Old Henry drove to Swinnerton, the neighboring town, and procured a doctor. Some friends called, and the immediate care of her was taken off his hands. Then one chill spring night she died, and old Henry, in a fog of sorrow and uncertainty, followed her body to the nearest graveyard, an unattractive space with a few pines growing in it. Although he might have gone to the daughter in Pemberton or sent for her, it was really too much trouble and he was too weary and fixed. It was suggested to him at once by one friend and another that he come to stay with them awhile, but he did not see fit. He was so old and so fixed in his notions and so accustomed to the exact surroundings he had known all his days, that he could not think of leaving. He wanted to remain near where they had put his Phoebe; and the fact that he would have to live alone did not trouble him in the least. The living children were notified and the care of him offered if he would leave, but he would not.

"I kin make a shift for myself," he continually announced to old Dr. Morrow, who had attended his wife in this case. "I kin cook a little, and, besides, it don't take much more'n coffee an' bread in the mornin's to satisfy me. I'll get along now well enough. Yuh just let me be." And after many pleadings and proffers of advice, with supplies of coffee and bacon and baked bread duly offered and accepted, he was left to himself. For a while he sat idly outside his door brooding in the spring sun. He tried to revive his interest in farming, and to keep himself busy and free from thought by looking after the fields, which of late had been much neglected. It was a gloomy thing to come in of an evening, however, or in the afternoon and find no shadow of Phoebe where everything suggested her. By degrees he put a few of her things away. At night he sat beside his lamp and read in the papers that were left him occasionally or in a Bible that he had neglected for years, but he could get little solace from these things. Mostly he held his hand over his mouth and looked at the floor as he sat and thought of what had become of her, and how soon he himself would die. He made a great business of making his coffee in the morning and frying himself a little bacon at night; but his appetite was gone. The shell in which he had been housed so long seemed vacant, and its shadows were suggestive of immedicable griefs. So he lived quite dolefully for five long months, and then a change began.

It was one night, after he had looked after the front and the back door, wound the clock, blown out the light, and gone through all the self-same motions that he had indulged in for years, that he went to bed not so much to sleep as to think. It was a moonlight night. The green-lichen-covered orchard just outside and to be seen from his bed where he now lay was a silvery affair, sweetly spectral. The moon shone through the east windows, throwing the pattern of the panes on the wooden floor, and making the old furniture, to which he was accustomed, stand out dimly in the room. As usual he had been thinking of Phoebe and the years when they had been young together, and of the children who had gone, and the poor shift he was making of his present days. The house was coming to be in a very bad state indeed. The bed-clothes were in disorder and not clean, for he made a wretched shift of washing. It was a terror to him. The roof leaked, causing things, some of them, to remain damp for weeks at a time, but he was getting into that brooding state where he would accept anything rather than exert himself. He preferred to pace slowly to and fro or to sit and think.

By twelve o'clock of this particular night he was asleep, however, and by two had waked again. The moon by this time had shifted to a position on the western side of the house, and it now shone in through the windows of the living-room and those of the kitchen beyond. A certain combination of furniture—a chair near a table, with his coat on it, the half-open kitchen door casting a shadow, and the position of a lamp near a paper—gave him an exact representation of Phoebe leaning over the table as he had often seen her do in life. It gave him a great start. Could it be she—or her ghost? He had scarcely ever believed in spirits, and still—— He looked at her fixedly in the feeble half-light, his old hair tingling oddly at the roots, and then sat up. The figure did not move. He put his thin legs out of the bed and sat looking at her, wondering if this could really be Phoebe. They had talked of ghosts often in their lifetime, of apparitions and omens; but they had never agreed that such things could be. It had never been a part of his wife's creed that she could have a spirit that could return to walk the earth. Her after-world was quite a different affair, a vague heaven, no less, from which the righteous did not trouble to return. Yet here she was now, bending over the table in her black skirt and gray shawl, her pale profile outlined against the moonlight.

"Phoebe," he called, thrilling from head to toe and putting out one bony hand, "have yuh come back?"

The figure did not stir, and he arose and walked uncertainly to the door, looking at it fixedly the while. As he drew near, however, the apparition resolved itself into its primal content—his old coat over the high-backed chair, the lamp by the paper, the half-open door.

"Well," he said to himself, his mouth open, "I thought shore I saw her." And he ran his hand strangely and vaguely through his hair, the while his nervous tension relaxed. Vanished as it had, it gave him the idea that she might return.

Another night, because of this first illusion, and because his mind was now constantly on her and he was old, he looked out of the window that was nearest his bed and commanded a hen-coop and pig-pen and a part of the wagon-shed, and there, a faint mist exuding from the damp of the ground, he thought he saw her again. It was one of those little wisps of mist, one of those faint exhalations of the earth that rise in a cool night after a warm day, and flicker like small white cypresses of fog before they disappear. In life it had been a custom of hers to cross this lot from her kitchen door to the pig-pen to throw in any scrap that was left from her cooking, and here she was again. He sat up and watched it strangely, doubtfully, because of his previous experience, but inclined, because of the nervous titillation that passed over his body, to believe that spirits really were, and that Phoebe, who would be concerned because of his lonely state, must be thinking about him, and hence returning. What other way would she have? How otherwise could she express herself? It would be within the province of her charity so to do, and like her loving interest in him. He quivered and watched it eagerly; but, a faint breath of air stirring, it wound away toward the fence and disappeared.

A third night, as he was actually dreaming, some ten days later, she came to his bedside and put her hand on his head.

"Poor Henry!" she said. "It's too bad."

He roused out of his sleep, actually to see her, he thought, moving from his bed-room into the living-room, her figure a shadowy mass of black. The weak straining of his eyes caused little points of light to flicker about the outlines of her form. He arose, greatly astonished, walked the floor in the cool room, convinced that Phoebe was coming back to him. If he only thought sufficiently, if he made it perfectly clear by his feeling that he needed her greatly, she would come back, this kindly wife, and tell him what to do. She would perhaps be with him much of the time, in the night, anyhow; and that would make him less lonely, this state more endurable.

In age and with the feeble it is not such a far cry from the subtleties of illusion to actual hallucination and in due time this transition was made for Henry. Night after night he waited, expecting her return. Once in his weird mood he thought he saw a pale light moving about the room, and another time he thought he saw her walking in the orchard after dark. It was one morning when the details of his lonely state were virtually unendurable that he woke with the thought that she was not dead. How he had arrived at this conclusion it is hard to say. His mind had gone. In its place was a fixed illusion. He and Phoebe had had a senseless quarrel. He had reproached her for not leaving his pipe where he was accustomed to find it, and she had left. It was an aberrated fulfillment of her old jesting threat that if he did not behave himself she would leave him.

"I guess I could find yuh ag'in," he had always said. But her cackling threat had always been:

"Yuh'll not find me if I ever leave yuh. I guess I kin git some place where yuh can't find me."

This morning when he arose he did not think to build the fire in the customary way or to grind his coffee and cut his bread, as was his wont, but solely to meditate as to where he should search for her and how he should induce her to come back. Recently the one horse had been dispensed with because he found it cumbersome and beyond his needs. He took down his soft crush hat after he had dressed himself, a new glint of interest and determination in his eye, and taking his black crook cane from behind the door, where he had always placed it, started out briskly to look for her among the nearest neighbors. His old shoes clumped soundly in the dust as he walked, and his gray-black locks, now grown rather long, straggled out in a dramatic fringe or halo from under his hat. His short coat stirred busily as he walked, and his hands and face were peaked and pale.

"Why, hello, Henry! Where're yuh goin' this mornin'?" inquired Farmer Dodge, who, hauling a load of wheat to market, encountered him on the public road. He had not seen the aged farmer in months, not since his wife's death, and he wondered now, seeing him looking so spry.

"Yuh ain't seen Phoebe, have yuh?" inquired the old man, looking up quizzically.

"Phoebe who?" inquired Farmer Dodge, not for the moment connecting the name with Henry's dead wife.

"Why, my wife Phoebe, o' course. Who do yuh s'pose I mean?" He stared up with a pathetic sharpness of glance from under his shaggy, gray eyebrows.

"Wall, I'll swan, Henry, yuh ain't jokin', are yuh?" said the solid Dodge, a pursy man, with a smooth hard, red face. "It can't be your wife yuh're talkin' about. She's dead."

"Dead! Shucks!" retorted the demented Reifsneider. "She left me early this mornin', while I was sleepin'. She allus got up to build the fire, but she's gone now. We had a little spat last night, an' I guess that's the reason. But I guess I kin find her. She's gone over to Matilda Race's; that's where she's gone."

He started briskly up the road, leaving the amazed Dodge to stare in wonder after him.

"Well, I'll be switched!" he said aloud to himself. "He's clean out'n his head. That poor old feller's been livin' down there till he's gone outen his mind. I'll have to notify the authorities." And he flicked his whip with great enthusiasm. "Geddap!" he said, and was off.

Reifsneider met no one else in this poorly populated region, until he reached the whitewashed fence of Matilda Race and her husband three miles away. He had passed several other houses en route, but these not being within the range of his illusion were not considered. His wife, who had known Matilda well, must be here. He opened the picket-gate which guarded the walk, and stamped briskly up to the door.

"Why, Mr. Reifsneider," exclaimed old Matilda herself, a stout woman, looking out of the door in answer to his knock, "what brings yuh here this mornin'?"

"Is Phoebe here?" he demanded eagerly.

"Phoebe who? What Phoebe?" replied Mrs. Race, curious as to this sudden development of energy on his part.

"Why, my Phoebe, o' course. My wife Phoebe. Who do yuh s'pose? Ain't she here now?"

"Lawsy me!" exclaimed Mrs. Race, opening her mouth. "Yuh pore man! So you're clean out'n your mind now. Yuh come right in and sit down. I'll git yuh a cup o' coffee. O' course your wife ain't here; but yuh come in an' sit down. I'll find her fer yuh after a while. I know where she is."

The old farmer's eyes softened, and he entered. He was so thin and pale a specimen, pantalooned and patriarchal, that he aroused Mrs. Race's extremest sympathy as he took off his hat and laid it on his knees quite softly and mildly.

"We had a quarrel last night, an' she left me," he volunteered.

"Laws! laws!" sighed Mrs. Race, there being no one present with whom to share her astonishment as she went to her kitchen. "The pore man! Now somebody's just got to look after him. He can't be allowed to run around the country this way lookin' for his dead wife. It's turrible."

She boiled him a pot of coffee and brought in some of her new-baked bread and fresh butter. She set out some of her best jam and put a couple of eggs to boil, lying whole-heartedly the while.

"Now yuh stay right there, Uncle Henry, till Jake comes in, an' I'll send him to look for Phoebe. I think it's more'n likely she's over to Swinnerton with some o' her friends. Anyhow, we'll find out. Now yuh just drink this coffee an' eat this bread. Yuh must be tired. Yuh've had a long walk this mornin'." Her idea was to take counsel with Jake, "her man," and perhaps have him notify the authorities.

She bustled about, meditating on the uncertainties of life, while old Reifsneider thrummed on the rim of his hat with his pale fingers and later ate abstractedly of what she offered. His mind was on his wife, however, and since she was not here, or did not appear, it wandered vaguely away to a family by the name of Murray, miles away in another direction. He decided after a time that he would not wait for Jake Race to hunt his wife but would seek her for himself. He must be on, and urge her to come back.

"Well, I'll be goin'," he said, getting up and looking strangely about him. "I guess she didn't come here after all. She went over to the Murrays', I guess. I'll not wait any longer, Mis' Race. There's a lot to do over to the house today." And out he marched in the face of her protests taking to the dusty road again in the warm spring sun, his cane striking the earth as he went.

It was two hours later that this pale figure of a man appeared in the Murrays' doorway, dusty, perspiring, eager. He had tramped all of five miles, and it was noon. An amazed husband and wife of sixty heard his strange query, and realized also that he was mad. They begged him to stay to dinner, intending to notify the authorities later and see what could be done; but though he stayed to partake of a little something, he did not stay long, and was off again to another distant farmhouse, his idea of many things to do and his need of Phoebe impelling him. So it went for that day and the next and the next, the circle of his inquiry ever widening.

The process by which a character assumes the significance of being peculiar, his antics weird, yet harmless, in such a community is often involute and pathetic. This day, as has been said, saw Reifsneider at other doors, eagerly asking his unnatural question, and leaving a trail of amazement, sympathy, and pity in his wake. Although the authorities were informed—the county sheriff, no less—it was not deemed advisable to take him into custody; for when those who knew old Henry, and had for so long, reflected on the condition of the county insane asylum, a place which, because of the poverty of the district, was of staggering aberration and sickening environment, it was decided to let him remain at large; for, strange to relate, it was found on investigation that at night he returned peaceably enough to his lonesome domicile there to discover whether his wife had returned, and to brood in loneliness until the morning. Who would lock up a thin, eager, seeking old man with iron-gray hair and an attitude of kindly, innocent inquiry, particularly when he was well known for a past of only kindly servitude and reliability? Those who had known him best rather agreed that he should be allowed to roam at large. He could do no harm. There were many who were willing to help him as to food, old clothes, the odds and ends of his daily life—at least at first. His figure after a time became not so much a common-place as an accepted curiosity, and the replies, "Why, no, Henry; I ain't see her," or "No, Henry; she ain't been here today," more customary.

For several years thereafter then he was an odd figure in the sun and rain, on dusty roads and muddy ones, encountered occasionally in strange and unexpected places, pursuing his endless search. Undernourishment, after a time, although the neighbors and those who knew his history gladly contributed from their store, affected his body; for he walked much and ate little. The longer he roamed the public highway in this manner, the deeper became his strange hallucination; and finding it harder and harder to return from his more and more distant pilgrimages, he finally began taking a few utensils with him from his home, making a small package of them, in order that he might not be compelled to return. In an old tin coffee-pot of large size he placed a small tin cup, a knife, fork, and spoon, some salt and pepper, and to the outside of it, by a string forced through a pierced hole, he fastened a plate, which could be released, and which was his woodland table. It was no trouble for him to secure the little food that he needed, and with a strange, almost religious dignity, he had no hesitation in asking for that much. By degrees his hair became longer and longer, his once black hat became an earthen brown, and his clothes threadbare and dusty.

For all of three years he walked, and none knew how wide were his perambulations, nor how he survived the storms and cold. They could not see him, with homely rural understanding and forethought, sheltering himself in hay-cocks, or by the sides of cattle, whose warm bodies protected him from the cold, and whose dull understandings were not opposed to his harmless presence. Overhanging rocks and trees kept him at times from the rain, and a friendly hay-loft or corn-crib was not above his humble consideration.

The involute progression of hallucination is strange. From asking at doors and being constantly rebuffed or denied, he finally came to the conclusion that although his Phoebe might not be in any of the houses at the doors of which he inquired, she might nevertheless be within the sound of his voice. And so, from patient inquiry, he began to call sad, occasional cries, that ever and anon waked the quiet landscapes and ragged hill regions, and set to echoing his thin "O-o-o Phoebe! O-o-o Phoebe!" It had a pathetic, albeit insane, ring, and many a farmer or plowboy came to know it even from afar and say, "There goes old Reifsneider."

Another thing that puzzled him greatly after a time and after many hundreds of inquiries was, when he no longer had any particular dooryard in view and no special inquiry to make, which way to go. These cross-roads, which occasionally led in four or even six directions, came after a time to puzzle him. But to solve this knotty problem, which became more and more of a puzzle, there came to his aid another hallucination. Phoebe's spirit or some power of the air or wind or nature would tell him. If he stood at the center of the parting of the ways, closed his eyes, turned thrice about, and called "O-o-o Phoebe!" twice, and then threw his cane straight before him, that would surely indicate which way to go for Phoebe, or one of these mystic powers would surely govern its direction and fall! In whichever direction it went, even though, as was not infrequently the case, it took him back along the path he had already come, or across fields, he was not so far gone in his mind but that he gave himself ample time to search before he called again. Also the hallucination seemed to persist that at some time he would surely find her. There were hours when his feet were sore, and his limbs weary, when he would stop in the heat to wipe his seamed brow, or in the cold to beat his arms. Sometimes, after throwing away his cane, and finding it indicating the direction from which he had just come, he would shake his head wearily and philosophically, as if contemplating the unbelievable or an untoward fate, and then start briskly off. His strange figure came finally to be known in the farthest reaches of three or four counties. Old Reifsneider was a pathetic character. His fame was wide.

Near a little town called Watersville, in Green County, perhaps four miles from that minor center of human activity, there was a place or precipice locally known as the Red Cliff, a sheer wall of red sandstone, perhaps a hundred feet high, which raised its sharp face for half a mile or more above the fruitful cornfields and orchards that lay beneath, and which was surmounted by a thick grove of trees. The slope that slowly led up to it from the opposite side was covered by a rank growth of beech, hickory, and ash, through which threaded a number of wagon-tracks crossing at various angles. In fair weather it had become old Reifsneider's habit, so inured was he by now to the open, to make his bed in some such patch of trees as this to fry his bacon or boil his eggs at the foot of some tree before laying himself down for the night. Occasionally, so light and inconsequential was his sleep, he would walk at night. More often, the moonlight or some sudden wind stirring in the trees or a reconnoitering animal arousing him, he would sit up and think, or pursue his quest in the moonlight or the dark, a strange, unnatural, half wild, half savage-looking but utterly harmless creature, calling at lonely road crossings, staring at dark and shuttered houses, and wondering where, where Phoebe could really be.

That particular lull that comes in the systole-diastole of this earthly ball at two o'clock in the morning invariably aroused him, and though he might not go any farther he would sit up and contemplate the darkness or the stars, wondering. Sometimes in the strange processes of his mind he would fancy that he saw moving among the trees the figure of his lost wife, and then he would get up to follow, taking his utensils, always on a string, and his cane. If she seemed to evade him too easily he would run, or plead, or, suddenly losing track of the fancied figure, stand awed or disappointed, grieving for the moment over the almost insurmountable difficulties of his search.

It was in the seventh year of these hopeless peregrinations, in the dawn of a similar springtime to that in which his wife had died, that he came at last one night to the vicinity of this self-same patch that crowned the rise to the Red Cliff. His far-flung cane, used as a divining-rod at the last cross-roads, had brought him hither. He had walked many, many miles. It was after ten o'clock at night, and he was very weary. Long wandering and little eating had left him but a shadow of his former self. It was a question now not so much of physical strength but of spiritual endurance which kept him up. He had scarcely eaten this day, and now exhausted he set himself down in the dark to rest and possibly to sleep.

Curiously on this occasion a strange suggestion of the presence of his wife surrounded him. It would not be long now, he counseled with himself, although the long months had brought him nothing, until he should see her, talk to her. He fell asleep after a time, his head on his knees. At midnight the moon began to rise, and at two in the morning, his wakeful hour, was a large silver disk shining through the trees to the east. He opened his eyes when the radiance became strong, making a silver pattern at his feet and lighting the woods with strange lusters and silvery, shadowy forms. As usual, his old notion that his wife must be near occurred to him on this occasion, and he looked about him with a speculative, anticipatory eye. What was it that moved in the distant shadows along the path by which he had entered—a pale, flickering will-o'-the-wisp that bobbed gracefully among the trees and riveted his expectant gaze? Moonlight and shadows combined to give it a strange form and a stranger reality, this fluttering of bogfire or dancing of wandering fire-flies. Was it truly his lost Phoebe? By a circuitous route it passed about him, and in his fevered state he fancied that he could see the very eyes of her, not as she was when he last saw her in the black dress and shawl but now a strangely younger Phoebe, gayer, sweeter, the one whom he had known years before as a girl. Old Reifsneider got up. He had been expecting and dreaming of this hour all these years, and now as he saw the feeble light dancing lightly before him he peered at it questioningly, one thin hand in his gray hair.

Of a sudden there came to him now for the first time in many years the full charm of her girlish figure as he had known it in boyhood, the pleasing, sympathetic smile, the brown hair, the blue sash she had once worn about her waist at a picnic, her gay, graceful movements. He walked around the base of the tree, straining with his eyes, forgetting for once his cane and utensils, and following eagerly after. On she moved before him, a will-o'-the-wisp of the spring, a little flame above her head, and it seemed as though among the small saplings of ash and beech and the thick trunks of hickory and elm that she signaled with a young, a lightsome hand.

"O Phoebe! Phoebe!" he called. "Have yuh really come? Have yuh really answered me?" And hurrying faster, he fell once, scrambling lamely to his feet, only to see the light in the distance dancing illusively on. On and on he hurried until he was fairly running, brushing his ragged arms against the trees, striking his hands and face against impeding twigs. His hat was gone, his lungs were breathless, his reason quite astray, when coming to the edge of the cliff he saw her below among a silvery bed of apple-trees now blooming in the spring.

"O Phoebe!" he called. "O Phoebe! Oh, no, don't leave me!" And feeling the lure of a world where love was young and Phoebe as this vision presented her, a delightful epitome of their quondam youth, he gave a gay cry of "Oh, wait, Phoebe!" and leaped.

Some farmer-boys, reconnoitering this region of bounty and prospect some few days afterward, found first the tin utensils tied together under the tree where he had left them, and then later at the foot of the cliff, pale, broken, but elate, a molded smile of peace and delight upon his lips, his body. His old hat was discovered lying under some low-growing saplings the twigs of which had held it back. No one of all the simple population knew how eagerly and joyously he had found his lost mate.

CHAPTER *four*

Psychotic
Symptoms

Certain symptoms can be considered evidence for a psychosis
and are a gross manifestation of the break with reality. Some of
the more important will be illustrated in this chapter.

Hallucinations

I. Hallucinations have already been discussed in the
section on schizophrenia. Hallucinations are disturbances in
perception, and therefore any of the five senses can be involved.
Auditory hallucinations are most characteristic of schizophrenia.
Frightening visual hallucinations are apt to occur in toxic states,
as do the tactile hallucinations that are common in delirium
tremens, a condition that occurs after prolonged alcoholism.
Olfactory hallucinations, though rare, occur in regressed
schizophrenics and are occasionally found as a single presenting
symptom. Hallucinations of taste, although uncommon, can be
found in depressed patients where everything may taste
bitter or sour. These generalizations are of limited value and
are subject to wide variations. The following examples
illustrate particularly interesting instances.

Edgar Allan Poe's story "The Tell-Tale Heart"
gives one an insight into the agonizing nature of some
hallucinations. Consider the terror and helplessness that any
individual would feel who could no longer trust his senses—
with which he organizes his perceptual world. What then can
he trust? The famous American psychiatrist Harry Stack
Sullivan said once that psychotic anxiety can be compared to

walking down stairs in pitch dark and suddenly finding that the next stair is missing. In "The Tell-Tale Heart" we see anxiety of psychotic proportion, and the beating of the heart is accepted without question as though it were a reality. It is Poe's genius that he leaves the reader unsure whether one is a witness to the uncanny, or to a psychotic distortion. This is of little consequence since it is this very quality of the uncanny which is so often felt by the psychotic.

THE TELL-TALE HEART

Edgar Allan Poe (1809–1849)

True!—nervous—very, very dreadfully nervous I had been and am! but why *will* you say that I am mad? The disease had sharpened my senses—not destroyed—not dulled them. Above all was the sense of hearing acute. I heard all things in the heaven and in the earth. I heard many things in hell. How, then, am I mad? Harken! and observe how healthily —how calmly I can tell you the whole story.

It is impossible to tell how first the idea entered my brain; but once conceived, it haunted me day and night. Object there was none. Passion there was none. I loved the old man. He had never wronged me. He had never given me insult. For his gold I had no desire. I think it was his eye! Yes, it was this! One of his eyes resembled that of a vulture—a pale blue eye, with a film over it. Whenever it fell upon me, my blood ran cold; and so by degrees—very gradually—I made up my mind to take the life of the old man, and thus rid myself of the eye forever.

Now this is the point. You fancy me mad. Madmen know nothing. But you should have seen *me*. You should have seen how wisely I pro-ceeded—with what caution—with what foresight—with what dissimulation I went to work!

I was never kinder to the old man than during the whole week before I killed him. And every night, about midnight, I turned the latch of his door and opened it—oh, so gently! And then, when I had made an open-ing sufficient for my head, I put in a dark lantern, all closed, closed, so that no light shone out, and then I thrust in my head. Oh, you would have laughed to see how cunningly I thrust it in! I moved it slowly—very, very slowly, so that I might not disturb the old man's sleep. It took me an hour to place my whole head within the opening so far that I could see him as he lay upon his bed. Ha!—would a madman have been so wise as this? And then, when my head was well in the room, I undid the lantern

"The Tell-Tale Heart," by Edgar Allan Poe.

cautiously—oh, so cautiously—cautiously (for the hinges creaked)—I undid it just so much that a single thin ray fell upon the vulture eye. And
this I did for seven long nights—every night just at midnight—but I
found the eye always closed; and so it was impossible to do the work;
for it was not the old man who vexed me, but his Evil Eye. And every
morning, when the day broke, I went boldly into the chamber, and spoke
courageously to him, calling him by name in a hearty tone, and inquiring
how he had passed the night. So you see he would have been a very profound old man, indeed, to suspect that every night, just at twelve, I looked
in upon him while he slept.

Upon the eighth night I was more than usually cautious in opening
the door. A watch's minute hand moves more quickly than did mine.
Never before that night had I *felt* the extent of my own powers—of my
sagacity. I could scarcely contain my feelings of triumph. To think that
there I was, opening the door, little by little, and he not even to dream
of my secret deeds or thoughts. I fairly chuckled at the idea; and perhaps
he heard me; for he moved on the bed suddenly, as if startled. Now you
may think that I drew back—but no. His room was as black as pitch with
the thick darkness (for the shutters were close fastened, through fear of
robbers), and so I knew that he could not see the opening of the door, and
I kept pushing it on steadily, steadily.

I had my head in, and was about to open the lantern, when my thumb
slipped upon the tin fastening, and the old man sprang up in bed, crying
out: "Who's there?"

I kept quite still and said nothing. For a whole hour I did not move a
muscle, and in the meantime I did not hear him lie down. He was still
sitting up in the bed listening;—just as I have done, night after night,
hearkening to the death watches in the wall.

Presently I heard a slight groan, and I knew it was the groan of mortal
terror. It was not a groan of pain or grief—oh no!—it was the low stifled
sound that arises from the bottom of the soul when overcharged with awe.
I knew the sound well. Many a night, just at midnight, when all the
world slept, it has welled up from my own bosom, deepening, with its
dreadful echo, the terrors that distracted me. I say I knew it well. I knew
what the old man felt, and pitied him, although I chuckled at heart. I knew
that he had been lying awake ever since the first slight noise, when he had
turned in the bed. His fears had been ever since growing upon him. He
had been trying to fancy them causeless, but could not. He had been saying to himself: "It is nothing but the wind in the chimney—it is only a
mouse crossing the floor," or "it is merely a cricket which has made a
single chirp." Yes, he had been trying to comfort himself with these suppositions; but he had found all in vain. *All in vain;* because Death, in
approaching him, had stalked with his black shadow before him, and enveloped the victim. And it was the mournful influence of the unperceived

shadow that caused him to feel—although he neither saw nor heard—to *feel*
the presence of my head within the room.

When I had waited a long time, very patiently, without hearing him
lie down, I resolved to open a little—a very, very little crevice in the lantern. So I opened it—you cannot imagine how stealthily, stealthily—until,
at lenth, a single dim ray, like the thread of the spider, shot from out the
crevice and full upon the vulture eye.

It was open—wide, wide open—and I grew furious as I gazed upon it.
I saw it with perfect distinctness—all a dull blue, with a hideous veil over
it that chilled the very marrow in my bones; but I could see nothing else
of the old man's face or person: for I had directed the ray, as if by instinct, precisely upon the damned spot.

And now—have I not told you that what you mistake for madness is
but over-acuteness of the senses?—now, I say, there came to my ears a low,
dull, quick sound, such as a watch makes when enveloped in cotton. I
knew *that* sound well too. It was the beating of the old man's heart. It increased my fury, as the beating of a drum stimulates the soldier into
courage.

But even yet I refrained and kept still. I scarcely breathed. I held the
lantern motionless. I tried how steadily I could maintain the ray upon the
eye. Meantime the hellish tattoo of the heart increased. It grew quicker
and quicker, and louder and louder every instant. The old man's terror
must have been extreme! It grew louder, I say, louder every moment!—do
you mark me well? I have told you that I am nervous: so I am. And now at
the dead hour of night, amid the dreadful silence of that old house, so
strange a noise as this excited me to uncontrollable terror. Yet, for some
minutes longer I refrained and stood still. But the beating grew louder,
louder! I thought the heart must burst. And now a new anxiety seized
me—the sound would be heard by a neighbor! The old man's hour had
come! With a loud yell, I threw open the lantern and leaped into the
room. He shrieked once—once only. In an instant I dragged him to the
floor, and pulled the heavy bed over him. I then smiled gaily, to find the
deed so far done. But, for many minutes, the heart beat on with a muffled
sound. This, however, did not vex me; it would not be heard through the
wall. At length it ceased. The old man was dead. I removed the bed and
examined the corpse. Yes, he was stone, stone dead. I placed my hand
upon the heart and held it there many minutes. There was no pulsation.
He was stone dead. His eye would trouble me no more.

If still you think me mad, you will think so no longer when I describe
the wise precautions I took for the concealment of the body. The night
waned, and I worked hastily, but in silence. First of all I dismembered the
corpse. I cut off the head and the arms and the legs.

I then took up three planks from the flooring of the chamber, and
deposited all between the scantlings. I then replaced the boards so cleverly,

so cunningly, that no human eye—not even *his*—could have detected anything wrong. There was nothing to wash out—no stain of any kind—no
blood-spot whatever. I had been too wary for that. A tub had caught all
—ha! ha!

When I had made an end of these labors, it was four o'clock—still
dark as midnight. As the bell sounded the hour, there came a knocking at
the street door. I went down to open it with a light heart—for what had I
now to fear? There entered three men, who introduced themselves, with
perfect suavity, as officers of the police. A shriek had been heard by a
neighbor during the night: suspicion of foul play had been aroused; information had been lodged at the police office, and they (the officers) had
been deputed to search the premises.

I smiled—for *what* had I to fear? I bade the gentlemen welcome. The
shriek, I said, was my own in a dream. The old man, I mentioned, was ab-
sent in the country. I took my visitors all over the house. I bade them
search—search *well*. I led them, at length, to *his* chamber. I showed them
his treasures, secure, undisturbed. In the enthusiasm of my confidence, I
brought chairs into the room, and desired them *here* to rest from their
fatigues, while I myself, in the wild audacity of my perfect triumph,
placed my own seat upon the very spot beneath which reposed the corpse
of the victim.

The officers were satisfied. My *manner* had convinced them. I was
singularly at ease. They sat, and while I answered cheerily, they chatted
familiar things. But ere long, I felt myself getting pale and wished them
gone. My head ached, and I fancied a ringing in my ears: but still they sat
and still chatted. The ringing became more distinct:—it continued and
became more distinct: I talked more freely to get rid of the feeling: but
it continued and gained definiteness—until, at length, I found that the
noise was *not* within my ears.

No doubt I now grew *very* pale;—but I talked more fluently, and
with a heightened voice. Yet the sound increased—and what could I do?
It was *a low, dull, quick sound—much such a sound as a watch makes
when enveloped in cotton*. I gasped for breath—and yet the officers heard
it not. I talked more quickly—more vehemently; but the noise steadily increased. Why *would* they not be gone? I paced the floor to and fro with
heavy strides, as if excited to fury by the observation of the men—but the
noise steadily increased. Oh, God; what *could* I do? I foamed—I raved—I
swore! I swung the chair upon which I had been sitting, and grated it upon
the boards, but the noise arose over all and continually increased. It grew
louder—louder—*louder!* And still the men chatted pleasantly, and smiled.
Was it possible they heard not? Almighty God!—no, no! They heard!—
they suspected—they *knew!*—they were making a *mockery* of my horror!
—this I thought, and this I think. But anything was better than this agony!
Anything was more tolerable than this derision! I could bear those hypo-

critical smiles no longer! I felt that I must scream or die!—and now again!
—hark! louder! louder! *louder!*—

"Villains!" I shrieked, "dissemble no more! I admit the deed!—tear
up the planks!—here, here!—it is the beating of his hideous heart!"

Visual Hallucinations in Schizophrenia

II. During the onset of a schizophrenic decompensation,
bizarre revelations often occur. These revelations have the
quality of suddenly providing an entirely new perspective on
life, usually a perspective that results in a major distortion
of reality. This strange experience frequently takes place
through the sudden appearance of some religious figure in a
visual hallucination who imparts a special grandiose mission,
or the very appearance suggests to the patient that he is
endowed with special powers. Careful study of such patients
suggests that these visual hallucinations have a reparative
function; they are considered secondary or restitutive
phenomena set up to cope with unbearable anxiety. These
hallucinatory experiences often help to organize a delusional
system, and once the delusion is formed much of the intense
anxiety that may have preceded the experience is relieved.
Such patients are apt to welcome or be fascinated by these
hallucinations rather than fear them. Chekhov illustrates
this in "The Black Monk."

THE BLACK MONK

Anton Chekhov   (1860–1904)

. . . But in the country Kovrin continued to live the
same nervous and untranquil life as he had lived in town. He read much,
wrote much, studied Italian; and when he went for walks, thought all
the time of returning to work. He slept so little that he astonished the
household; if by chance he slept in the daytime for half an hour, he
could not sleep all the following night. Yet after these sleepless nights
he felt active and gay.

He talked much, drank wine, and smoked expensive cigars. Often,

From "The Black Monk," by Anton Chekhov. Reprinted with permission of The
Macmillan Company from *The Lady with the Dog* by Anton Chekhov. Copyright
1917 by The Macmillan Company, renewed 1945 by Constance Garnett.

nearly every day, young girls from the neighbouring country-houses drove over to Borisovka, played the piano with Tanya, and sang. Sometimes the visitor was a young man, also a neighbour, who played the violin well. Kovrin listened eagerly to their music and singing, but was exhausted by it, so exhausted sometimes that his eyes closed involuntarily, and his head drooped on his shoulder.

One evening after tea he sat upon the balcony, reading. In the drawing-room Tanya—a soprano, one of her friends—a contralto, and the young violinist studied the well-known serenade of Braga. Kovrin listened to the words, but though they were Russian, could not understand their meaning. At last, laying down his book and listening attentively, he understood. A girl with a disordered imagination heard by night in a garden some mysterious sounds, sounds so beautiful and strange that she was forced to recognise their harmony and holiness, which to us mortals are incomprehensible, and therefore flew back to heaven. Kovrin's eyelids drooped. He rose, and in exhaustion walked up and down the drawing-room, and then up and down the hall. When the music ceased, he took Tanya by the hand and went out with her to the balcony.

"All day—since early morning," he began, "my head has been taken up with a strange legend. I cannot remember whether I read it, or where I heard it, but the legend is very remarkable and not very coherent. I may begin by saying that it is not very clear. A thousand years ago a monk, robed in black, wandered in the wilderness—somewhere in Syria or Arabia. . . . Some miles away the fishermen saw another black monk moving slowly over the surface of the lake. The second monk was a mirage. Now put out of your mind all the laws of optics, which legend, of course, does not recognise, and listen. From the first mirage was produced another mirage, from the second, a third, so that the image of the Black Monk is eternally reflected from one stratum of the atmosphere to another. At one time it was seen in Africa, then in Spain, then in India, then in the Far North. At last it issued from the limits of the earth's atmosphere, but never came across conditions which would cause it to disappear. Maybe it is seen to-day in Mars or in the constellation of the Southern Cross. Now the whole point, the very essence of the legend, lies in the prediction that exactly a thousand years after the monk went into the wilderness, the mirage will again be cast into the atmosphere of the earth and show itself to the world of men. This term of a thousand years, it appears, is now expiring. . . . According to the legend we must expect the Black Monk today or tomorrow."

"It is a strange story," said Tanya, whom the legend did not please.

"But the most astonishing thing," laughed Kovrin, "is that I cannot remember how this legend came into my head. Did I read it? Did I hear it? Or can it be that I dreamed of the Black Monk? I cannot remember. But the legend interests me. All day long I thought of nothing else."

Releasing Tanya, who returned to her visitors, he went out of the house, and walked lost in thought beside the flower-beds. Already the sun was setting. The freshly watered flowers exhaled a damp, irritating smell. In the house the music had again begun, and from the distance the violin produced the effect of a human voice. Straining his memory in an attempt to recall where he had heard the legend, Kovrin walked slowly across the park, and then, not noticing where he went, to the river-bank.

By the path which ran down among the uncovered roots to the water's edge Kovrin descended, frightening the snipe, and disturbing two ducks. On the dark pine trees glowed the rays of the setting sun, but on the surface of the river darkness had already fallen. Kovrin crossed the stream. Before him now lay a broad field covered with young rye. Neither human dwelling nor human soul was visible in the distance; and it seemed that the path must lead to the unexplored, enigmatical region in the west where the sun had already set—where still, vast and majestic, flamed the afterglow.

"How open it is—how peaceful and free!" thought Kovrin, walking along the path. "It seems as if all the world is looking at me from a hiding-place and waiting for me to comprehend it."

A wave passed over the rye, and the light evening breeze blew softly on his uncovered head. Yet a minute more and the breeze blew again, this time more strongly, the rye rustled, and from behind came the dull murmur of the pines. Kovrin stopped in amazement. On the horizon, like a cyclone or waterspout, a great, black pillar rose up from earth to heaven. Its outlines were undefined; but from the first it might be seen that it was not standing still, but moving with inconceivable speed towards Kovrin; and the nearer it came the smaller and smaller it grew. Involuntarily Kovrin rushed aside and made a path for it. A monk in black clothing, with grey hair and black eyebrows, crossing his hands upon his chest, was borne past. His bare feet were above the ground. Having swept some twenty yards past Kovrin, he looked at him, nodded his head, and smiled kindly and at the same time slyly. His face was pale and thin. When he had passed by Kovrin he again began to grow, flew across the river, struck inaudibly against the clay bank and pine trees, and, passing through them, vanished like smoke.

"You see," stammered Kovrin, "after all, the legend was true!"

Making no attempt to explain this strange phenomenon; satisfied with the fact that he had so closely and so plainly seen not only the black clothing but even the face and eyes of the monk; agitated agreeably, he returned home.

In the park and in the garden visitors were walking quietly; in the house the music continued. So he alone had seen the Black Monk. He felt a strong desire to tell what he had seen to Tanya and Yegor Semionovich, but feared that they would regard it as an hallucination, and decided to keep his counsel. He laughed loudly, sang, danced a mazurka, and felt in the best of spirits; and the guests and Tanya noticed upon his face a peculiar expression of ecstasy and inspiration, and found him very interesting. . . .

Hardly had he called to mind the legend and painted in imagination the black apparition in the rye-field when from behind the pine trees opposite to him, walked inaudibly—without the faintest rustling—a man of middle height. His grey head was uncovered, he was dressed in black, and barefooted like a beggar. On his pallid, corpse-like face stood out sharply a number of black spots. Nodding his head politely the stranger or beggar walked noiselessly to the bench and sat down, and Kovrin recognised the Black Monk. For a minute they looked at one another, Kovrin with astonishment, but the monk kindly and, as, before, with a sly expression on his face.

"But you are a mirage," said Kovrin. "Why are you here, and why do you sit in one place? That is not in accordance with the legend."

"It is all the same," replied the monk softly, turning his face toward Kovrin. "The legend, the mirage, I—all are products of your own excited imagination. I am a phantom."

"That is to say you don't exist?" asked Kovrin.

"Think as you like," replied the monk, smiling faintly. "I exist in your imagination, and as your imagination is a part of Nature, I must exist also in Nature."

"You have a clever, a distinguished face—it seems to me as if in reality you had lived more than a thousand years," said Kovrin. "I did not know that my imagination was capable of creating such a phenomenon. Why do you look at me with such rapture? Are you pleased with me?"

"Yes. For you are one of the few who can justly be named the elected of God. You serve eternal truth. Your thoughts, your intentions, your astonishing science, all your life bear the stamp of divinity, a heavenly impress; they are dedicated to the rational and the beautiful, and that is, to the Eternal."

"You say, to eternal truth. Then can eternal truth be accessible and necessary to men if there is no eternal life?"

"There is eternal life," said the monk.

"You believe in the immortality of men."

"Of course. For you, men, there awaits a great and a beautiful future. And the more the world has of men like you the nearer will this future be brought. Without you, ministers to the highest principles, living freely and consciously, humanity would be nothing; developing in the natural order it must wait the end of its earthly history. But you, by some thousands of years, hasten it into the kingdom of eternal truth—and in this is your high service. You embody in yourself the blessing of God which rested upon the people."

"And what is the object of eternal life?" asked Kovrin.

"The same as all life—enjoyment. True enjoyment is in knowledge, and eternal life presents innumerable, inexhaustible fountains of knowledge; it is in this sense it was said: 'In My Father's house are many mansions. . . .' "

"You cannot conceive what a joy it is to me to listen to you," said Kovrin, rubbing his hands with delight.

"I am glad."

"Yet I know that when you leave me I shall be tormented by doubt as to your reality. You are a phantom, a hallucination. But that means that I am physically diseased, that I am not in a normal state?"

"What if you are? That need not worry you. You are ill because you have overstrained your powers, because you have borne your health in sacrifice to one idea, and the time is near when you will sacrifice not merely it but your life also. What more could you desire? It is what all gifted and noble natures aspire to."

"But if I am physically diseased, how can I trust myself?"

"And how do you know that the men of genius whom all the world trusts have not also seen visions? Genius, they tell you now, is akin to insanity. Believe me, the healthy and the normal are but ordinary men—the herd. Fears as to a nervous age, over-exhaustion and degeneration can trouble seriously only those whose aims in life lie in the present—that is the herd."

"The Romans had as their ideal: *mens sana in corpore sano.*"

"All that the Greeks and Romans said is not true. Exaltations, aspirations, excitements, ecstasies—all those things which distinguish poets, prophets, martyrs to ideas from ordinary men are incompatible with the animal life, that is, with physical health. I repeat, if you wish to be healthy and normal go with the herd."

"How strange that you should repeat what I myself have so often thought!" said Kovrin. "It seems as if you had watched me and listened to my secret thoughts. But do not talk about me. What do you imply by the words: eternal truth?"

The monk made no answer. Kovrin looked at him, but could not make out his face. His features clouded and melted away; his head and arms disappeared; his body faded into the bench and into the twilight, and vanished utterly.

"The hallucination has gone," said Kovrin, laughing. "It is a pity."

He returned to the house lively and happy. What the Black Monk had said to him flattered, not his self-love, but his soul, his whole being. To be the elected, to minister to eternal truth, to stand in the ranks of those who hasten by thousands of years the making mankind worthy of the kingdom of Christ, to deliver humanity from thousands of years of struggle, sin, and suffering, to give to one idea everything, youth, strength,

health, to die for the general welfare—what an exalted, what a glorious
ideal! And when through his memory flowed his past life, a life pure and
chaste and full of labour, when he remembered what he had learnt and
what he had taught, he concluded that in the words of the monk, there
was no exaggeration. . . .

Disturbances in the Body Image

III. One of the less frequently discussed symptoms
of schizophrenia is the disturbance of the person's sense of his
own body. He may have all sorts of bizarre notions about
changes in his size, changes in his body make-up; he may believe
he is changing sexes or that he is disintegrating. Such fantasies
are usually terrifying, and Rilke has captured these feelings
with incredible intuition in his remarkable study, *The
Notebooks of Malte Laurids Brigge.* (Such symptoms of a less
intense or more transient nature may occur in persons not
psychotic.) This particular story also conveys the regression
typical of schizophrenia.

THE NOTEBOOKS OF MALTE LAURIDS BRIGGE
Rainer Maria Rilke (1875–1926)

. . . The doctor did not understand me. Nothing. And
certainly it was difficult to describe. They wanted to try electric treatment. Good. I received a slip of paper: I had to be at the Salpêtrière at
one o'clock. I was there. I had to pass a long row of barracks and traverse
a number of courtyards, where people in white bonnets stood here and
there under the bare trees like convicts. Finally I entered a long, gloomy,
corridor-like room, that had on one side four windows of dim, greenish
glass, one separated from the other by a broad, black partition. In front
of them a wooden bench ran along, past everything, and on this bench
they who knew me sat and waited. Yes, they were all there. When I
became accustomed to the twilight of the place, I noticed that among
them, as they sat shoulder to shoulder in an endless row, there could also
be other people, little people, artisans, char-women, truckmen. Down at

the narrow end of this corridor, on special chairs, two stout women had spread themselves out and were conversing, concierges probably. I looked at the clock; it was five minutes to one. In five minutes, or say ten, my turn would come; so it was not so bad. The air was foul, heavy, impregnated with clothes and breaths. At a certain spot the strong, intensifying coolness of ether came through a crack in a door. I began to walk up and down. It crossed my mind that I had been directed here, among these people, to this overcrowded, general consultation. It was, so to speak, the first public confirmation of the fact that I belonged among the outcast; had the doctor known by my appearance? Yet I had paid my visit in a tolerably decent suit; I had sent in my card. Despite that he must have learned it somehow; perhaps I had betrayed myself. However, now that it was a fact I did not find it so bad after all; the people sat quietly and took no notice of me. Some were in pain and swung one leg a little, the better to endure it. Various men had laid their heads in the palms of their hands; others were sleeping deeply, with heavy, fatigue-crushed faces. A stout man with a red, swollen neck sat bending forward, staring at the floor, and from time to time spat with a smack at a spot he seemed to find suitable for the purpose. A child was sobbing in a corner; it had drawn its long thin legs close up on the bench, and now clasped and held them tightly to its body, as though it must bid them farewell. A small, pale woman on whose head a crape hat adorned with round, black flowers, sat awry, wore the grimace of a smile about her meager lips, but her sore eyes were constantly overflowing. Not far from her had been placed a girl with a round, smooth face and protruding eyes that were without expression; her mouth hung open, so that one saw her white, slimy gums with their old stunted teeth. And there were many bandages. Bandages that swathed a whole head layer upon layer, until only a single eye remained that no longer belonged to anyone. Bandages that hid, and bandages that revealed, what was beneath them. Bandages that had been undone, in which, as in a dirty bed, a hand now lay that was a hand no longer; and a bandaged leg that protruded from the row on the bench, as large as a whole man. I walked up and down, and endeavored to be calm. I occupied myself a good deal with the wall facing me. I noticed that it contained a number of single doors, and did not reach up to the ceiling, so that this corridor was not completely separated from the rooms that must adjoin it. I looked at the clock; I had been pacing up and down for an hour. A while later the doctors arrived. First a couple of young fellows who passed by with indifferent faces, and finally the one I had consulted, in light gloves, chapeau à huit reflets, impeccable overcoat. When he saw me he lifted his hat a little and smiled absent-mindedly. I now hoped to be called immediately, but another hour passed. I cannot remember how I spent it. It passed. An old man wearing a soiled apron, a sort of attendant, came and touched me on the shoulder. I entered one of the adjoining rooms. The doctor and the young fellows sat round a table and looked at me, someone gave me a chair. So far so good. And now I had to describe what it was that was the matter with me. As briefly as possible, s'il vous plaît. For much time these gentlemen had not. I felt very old. The young fellows sat and looked at me with that superior, professional curiosity they had learned. The doctor I knew stroked his pointed black beard and smiled absently. I thought I should burst into tears, but I heard myself saying in French: "I have already had the honor, monsieur, of giving you all the details that I can give. If you consider it indispensable that these gentlemen should be initiated, you are certainly able, after our conversation, to do this in a few words, while I find it very difficult." The doctor rose, smiling politely, and going toward the window with his assistants said a few words, which he accompanied with a horizontal, wavering movement of his hands. Three minutes later one of the young men, short-sighted and jerky, came back to the table, and said, trying to look at me severely, "You sleep well, sir?" "No, badly." Whereupon he sprang back again to the group at the window. There they discussed a while longer, then the doctor turned to me and informed me that I would be summoned again. I reminded him that my appointment had been for one o'clock. He smiled and made a few swift, abrupt movements with his small white hands, which were meant to signify that he was uncommonly busy. So I returned to my hallway, where the air had become much more oppressive, and began again to pace up and down, although I felt mortally tired. Finally the moist, accumulated smell made me dizzy; I stopped at the entrance door and opened it a little. I saw that outside it was still afternoon, with some sun, and that did me ever so much good. But I had hardly stood a minute thus when I heard someone calling me. A female sitting at a table two or three steps away hissed something to me. Who had told me to open the door? I said I could not stand the atmosphere. Well, that was my own affair, but the door had to be kept shut. Was it not permissible, then, to open a window? No, that was forbidden. I decided to resume my walking up and down, for after all that was a kind of anodyne and it hurt nobody. But now this too displeased the woman sitting at the little table. Did I not have a seat? No, I hadn't. Walking about was not allowed; I would have to find a seat. There ought to be one. The woman was right. In fact, a place was promptly found next the girl with the protruding eyes. There I now sat with the feeling that this state must certainly be the preparation for something dreadful. On my left, then, was this girl with the decaying gums; what was on my right I could not make out till after some time. It was a huge, immovable mass, having a face and a large, heavy, inert hand. The side of the face that I saw was empty, quite without features and without memories; and it was gruesome that the clothes were like that of a corpse dressed for the coffin. The narrow, black cravat had been buckled in the same loose, impersonal way around the collar, and the coat showed that it had been put on the will-less body by other hands. The hand had been placed on the trousers exactly where it lay, and even the hair looked as if it had been combed by those women who lay out the dead, and was stiffly arranged, like the hair of stuffed animals. I observed all these things with attention, and it occurred to me that this must be the place that had been destined for me; for I now believed I had at last arrived at that point of my life at which I would remain. Yes, fate goes wonderful ways.

Suddenly there rose quite nearby in quick succession the frightened, defensive cries of a child, followed by a low, hushed weeping. While I was straining to discover where this could have come from, a little, sup-pressed cry quavered away again, and I heard voices, questioning, a voice giving orders in a subdued tone, and then some sort of machine started up and hummed indifferently along. Now I recalled that half wall, and it was clear to me that all this came from the other side of the doors and that work was going on in there. Actually, the attendant with the soiled apron appeared from time to time and made a sign. I had given up thinking that he might mean me. Was it intended for me? No. Two men appeared with a wheelchair; they lifted the mass beside me into it, and I now saw that it was an old paralytic who had another, smaller side to him, worn out by life, and an open, dim and melancholy eye. They wheeled him inside, and now there was lots of room beside me. And I sat and wondered what they were likely to do to the imbecile girl and whether she too would scream. The machines back there kept up such an agreeable mechanical whirring, there was nothing disturbing about it.

But suddenly everything was still, and in the stillness a superior, self-complacent voice, which I thought I knew, said: "Riez!" A pause. "Riez! Mais riez, riez!" I was already laughing. It was inexplicable that the man on the other side of the partition didn't want to laugh. A machine rattled, but was immediately silent again, words were exchanged, then the same energetic voice rose again and ordered: "Dites-nous le mot: avant." And spelling it: "A-v-a-n-t." Silence. "On n'entend rien. Encore une fois. . . ."

And then, as I listened to the hot, flaccid stuttering on the other side of the partition, then for the first time in many, many years it was there again. That which had struck into me my first, profound terror, when as a child I lay ill with fever: the Big Thing. Yes, that was what I had al-ways called it, when they all stood around my bed and felt my pulse and asked me what had frightened me: the Big Thing. And when they got the doctor and he came and spoke to me, I begged him only to make the Big Thing go away, nothing else mattered. But he was like the rest. He could not take it away, though I was so small then and might so easily have been helped. And now it was there again. Later it had simply stayed away; it had not come back even on nights when I had fever; but now it was there, although I had no fever. Now it was there. Now it grew out of me like a tumor, like a second head, and was a part of me, though it could not belong to me at all, because it was so big. It was there like a huge, dead beast, that had once, when it was still alive, been my hand or my arm. And my blood flowed both through me and through it, as if through one and the same body. And my heart had to make a great effort to drive the blood into the Big Thing; there was hardly enough blood. And the blood entered the Big Thing unwillingly and came back sick and tainted. But the Big Thing swelled and grew over my face like a warm bluish boil and grew over my mouth, and already the shadow of its edge lay upon my remaining eye.

I cannot recall how I got out through the numerous courtyards. It was evening, and I lost my way in this strange neighborhood and went up boulevards with interminable walls in one direction and, when there was no end to them, returned in the opposite direction until I reached some square or other. Thence I began to walk along a street, and other streets came that I had never seen before, and still other streets. Electric cars would come racing up and past, too brilliantly lit and with harsh, beating clang of bells. But on their signboards stood names I did not know. I did not know in what city I was or whether I had a lodging somewhere here or what I must do in order not to have to go on walking.

And now this illness too, which has always affected me so strangely. I am sure it is underestimated. Just as the importance of other diseases is exaggerated. This disease has no particular characteristics; it takes on those of the person it attacks. With a somnambulic certainty it drags out of each his deepest danger, that seemed passed, and sets it before him again, quite near, imminent. Men, who once in their school-days attempted the helpless vice that has for its duped intimate the poor, hard hands of boys, find themselves at it again; or an illness they had conquered in childhood begins in them again; or a lost habit reappears, a certain hesitant turn of the head that had been peculiar to them years before. And with whatever comes there rises a whole tangle of insane memories, which hangs about it like wet seaweed on some sunken thing. Lives of which one would never have known mount to the surface and mingle with what has actually been, and push aside past matters that one had thought to know: for in that which ascends is a rested, new strength, but that which has always been there is wearied by too frequent remembrance.

I am lying in my bed, five flights up, and my day, which nothing interrupts, is like a dial without hands. As a thing long lost lies one morning in its old place, safe and well, fresher almost than at the time of its loss, quite as though someone had cared for it—: so here and there on my coverlet lie lost things out of my childhood and are as new. All forgotten fears are there again.

The fear that a small, woollen thread that sticks out of the hem of my blanket may be hard, hard and sharp like a steel needle; the fear that this little button on my night-shirt may be bigger than my head, big and heavy; the fear that this crumb of bread now falling from my bed may arrive glassy and shattered on the floor, and the burdensome worry lest at that really everything will be broken, everything for ever; the fear that the torn border of an opened letter may be something forbidden that no one ought to see, something indescribably precious for which no place in the room is secure enough; the fear that if I fell asleep I might swallow the piece of coal lying in front of the stove; the fear that some number may begin to grow in my brain until there is no more room for it inside me; the fear that it may be granite I am lying on, grey granite; the fear that I may shout, and that people may come running to my door and finally break it open; the fear that I may betray myself and tell all that I dread; and the fear that I might not be able to say anything, because everything is beyond utterance,—and the other fears . . . the fears.

I asked for my childhood and it has come back, and I feel that it is just as difficult as it was before, and that it has been useless to grow older. . . .

Ideas of Reference

IV. Schizophrenic patients commonly misinterpret the events in the world around them. One method of misinterpretation is so common that it has been given a special designation: ideas of reference. A patient suffering with ideas of reference believes that every irrelevant or coincidental action or happening in the world around him is related to him, caused by him, or arranged for him. If strangers cross the street, it is to avoid him because they have been warned. If three men pass wearing hats, it was prearranged to show him that he is a fool for not wearing a hat. If all the traffic lights are red, it has been set up to test his restraint, etc. If some passing stranger spits, it is meant to be a direct insult and challenge to his masculinity. Whispered conversation always refers to him, and laughter is always directed at him. Rilke, in *The Notebooks of Malte Laurids Brigge*, illustrates this pattern.

THE NOTEBOOKS OF MALTE LAURIDS BRIGGE
Rainer Maria Rilke   (1875–1926)

. . . Who are these people? What do they want of me? Are they waiting for me? How do they recognize me? It is true, my beard looks somewhat neglected, and very, very slightly resembles their own sickly, aged, faded beards that have always impressed me. But haven't I the right to neglect my beard? Many busy men do that, and it never occurs to anyone promptly to reckon them on that account among the outcast. For it is clear to me that these are the outcast, not simply beggars; no, they are really not beggars; one must make distinctions. They are refuse, husks of humanity that fate has spewed out. Moist with the spittle of destiny they are stuck to a wall, a lamp-post, an advertisement-pillar, or they trickle slowly down the alley, with a dark, dirty track behind them. What in the world did that old woman want with me, who had crawled out of some hole, carrying the drawer of a night-stand with a few buttons and needles rolling about in it? Why did she keep walking beside me and watching me? As if she were trying to recognize me with her bleared eyes, that looked as though some diseased person had spat slime into the bloody lids? And how came that little grey woman to stand that time for a whole quarter of an hour by my side before a shop-window, showing me an old, long pencil, that came pushing infinitely slowly out of her miserable, clenched hands? I pretended to look at the display in the window and not notice anything. But she knew I had seen her, she knew I stood there wondering what she was really doing. For I understood quite well that the pencil in itself was of no consequence: I felt it was a sign, a sign for the initiated, a sign the outcast know; I guessed she was indicating to me that I should go somewhere or do something. And the strangest part was that I could not rid myself of the feeling that there actually existed a certain compact to which this sign belonged, and that this scene was in truth something I should have expected.

That was two weeks ago. But scarcely a day passes now without such an encounter. Not only in the twilight; it happens at midday in the most crowded streets, that a little man or an old woman is suddenly there, nods to me, shows me something, and then vanishes, as though all the necessary were now done. It is possible that one day it may occur to them to come as far as my room; they certainly know where I live, and they will take care that the concierge does not stop them. But here, my dears, here I am safe from you. One must have a special card in order to get into this

room. In this card I have the advantage of you. I go a little shyly, as one
may imagine, through the streets, but finally I stand before a glass door,
open it as if I were at home, show my card at the next door (just exactly
as you show me your things, only with the difference that people understand me and know what I mean—), and then I am among these books,
and taken away from you as though I had died, and sit and read a
poet. . . .

Paranoid Jealousy

V. One form of paranoid symptom that is common
enough to deserve separate consideration is paranoid jealousy.
Somewhat more common in men than in women, the condition
involves a nearly total preoccupation with the fidelity of the
spouse. The afflicted man is obsessed by fantasies in which he
imagines his wife in the arms of another man. Every shred of
evidence that his wife even thinks of another man are seized on,
exaggerated, and reacted to as if they were consummated
acts of infidelity. Freud has done much to explain this condition.
Psychoanalysis of patients who suffered from it revealed a strong
undercurrent of latent homosexuality. Their jealousy was a
way of displacing their own unacceptable sexual fantasies onto
their wives. Thus they blamed their wives for their own
unconscious sexual impulses. Such an explanation is hard to
believe, but case after case confirms it, and in rare instances
such patients may eventually display overt homosexuality.
Neurotic men may have quite similar fantasies to those found
in paranoid jealousy. The sole difference seems to be
quantitative; that is, how important, how involving do the
fantasies become. Mallea, a Latin-American author, has
intuitively documented an example of paranoid jealousy.

The Heart's Reason

Eduardo Mallea   (1903–   )

. . . At noon he went out for lunch in the company of
his annoyance and his disturbance. As a rule he lunched at a restaurant

From "The Heart's Reason" by Eduardo Mallea. Translated by Harriet de Onis. By
permission of Harriet de Onis and Washington Square Press, Inc.

there on the square, in a kind of artificially lighted basement decorated with fish tanks and bad frescoes. He had no desire to enter into a conversation with the waiter, and he quickly ordered a cold plate and the fruits in season. He saw Rodas, a pompous agent of the company, at a table, and the sight filled him with such exasperation that he avoided speaking to him. He stood the menu up in front of him against the water pitcher and pretended to be studying the long list of dishes. But his imagination was in the house of Olivos. Alicia would be having lunch at this same time, comfortable in her solitude, without doubt at ease about the hour when she would be going out, her plans complete and her spirit satisfied. She had the whole afternoon to herself, the whole long afternoon, and she did not have to be back until eight or nine, her secret hermetically sealed within her, cloaked in the memory of her private, invulnerable acts.

"By three or four in the afternoon she will be in Bordiguera's flat," Montuvio thought. The precision of the idea provided him the opportunity to refute it with equal precision. It was no longer a matter of nebulosities, hypotheses, confused conjecturing. It was a question of an act. And that act—was impossible.

He calmly peeled his fruit. No, that act was impossible. A kind of animation, born of a clear-cut sense of relief, came over him, and calling the waiter, he made a jocose remark having to do with a couple who always came to the restaurant and about whom he had spoken with him before.

"No, it's impossible," he went out saying to himself. In his mouth was the taste of coffee, and along with the taste of coffee, the taste of such a palpable satisfying comfort. It was a sunny afternoon, warm, the square once more full after the lull of midday, and leaden-hued pigeons promenading their bulging crops along the cornices of the buildings. Montuvio crossed two or three streets with the laudable intention of winding up once and for all that long-drawn-out business with the manager of Vares Rey, who was reluctant to sign up for even a third-class policy. But the manager was not in. He would not be back until five. Montuvio, promising to return, descended again in the black cage of the elevator. Only when he reached the ground floor was he seized, openly, by that need, that inclination or drift, really unjustifiable, which was not yet a plan.

"An idea is one thing," the newborn tendency seemed to insinuate, "and facts are another. An idea cannot be completely done away with until it is confronted with reality itself."

He started to walk quickly where he was going to spare himself the shame of thinking it over. He had plenty of time. Bordiguera's flat was near the Plaza de la República; it was in the second of three houses, all alike, in a street that ran east and west and was filled with shops and

motion-picture theaters. Montuvio crossed the streets with the nervousness of a student at examination time or an actor making his debut, and as
he stole a glance at himself in the show-window of a photographer's
studio, he noticed that he was pale, with a greenish pallor, and that the
shadows on his face did not come from needing a shave, but from his bad
color.

In his heart he knew he would not be satisfied until he had seen for
himself. On more than one occasion he had been the plaything of his
ideas. What he liked was the practical, the visible, that which left no room
for doubt. This sudden need for spying, this base, shameful action would
have been unbearably humiliating to him if he had not considered it, as he
did now, in the light of the exigencies of his very make-up. So he accepted it as a natural demand of the deepest fibers of his being, the least
praiseworthy, perhaps, but the most human.

It did not take him more than ten minutes to reach the block where
the apartment building stood, on one of whose floors Bordiguera had his
bachelor establishment. All the way Montuvio felt that vague fear inherent in every test we undertake, still safe as we embark upon it, but
from which we may emerge utterly routed. Naturally, there contributed
to this, in a heavy, dragging, almost visceral manner, the needless and
absurd nature of the proof to which he was lending himself; and still no
power in the world could now have persuaded him not to carry it out; on
the contrary, an obstacle that might have suddenly arisen to prevent him
from keeping watch over Bordiguera's doorway would have aroused his
anger, a confused but virulent, savage, almost animal protest.

Now he had to see. Once admitting conjecture, could he reject the
supreme proof, that which the eyes give, the evidence? He felt a strange
mixture of disgust and sadness as he passed, on the opposite side of the
street, the door of the apartment house. The wide, dark foyer stretched
deserted toward the elevators. Montuvio walked by. He stopped just before he reached the corner, in the entrance of one of the narrow doorways, from which he could comfortably watch both the house that had
become his preoccupation and a long stretch of the street. Across from
where he stood were the two show-windows of a shop selling Chinese
goods; in the windows were displayed, on two male mannequins, two
Asiatic garments of pale blue, of silk so thin that the creases seemed additional, designed pleats; on the floor of the windows beside these dynastic
vestments was an assemblage of small jade dragons, curtains of painted
straw, an old scepter, and two tiny pairs of black sandals.

Montuvio, after taking his position in the doorway he had chosen,
prepared to wait. He carefully observed the shops alongside the Chinese
store, but none of them could compare with it in age and attractiveness.
His eyes rested for a few minutes on its exotic variety. But at once,
quickly and by degrees, as though borne on the mingled stream of a single

current of thought, of a single liquid flow, the idea came to him of what would happen if Alicia, at a given moment, came out of that house. The conjecture began turning into anger. He acquired a feeling of the assurance and the superiority it would give him to have the proof in his hands if the fault did exist; and this feeling hardened and exasperated him. It was as though he said to himself: "Now I've got you; you are in the trap; you can't flee from the deceit into evasions, but straight into me, before my eyes." He felt reassured, and thought that he could wait for hours without moving from the spot.

He remained thus for some time. People passed by, brisk, objective, without worries of the caliber of his, all ostensibly free from intimate problems; he alone had that matter to settle. His gaze clung to the show-windows of the Chinese shop, but within him the wheels turned without stopping in his effort to bring pressure on his memory to give him some point of support for the possible presence of his wife at Bordiguera's house. He recalled gestures and smiles. He recalled himself, he saw himself alone and wronged by the amatory complicity of Alicia and Bordiguera; and a sour, nauseating hatred brewed in his liver against that witty talker, with his honeyed glance, his refined manners, whom he had once brought to his house. After the first quarter-hour of his vigil, a restless, gnawing impatience began to grow in him, a kind of feeling as though he himself had invited misfortune, and that he now could escape neither the fact nor the consequences of having given it origin.

When nobody came out of the house by half past five, he began to think, cautiously and with precarious relief, that undoubtedly there was no one in Bordiguera's flat, not even Bordiguera himself, and that perhaps the sensible and manly thing to do was to consider the proof finished, and rid himself, with a normal disdain, of suspicions, base ideas, and shameful imaginings. But this was instantly followed by the thought that, now that he was here, if he waited a little longer he would be even surer of how childish, unwarranted, and insulting his imagining had been.

With this he began to wait more calmly, firm in the conviction that nobody would come out of the house. The longer he waited, the greater his satisfaction. He could stay there until eight or nine; perhaps until he saw Bordiguera come in at dinner-time. Yes, perhaps even this was possible. Filled with a sense of calm and assurance, he left the spot where he had stationed himself and leisurely crossed over to the Chinese shop, where he stopped to admire the objects exhibited there. He found them impressive, extraordinary in their totality and in their details, the expression of a subtle, alien civilization in which he would have been unable to live even for an hour. Then he crossed back to his watching-post; killing time with a certain impatience, he tried to find something on which to fix his attention on that side of the street; but there was nothing but the meaningless window of a dry-cleaning establishment and a monotonous list of professional signs tacked in the corner of an old doorway. He went over to read one of those signs.

At that moment he had his back turned to the house he was watching, when his instinct suddenly warned him, making him turn, startled and confused: Bordiguera was coming out of the doorway of his house, and with him was a woman, a slender woman wearing a light dress and light shoes. He saw them from the distance, and barely had time to hide and then look again, poking his head out, his heart thudding heavily, at the woman as Bordiguera hailed a cab and they got into it. After they had been hidden from view for a fraction of a second by the body of the car, it started off quickly, toward the street intersection, passing before Montuvio's very eyes. . . .

God above! He saw it so clearly. His heart stopped beating. He stepped back, as though dodging a blow from the flat of an ax. His face felt white and his veins white, as though they had no blood. The automobile passed and disappeared in the distance. Montuvio, with the weakness that follows a shock, took one liberating step into the street.

The person who had just come out with Bordiguera was not Alicia. Thank God! The man was not having an affair with his wife. He had had the proof at first glance, in a lightning flash, when he saw her standing on the sidewalk, and then as the features of the woman who had entered the cab with Bordiguera whirled past him. It was a thin face, very delicately modeled, very pale, whose features he could not describe exactly, and she was wearing clothes that were loose and too light, which somehow gave the impression that she was a foreigner.

Montuvio felt a kind of glory, as though all his blood vessels had dilated in a burst of instant well-being. A kind of shame of himself came over him at the same time, bringing with it happiness and a strange, impulsive feeling of sympathy, almost of gratitude, toward Bordiguera. He would have thrown his arms around him, glorified him, at that moment. And his mind flew to the house in Olivos, bringing him anew the vision of a happy, noble home ruled over, as never before, by the decorous figure of his wife, innocent of all suspicion and above suspicion itself. It seemed to him that he would have to tell her about it that very night, mingling his account with a tacit plea for forgiveness.

As it was summer, the afternoon sun was still high. A bright golden haze outlined the outer edges of the buildings, luminously dividing matter from space. The city glowed, day's transit was reaching its peak. Montuvio drank in the light. He would have called his house at that very moment, but his wife at this time would be somewhere not far from him, on streets like these. He thought he had plenty of time to call on the manager of Varas Rey. Happy, self-assured, buoyed up, he started down one of the streets; with light step he crossed the square. The very elevator-operator seemed a witness and a friend.

The manager of Varas Rey, with his Herculean shoulders and his un-expectedly small ironical mouth, received him more coolly than on other occasions. He was alone, slouched down in his chair, in his office, similar to the five hundred other offices of the marble, presumptuous, glowing building. "It's like this," the manager began. "It's like this . . ." and for the seventh or eighth time he monotonously expounded his reasons for not wanting to take out insurance, for preferring not to take out in-surance.

"It's not right for me to saddle myself with more expense now," the manager argued, excusing himself with a shrug of his expressive, powerful shoulders.

"But of course," Montuvio burst out. "You are absolutely right. In my opinion you are absolutely right. Forgive me. I am not going to insist." And he smiled with lips and soul. "Absolutely right."

He finally took his leave, reiterating excuses. He would have given a medal to the stubborn manager, he would have asked forgiveness on bended knee for his intrusion, for his importunacy, for his insistence. He went out tripping over his own excuses.

What did all this matter to him? Happiness rained on him. He ad-mired his wife. He felt that a new life was beginning. In a few more months the house in Olivos would be his. That evening he would have dinner with Alicia, he would open the windows to the cool of summer, the house would be the abode of the noble calm where peace reigned. What more could he ask? Bordiguera could go on coming till the end of time; as sure as his name was Montuvio, a suspicion would never again cross his mind. God, if we are the rulers of our reason, why are we not the rulers of our reasoning? Why do we allow our inner garden to be profaned by wild birds that do not belong there?

He looked at his watch; it was half past six, and he did not intend to go back to the office. What for? The vast afternoon was ripening. A bluish gold vied with the breezes. The best thing was to feel free, to watch the people, to stop before the show-windows, to loiter among the hurrying throngs. He walked for about an hour, he visited the shops full of luxurious objects, he read the stock-exchange quotations, looked at the women going by, stopped before stores selling the things that appealed least to him; but then a vague boredom began to assail him, a certain las-situde. What could he do? He thought of Gambrinus's beer-garden, which he liked so well, and set out for it.

It was a big, dark beer-garden, shadowy, wainscoted in somber wood, with imposing Bavarian steins and railings and bluish glass separating the small booths. The only light of day that entered the place came through the high skylight. And from a hook hung newspapers printed in barbaric, undecipherable, Gothic characters.

Montuvio seated himself at one of the tables in the main room and ordered his usual bock. A sensation of rest and infinite coolness came over him. On the table stood a dish of pretzels and a little white jar of mustard.

He began to recall his day, slowly, from the start: the conversation with Alicia, the bus trip to the city, the building up of his doubts, the bitter lunch, the vicissitudes of his spying, the anxiety, and, finally, the surprising revelation. The scene had acquired the swift illumination of a flash of light. In seconds it was over and had disappeared. Nevertheless, he had had more than enough time to take in the woman's appearance, her clothing, her features, so different from Alicia's. He had had time to see Bordiguera's amatory solicitude toward her. As the car passed him, they were both laughing: she leaning back a little against the upholstery, Bordiguera attentive, gay. The woman was wearing a very light dress, white, almost cream-colored, and a simple hat, turned up a little, a hat that covered only one side of her head. How Montuvio had stared at her as the car rushed swiftly by! He would not have been able to recall the woman's features, he only knew they were not Alicia's, with a kind of illumined and general knowledge, revealed, above specific knowing. His eyes had clung anxiously to this lightning flash as it passed; it was not she; that was enough. He had seen enough.

Montuvio took a swallow of his beer, and it suddenly occurred to him that he might take something home with him that evening—chicken in aspic or a baked ham, both favorites of Alicia's. For a long time he had been coming in emptyhanded; he had not noticed it before, now he did. We all have a responsibility for those shifts of wind that come up and gradually change, becloud our relationships. The delicate shades of courtesy are always important; a feeling we trample on or offend in another may suddenly turn into a bitter poison, a wound, a corrosive acid. Alicia's sullenness might well be owing to a series of unconscious provocations on his part, subtle provocations, muted, subliminal, those which begin and develop insidiously, secretly, like a mortal disease. His eyes wandered over the room, which was cool and dim. He looked at the black railings and the plants. A mental breeze brought him once more, as a result of his lassitude, the image of the woman he saw come out with Bordiguera, the image of the automobile, and of the liberation the scene had brought him. Step by step the idea began to grow in him that there was just one thing that was odd. He turned the question over in his mind. How could he explain the fact that he was absolutely unable to recall the woman's features clearly? Perhaps it was owing only to the speed at which the car was traveling, his great confusion at the moment, the need to obtain the negation of one set of features before being able to take in clearly the lineaments of another. The fact was that all he saw was a specter that was not Alicia. Aside from this, aren't all specters alike? Especially if the clothes they wear define them as being of one sex, which in turn separates them from other specters. That was not Alicia's face, nor her dress, no.

To be sure, all women make themselves up alike; Alicia was blonde like the woman in the car. But why hadn't he looked more closely at her features, why didn't he know definitely what they were like? Montuvio put his glass down on the table. Had he seen right?

Suddenly a kind of disquiet, a malaise, took possession of him, an inexplicable mental distress that had arisen against his will. He was a hopeless fool! Tormenting himself with doubts! How could he ask himself such a question? He had seen with his eyes, with his own eyes. Not another's, *his*. And that woman *was not* Alicia. Different features, a different person altogether. And then that dress. Though Alicia did have a white dress. A white silk dress; only it was put away until now, until summer. Montuvio scoffed at himself. He had always been an easy prey to conflicting impressions.

But behind the scoffing—which was in his favor—remained the doubt —which was against him. Against all his will his mind kept turning things over. He raised his eyes and saw the people, the few, who were talking in the beer-garden, and a fat plain woman, blonde, who was arguing with two Germans. She did not look like the woman in the car, either. But just what was the woman in the car like? He tried to think, and his memory made a feeble, vague endeavor. He could not get beyond a woman's face, a generic face, no matter how hard he tried. But it was not Alicia, that was clear. Even supposing there could be a confusion about the dress, the features were clearly different, the whole appearance. What he had had was not an impression, it was proof. Naturally the light, as it fell, could modify the peculiarities of a face, if the coloring, the shade of the skin, were similar. But what was the sense of such reasoning, since the woman was another, definitely another. Proof is not an impression. The evanescence, the rapidity of an impression can change it, deform it; but they cannot change or deform proof.

He called the waiter and ordered another beer. His head drooped, he was tired and much less happy than he had been moments before. He was accustomed to this kind of rage or disappointment at himself, which often attacked him, this cruel confusion that had darkened many moments of his life. Almost with fury against himself, he called up in his mind an image: the moment when he was standing opposite Bordiguera's house, and the categorical assurance with which he had distinguished from his wife the woman who came out. He clung to the vision, struggling to give his mind the grip of a claw. But his mind was not a claw, and little by little there began to issue from it threads of arguments, evil suppositions, contradictory factors that he could neither contain nor suppress. He was a fool. Why this doubt? Was it possible that he had not seen clearly?

Allowing himself to be swept along by a succession of rememorative ideas which superimposed themselves on the events of the afternoon, he realized that there had been a reason for his going there to spy. It was evident—the word his mind selected frightened him—that there was something going on in Alicia. And the automobile in which Bordiguera and his friend had passed was going at such a speed that it made only the most dizzying impact on the eyes. Dizzying? Naturally, producing dizziness. Was it possible that he had been misled by this dizziness? For a few moments he was morally crushed by the idea, and then another motive came to his mind: the remote, intimate suggestion that his desire not to recognize Alicia had led him to twist even his visual impression. Impression? But wasn't it proof that he had, which had nothing to do with an impression? Now it turned out that they were the same thing. He sat there actually gripped by fear, and it took him several minutes to recover.

With disgust, almost with revulsion, he thought that the color of the woman's hair could have seemed, from a distance, the same as Alicia's and if he recalled the white dress he had seen her wear the summer before, he could not honestly refrain from doubt. Who would not be confused by a rapid vision? A certain face, a certain figure, could it not suddenly seem another under the influence of certain psychic conditions in the observer, and changes caused in the image by the angle of vision? Maybe the woman who had not looked to him like Alicia was Alicia herself. Why not? Could he trust, absolutely, a vision that was relative? Could he even hold fast to an image that he could not reconstruct in memory, that he could not describe? And, on the other hand, the other impression was alive, the other intuition, the other idea: the shadow of that inner conviction which had led him to think, gradually and insistently, that there was evidently something between his wife and Bordiguera. But why was he mixing the proofs like this? Yes, he was mixing them; he couldn't help mixing them, he could not resist this inner prompting, and now the two proofs, the inductive and the visual, were struggling for supremacy, and he felt with a vague terror that little by little the first was getting the upper hand.

In the last analysis, in point of certainty, in a clear, trustworthy manner, he knew nothing about the woman he had seen come out with Bordiguera. It might have been any woman. Even Alicia. Even any other. Any other, like Alicia. "Let's see," he asked himself, and he tormented and baited himself like a witness under examination, "let's see: how was she different, how was she another?"

The question left him overwhelmed, unable to find an answer. And it began to seem to him clear, possible, capable of proof that he had been deceived by the fleetingness of what he had seen, and that the woman, in effect, might very well have been Alicia.

A great agitation seized Montuvio, and a troop of contradictory ideas filled his mind. Had he once more suffered a deception? Had he? Was this conceivable? He could not be sure. He wasn't sure of anything. He would have given anything to turn time back to the moment when he saw the woman come out with Bordiguera, anything to detain that moment now beyond proof, to whose veracity he could not swear. The most fantastic and counterpoised ideas throbbed in his head; he was like an over-wound watch; there seemed no floor under his feet, or body about his fainting spirit; his pulse began to thud violently, and a wave of his former hatred toward Bordiguera and of rancor and bitterness toward his wife jarred his soul.

He got up with uncontrolled violence, almost upsetting the mustard jar, the dish of pretzels, and the stein on the table, and turning toward the counter, he stumblingly made his way to the telephone. He swiftly dialed the number of his house in Olivos, and for a moment, not breathing, he waited for the sound of the ringing to be interrupted by the lifting of the receiver. But the isochronous insistence of the ringing went on without the slightest change, threatening to become eternalized in its unanswered repetition.

Montuvio went back to his table. It seemed to him that he was seeing the scene of the afternoon, the woman coming out of Bordiguera's house; but the one who came out in his mind now was his wife; it was his wife, but not on that account was the impression that remained of the other woman changed. Had there been another? The images matched. He could not swear that they were different. Nor that they weren't. Were they one or two? One thing was as possible as the other, and he had no way of proving it; he saw himself at the center of a fixed uncertainty.

He was blasted by a chill despair, a quivering frenzy brought on by his impotence to decide between the allegations of his reason and the embers of his memory. Not one detail of what he had seen stood out bright, separate, clear, determinate. He knew just as much as before he took his stand across from Bordiguera's house. He was ignorant as when he went there. And much more bewildered, much more impotently lost.

He tossed a handful of change on the table and blundered out to the street. And there he stood, he, Celedonio Montuvio, insurance agent, his back to the door of Gambrinus's café, without knowing what to do or which way to go, his lower lip hanging idiotically, terrified, paralyzed, as though struck by lightning.

Autism

VI. One of the major symptoms of schizophrenia described by Bleuler was a gradual turning away from the external world of reality towards the person's own internal world of fantasy and hallucination. Autism cannot be equated with schizophrenia, but it implies that the individual is more emotionally invested in his own fantasies and imagination than in people or objects in reality. Such a greater investment in the inner life loosens the ties with reality and interferes with performance and function in conventional areas of society. Conrad Aiken, in his famous story, has described a crucial period in a child's life where he makes the turn toward autism. Aiken knowingly presents the gratifying and creative side of autism alongside the maladaptive and pathological side. No doubt this child is moving toward schizophrenia.

Silent Snow, Secret Snow
Conrad Aiken   (1889–   )

. . . After supper, the inquisition began. He stood before the doctor, under the lamp, and submitted silently to the usual thumpings and tappings.

"Now will you please say 'Ah!'?"

"Ah!"

"Now again please, if you don't mind."

"Ah."

"Say it slowly, and hold it if you can—"

"Ah-h-h-h-h-h—"

"Good."

How silly all this was. As if it had anything to do with his throat! Or his heart or lungs!

Relaxing his mouth, of which the corners, after all this absurd stretching, felt uncomfortable, he avoided the doctor's eyes, and stared towards the fireplace, past his mother's feet (in gray slippers) which projected from the green chair, and his father's feet (in brown slippers) which stood neatly side by side on the hearth rug.

"Hm. There is certainly nothing wrong there . . ."

He felt the doctor's eyes fixed upon him, and, as if merely to be polite, returned the look, but with a feeling of justifiable evasiveness.

"Now, young man, tell me,—do you feel all right?"

"Yes, sir, quite all right."

"No headaches? No dizziness?"

"No, I don't think so."

"Let me see. Let's get a book, if you don't mind—yes, thank you, that will do splendidly—and now, Paul, if you'll just read it, holding it as you would normally hold it—"

He took the book and read:

"And another praise have I to tell for this the city our mother, the gift of a great god, a glory of the land most high; the might of horses, the might of young horses, the might of the sea. . . . For thou, son of Cronus, our lord Poseidon, hast throned herein this pride, since in these roads first thou didst show forth the curb that cures the rage of steeds. And the shapely oar, apt to men's hands, hath a wondrous speed on the brine, following the hundred-footed Nereids. . . . O land that art praised above all lands, now is it for thee to make those bright praises seen in deeds."

He stopped, tentatively, and lowered the heavy book.

"No—as I thought—there is certainly no superficial sign of eye-strain."

Silence thronged the room, and he was aware of the focused scrutiny of the three people who confronted him. . . .

"We could have his eyes examined—but I believe it is something else."

"What could it be?" This was his father's voice.

"It's only this curious absent-minded—" This was his mother's voice.

In the presence of the doctor, they both seemed irritatingly apologetic.

"I believe it is something else. Now Paul—I would like very much to ask you a question or two. You will answer them, won't you—you know I'm an old, old friend of yours, eh? That's right! . . ."

His back was thumped twice by the doctor's fat fist,—then the doctor was grinning at him with false amiability, while with one fingernail he was scratching the top button of his waistcoat. Beyond the doctor's shoulder was the fire, the fingers of flame making light prestidigitation against the sooty fireback, the soft sound of their random flutter the only sound.

"I would like to know—is there anything that worries you?"

The doctor was again smiling, his eyelids low against the little black pupils, in each of which was a tiny white bead of light. Why answer him? why answer him at all? "At whatever pain to others"—but it was all a nuisance, this necessity for resistance, this necessity for attention: it was as if one had been stood up on a brilliantly lighted stage, under a great round blaze of spotlight; as if one were merely a trained seal, or a performing dog, or a fish, dipped out of an aquarium and held up by the tail. It would serve them right if he were merely to bark or growl. And meanwhile, to miss these last few precious hours, these hours of which every minute was more beautiful than the last, more menacing—? He still looked, as if from a great distance, at the beads of light in the doctor's eyes, at the fixed false smile, and then, beyond, once more at his mother's slippers, his father's slippers, the soft flutter of the fire. Even here, even amongst these hostile presences, and in this arranged light, he could see the snow, he could hear it—it was in the corners of the room, where the shadow was deepest, under the sofa, behind the half-opened door which led to the dining room. It was gentler here, softer, its seethe the quietest of whispers, as if, in deference to a drawing room, it had quite deliberately put on its "manners"; it kept itself out of sight, obliterated itself, but distinctly with an air of saying, "Ah, but just wait! Wait till we are alone together! Then I will begin to tell you something new! Something white! something cold! something sleepy! something of cease, and peace, and the long bright curve of space! Tell them to go away. Banish them. Refuse to speak. Leave them, go upstairs to your room, turn out the light and get into bed—I will go with you, I will be waiting for you, I will tell you a better story than Little Kay of the Skates, or The Snow Ghost—I will surround your bed, I will close the windows, pile a deep drift against the door, so that none will ever again be able to enter. Speak to them! . . ." It seemed as if the little hissing voice came from a slow white spiral of falling flakes in the corner by the front window—but he could not be sure. He felt himself smiling, then, and said to the doctor, but without looking at him, looking beyond him still—

"Oh, no, I think not—"

"But are you sure, my boy?"

His father's voice came softly and coldly then—the familiar voice of silken warning. . . .

"You needn't answer at once, Paul—remember we're trying to help you—think it over and be quite sure, won't you?"

He felt himself smiling again, at the notion of being quite sure. What a joke! As if he weren't so sure that reassurance was no longer necessary, and all this cross-examination a ridiculous farce, a grotesque parody! What could they know about it? These gross intelligences, these hum-drum minds so bound to the usual, the ordinary? Impossible to tell them about it! Why, even now, even now, with the proof so abundant, so formidable, so imminent, so appallingly present here in this very room, could they believe it?—could even his mother believe it? No—it was only too plain that if anything were said about it, the merest hint given, they would be incredulous—they would laugh—they would say "Absurd!"— think things about him which weren't true. . . .

"Why no, I'm not worried—why should I be?"

He looked then straight at the doctor's low-lidded eyes, looked from one of them to the other, from one bead of light to the other, and gave a little laugh.

The doctor seemed to be disconcerted by this. He drew back in his chair, resting a fat white hand on either knee. The smile faded slowly from his face.

"Well, Paul!" he said, and paused gravely, "I'm afraid you don't take this quite seriously enough. I think you perhaps don't quite realize—" He took a deep quick breath, and turned, as if helplessly, at a loss for words, to the others. But Mother and Father were both silent—no help was forthcoming.

"You must surely know, be aware, that you have not been quite yourself of late? don't you know that? . . ."

It was amusing to watch the doctor's renewed attempt at a smile, a queer disorganized look, as of confidential embarrassment.

"I feel all right, sir," he said, and again gave the little laugh.

"And we're trying to help you." The doctor's tone sharpened.

"Yes sir, I know. But why? I'm all right. I'm just *thinking*, that's all."

His mother made a quick movement forward, resting a hand on the back of the doctor's chair.

"Thinking?" she said. "But my dear, about what?"

This was a direct challenge—and would have to be directly met. But before he met it, he looked again into the corner by the door, as if for reassurance. He smiled again at what he saw, at what he heard. The little spiral was still there, still softly whirling, like the ghost of a white kitten chasing the ghost of a white tail and making as it did so the faintest of whispers. It was all right! If only he could remain firm, everything was going to be all right.

"Oh, about anything, about nothing,—*you* know the way you do!"

"You mean—day-dreaming?"

"Oh, no—thinking!"

"But thinking about *what?*"

"Anything."

He laughed a third time—but this time, happening to glance upward towards his mother's face, he was appalled at the effect his laughter seemed to have upon her. Her mouth had opened in an expression of horror. . . . This was too bad! Unfortunate! He had known it would cause pain, of course—but he hadn't expected it to be quite so bad as this. Perhaps—perhaps if he just gave them a tiny gleaming hint—?

"About the snow," he said.

"What on earth!" This was his father's voice. The brown slippers came a step nearer on the hearth-rug.

"But my dear, what do you mean!" This was his mother's voice.

The doctor merely stared.

"Just *snow*, that's all. I like to think about it."

"Tell us about it, my boy."

"But that's all it is. There's nothing to tell. *You* know what snow is?"

This he said almost angrily, for he felt that they were trying to corner him. He turned sideways so as no longer to face the doctor, and the better to see the inch of blackness between the window-sill and the lowered curtain—the cold inch of beckoning and delicious night. At once he felt better, more assured.

"Mother—can I go to bed, now, please? I've got a headache."

"But I thought you said—"

"It's just come. It's all these questions—! Can I, mother?"

"You can go as soon as the doctor has finished."

"Don't you think this thing ought to be gone into thoroughly, and *now?*" This was Father's voice. The brown slippers again came a step nearer, the voice was the well-known "punishment" voice, resonant and cruel.

"Oh, what's the use, Norman—"

Quite suddenly, everyone was silent. And without precisely facing them, nevertheless he was aware that all three of them were watching him with an extraordinary intensity—staring hard at him—as if he had done something monstrous, or was himself some kind of monster. He could hear the soft irregular flutter of the flames; the cluck-click-cluck-click of the clock; far and faint, two sudden spurts of laughter from the kitchen, as quickly cut off as begun; a murmur of water in the pipes; and then, the silence seemed to deepen, to spread out, to become world-long and world-wide, to become timeless and shapeless, and to center inevitably and rightly, with a slow and sleepy but enormous concentration of all power, on the beginning of a new sound. What this new sound was going to be, he knew perfectly well. It might begin with a hiss, but it would end with a roar—there was no time to lose—he must escape. It mustn't happen here—

Without another word, he turned and ran up the stairs.

Not a moment too soon. The darkness was coming in long white waves. A prolonged sibilance filled the night—a great seamless seethe of wild influence went abruptly across it—a cold low humming shook the windows. He shut the door and flung off his clothes in the dark. The bare black floor was like a little raft tossed in waves of snow, almost overwhelmed, washed under whitely, up again, smothered in curled billows of feather. The snow was laughing: it spoke from all sides at once: it pressed closer to him as he ran and jumped exulting into his bed.

"Listen to us!" it said. "Listen! We have come to tell you the story we told you about. You remember? Lie down. Shut your eyes, now— you will no longer see much—in this white darkness who could see, or want to see? We will take the place of everything. . . . Listen—"

A beautiful varying dance of snow began at the front of the room, came forward and then retreated, flattened out toward the floor, then rose fountain-like to the ceiling, swayed, recruited itself from a new stream of flakes which poured laughing in through the humming window, advanced again, lifted long white arms. It said peace, it said remoteness, it said cold—it said—

But then a gash of horrible light fell brutally across the room from the opening door—the snow drew back hissing—something alien had come into the room—something hostile. This thing rushed at him, clutched at him, shook him—and he was not merely horrified, he was filled with such a loathing as he had never known. What was this? this cruel disturbance? this act of anger and hate? It was as if he had to reach up a hand toward another world for any understanding of it,—an effort of which he was only barely capable. But of that other world he still remembered just enough to know the exorcising words. They tore themselves from his other life suddenly—

"Mother! Mother! Go away! I hate you!"

And with that effort, everything was solved, everything became all right: the seamless hiss advanced once more, the long white wavering lines rose and fell like enormous whispering sea-waves, the whisper becoming louder, the laughter more numerous.

"Listen!" it said. "We'll tell you the last, the most beautiful and secret story—shut your eyes—it is a very small story—a story that gets smaller and smaller—it comes inward instead of opening like a flower—it is a flower becoming a seed—a little cold seed—do you hear? we are leaning closer to you—"

The hiss was now becoming a roar—the whole world was a vast moving screen of snow—but even now it said peace, it said remoteness, it said cold, it said sleep.

Idiot Savant

VII. Those who have studied very serious emotional disorders in childhood have been impressed with what they called "atypical development." The child with "atypical development" will have many areas of cognitive and emotional functioning which are grossly impaired. On the other hand, one skill or one talent is enormously hypertrophied and precocious. The presence of this one talent suggests that mental retardation is not present, or, if it is, was strangely selective. The one isolated talent may be quite bizarre; e.g., the capacity to remember television commercials verbatim and recite them in the tones of the different announcers, although social speech and understanding is rudimentary; the capacity to calculate

the day of the week on which a given date in any year will fall;
the capacity to imitate long pieces of music without formal
musical comprehension. Each of these unusual capacities will
occur in a child who to all intents and purposes has little or no
other measurable intelligence or capacity. Cases like these in
the past were known as idiot savants. In light of our present day
understanding they would probably be considered cases of
"atypical development" or childhood schizophrenia. John
Steinbeck presents one fascinating example of such a person.
Johnny Bear, now a grownup, is capable of repeating large
sections of conversation without any clear comprehension
of the meaning, emotional importance, or significance
of what he repeats.

JOHNNY BEAR

John Steinbeck   (1902–   )

. . . There began a curious pantomime. Johnny Bear
moved to the door and then he came creeping back. The foolish smile
never left his face. In the middle of the room he crouched down on his
stomach. A voice came from his throat, a voice that seemed familiar to me.

"But you are too beautiful to live in a dirty little town like this."

The voice rose to a soft throaty tone, with just a trace of accent in
the words. "You just tell me that."

I'm sure I nearly fainted. The blood pounded in my ears. I flushed.
It was my voice coming out of the throat of Johnny Bear, my words, my
intonation. And then it was the voice of Mae Romero—exact. If I had not
seen the crouching man on the floor I would have called to her. The
dialogue went on. Such things sound silly when someone else says them.
Johnny Bear went right on, or rather I should say I went right on. He
said things and made sounds. Gradually the faces of the men turned from
Johnny Bear, turned toward me, and they grinned at me. I could do nothing. I knew that if I tried to stop him I would have a fight on my hands,
and so the scene went on, to a finish. When it was over I was cravenly
glad Mae Romero had no brothers. What obvious, forced, ridiculous
words had come from Johnny Bear. Finally he stood up, still smiling the
foolish smile, and he asked again, "Whiskey?"

I think the men in the bar were sorry for me. They looked away
from me and talked elaborately to one another. Johnny Bear went to the

From "Johnny Bear" by John Steinbeck. Reprinted by permission of The Viking
Press, Inc.

back of the room, crawled under a round cardtable, curled up like a dog and went to sleep.

Alex Hartnell was regarding me with compassion. "First time you ever heard him?"

"Yes, what in hell is he?"

Alex ignored my question for a moment. "If you're worrying about Mae's reputation, don't. Johnny Bear has followed Mae before."

"But how did he hear us? I didn't see him."

"No one sees or hears Johnny Bear when he's on business. He can move like no movement at all. Know what our young men do when they go out with girls? They take a dog along. Dogs are afraid of Johnny and they can smell him coming."

"But good God! Those voices——"

Alex nodded. "I know. Some of us wrote up to the university about Johnny, and a young man came down. He took a look and then he told us about Blind Tom. Ever hear of Blind Tom?"

"You mean the Negro piano player? Yes, I've heard of him."

"Well, Blind Tom was a half-wit. He could hardly talk, but he could imitate anything he heard on the piano, long pieces. They tried him with fine musicians and he reproduced not only the music but every little personal emphasis. To catch him they made little mistakes, and he played the mistakes. He photographed the playing in the tiniest detail. The man says Johnny Bear is the same, only he can photograph words and voices. He tested Johnny with a long passage in Greek and Johnny did it exactly. He doesn't know the words he's saying, he just says them. He hasn't brains enough to make anything up, so you know that what he says is what he heard."

"But why does he do it? Why is he interested in listening if he doesn't understand?"

Alex rolled a cigarette and lighted it. "He isn't, but he loves whiskey. He knows if he listens in windows and comes here and repeats what he hears, someone will give him whiskey. He tries to palm off Mrs. Ratz' conversation in the store, or Jerry Noland arguing with his mother, but he can't get whiskey for such things.". . .

CHAPTER five

The Neuroses:
Anxiety and Its Manifestations

The diagnostic concepts of neurosis were originally modeled on medical nosology. This evolution led to an overemphasis on symptoms. The medically trained psychiatrist focused on the hysterical paralysis, the acute anxiety attack, etc. However, as these patients were studied in the setting of psychoanalysis, it became apparent that alongside their *"symptom neurosis"* was what came to be called a *"character neurosis."* The *"character neurosis"* proved to be at least equally troublesome to the patients and more difficult to alter.

Neurotic character is the end product of the gradual shaping of the personality in the course of development. It is the historical record of the ego's attempts to cope with inner needs in the face of outer restraints, losses, and opportunities. Thus, neurotic character is one outcome of the "struggle with impulses."

The diagnostic categories of neurosis have been maintained despite these inherent difficulties. There is practical value in this since some patients do show a predominance of symptoms. Furthermore, contemporary study of the neuroses has produced a unifying point of view around the concept of anxiety. As was discussed in Chapter 1, the neuroses can be viewed as either expressing anxiety, e.g., the acute anxiety attack; compartmentalizing anxiety, e.g., the phobia; transforming anxiety, e.g., the conversion hysteria with "la belle indifference."

Each of the major neuroses will be illustrated.

Hysteria

I. Hysteria, one of the oldest medical diagnoses, was used as far back as the 4th century B.C. The word *hysteria* derives from the Greek *hystera*, meaning womb. The term arose since the Greeks believed that the womb migrated through the body of afflicted women, causing various otherwise unexplainable symptoms in the course of its passage. Hippocrates, the first great physician, is known to have used this diagnosis in his time to account for cases in which other causes could not be identified.

Through the years the diagnosis "hysteria" has continued to be used by physicians to designate physical symptoms without known physical cause. These conditions are now thought to have their origin in emotional disturbances. Beatrice Trueblood, in the first chapter, illustrated one typical example, the conversion reaction.

A common form of hysteria frequently diagnosed in the 19th century was neurasthenia, a poorly defined group of physical symptoms in which the patient complains of weakness, lassitude, and lack of energy. Freud believed that such instances of neurasthenia were related to the repression of libidinal (sexual) impulses. Perhaps the most famous example of this condition is Elizabeth Barrett. The brilliant invalid of Wimpole Street was caught up in an intense relationship to her father. His love, frustrated in his wife, turned toward his attractive daughter. Caught in the heat of this attachment, his daughter found safety in illness. Through her illness she avoided the feminine sexual aspects of her nature, attaining closeness instead in an infantile sick manner. Finally, the dashing Browning rescued her, permitting her feminine sexual feelings, a safe, non-incestuous outlet. The highlights of Rudolph Besier's play demonstrate both the illness, and the currents that underlay it.

The Barretts of Wimpole Street
Rudolf Besier   (1878–1942)

EDWARD MOULTON-BARRETT *enters. He is a well-set-up handsome man of sixty.*

ELIZABETH. Papa . . . (*An uneasy silence falls.* HENRIETTA, *in the middle of the room, stops dead.* BARRETT *stands for a moment just beyond the threshold, looking before him with a perfectly expressionless face*) Good evening, Papa. . . .

[*Without replying,* BARRETT *crosses the room and takes his stand with his back to the fireplace. A pause. No one moves.*

BARRETT (*in a cold, measured voice*). I am most displeased. (*A pause*) It is quite in order that you should visit your sister of an evening and have a few quiet words with her. But I think I have pointed out, not once, but several times, that, in her very precarious state of health, it is inadvisable for more than three of you to be in her room at the same time. My wishes in this matter have been disregarded—as usual. (*A pause*) You all know very well that your sister must avoid any kind of excitement. Absolute quiet is essential, especially before she retires for the night. And yet I find you romping around her like a lot of disorderly children. . . . I am gravely displeased. (HENRIETTA *gives a nervous little giggle*) I am not aware that I have said anything amusing, Henrietta?

HENRIETTA. I—I beg your pardon, Papa.

BARRETT. And may I ask what you were doing as I came into the room?

HENRIETTA. I was showing Ba how to polk.

BARRETT. To . . . polk?

HENRIETTA. How to dance the polka.

BARRETT. I see.

[*A pause*

OCTAVIUS (*nervously*). Well, B-Ba, I think I'll say g-good-night, and——

BARRETT. I should be grateful if you would kindly allow me to finish speaking.

OCTAVIUS. Sorry, sir. I—I thought you'd d-done.

BARRETT (*with frigid anger*). Are you being insolent, sir?

OCTAVIUS. N-no indeed, sir—I assure you, I——

BARRETT. Very well. Now——

ELIZABETH (*quickly, nervously*). As I am really the cause of your displeasure, Papa, I ought to tell you that I like nothing better than a—

a little noise occasionally. (*A slight pause*) It—it's delightful having all the family here together—and can't possibly do me any harm. . . .

BARRETT. Perhaps you will forgive my saying, Elizabeth, that you are not the best judge of what is good or bad for you. . . . And that brings me to what I came here to speak to you about. Doctor Chambers told me just now that you had persuaded him to allow you to discontinue drinking porter with your meals.

ELIZABETH. It needed very little persuasion, Papa. I said I detested porter, and he agreed at once that I should take milk instead.

BARRETT. I questioned him closely as to the comparative strength-giving values of porter and milk, and he was forced to admit that porter came decidedly first.

ELIZABETH. That may be, Papa. But when you dislike a thing to loathing, I don't see how it can do you any good.

BARRETT. I said just now that you are not the best judge of what is good or bad for you, my child. May I add that self-discipline is always beneficial, and self-indulgence invariably harmful?

ELIZABETH. If you think my drinking milk shows reckless self-indulgence, Papa, you're quite wrong. I dislike it only less than porter.

BARRETT. Your likes and dislikes are quite beside the point in a case like this.

ELIZABETH. But, Papa—

BARRETT. Believe me, Elizabeth, I have nothing but your welfare at heart when I warn you that if you decide to discontinue drinking porter, you will incur my grave displeasure.

ELIZABETH (*indignantly*). But—but when Doctor Chambers himself—

BARRETT. I have told you what Doctor Chambers said.

ELIZABETH. Yes, but—

BARRETT. Did you drink your porter at dinner?

ELIZABETH. No.

BARRETT. Then I hope you will do so before you go to bed.

ELIZABETH. No, Papa, that's really asking too much! I—I can't drink the horrible stuff in cold blood.

BARRETT. Very well. Of course, I have no means of coercing you. You are no longer a child. But I intend to give your better nature every chance of asserting itself. A tankard of porter will be left at your bedside. And I hope that to-morrow you will be able to tell me that—you have obeyed your Father.

ELIZABETH. I am sorry, Papa—but I sha'n't drink it.

BARRETT (*to* HENRIETTA). Go down to the kitchen and fetch a tankard of porter.

HENRIETTA. No.

BARRETT. I beg your pardon?

HENRIETTA (*her voice trembling with anger and agitation*). It's—it's sheer cruelty. You know how Ba hates the stuff. The Doctor has let her off. You're just torturing her because you—you like torturing.

BARRETT. I have told you to fetch a tankard of porter from the kitchen.

HENRIETTA. I won't do it.

BARRETT. Must I ask you a third time? (*Suddenly shouting*) Obey me this instant!

ELIZABETH (*sharply*). Papa . . . Go and fetch it, Henrietta! Go at once! I can't stand this. . . .

HENRIETTA. No, I——

ELIZABETH. Please—please . . .

[*After a moment's indecision,* HENRIETTA *turns and goes out.*

BARRETT (*quietly, after a pause*). You had all better say good night to your sister.

ARABEL (*in a whisper*). Good night, dearest.

[*She kisses* ELIZABETH *on the cheek.*

ELIZABETH (*receiving the kiss impassively*). Good night.

[ARABEL *leaves the room. Then each of the brothers in turn goes to* ELIZABETH *and kisses her cheek.*

GEORGE. Good night, Ba.

ELIZABETH. Good night.

[GEORGE *goes out.*

ALFRED. Good night, Ba.

ELIZABETH. Good night.

[ALFRED *goes out.*

HENRY. Good night, Ba.

ELIZABETH. Good night.

|HENRY *goes out.*

CHARLES. Good night, Ba.

ELIZABETH. Good night.

[CHARLES *goes out.*

SEPTIMUS. Good night, Ba.

ELIZABETH. Good night.

[SEPTIMUS *goes out.*

OCTAVIUS. G-good night, Ba.

ELIZABETH. Good night.

[OCTAVIUS *goes out.*

BARRETT, *standing before the fireplace, and* ELIZABETH, *on her sofa, look before them with expressionless faces. A pause.* HENRIETTA *enters with a tankard on a small tray. She stands a little beyond the threshold, glaring at her father and breathing quickly.*

ELIZABETH. Give it to me, please.

[HENRIETTA *goes to her.* ELIZABETH *takes the tankard and is putting*
it to her lips, when BARRETT *suddenly, but quietly, intervenes.*

BARRETT. No. (*Putting* HENRIETTA *aside, he takes the tankard from*
ELIZABETH. *To* HENRIETTA) You may go.

HENRIETTA. Good night, Ba darling.

[*She moves forward to* ELIZABETH, *but* BARRETT *waves her back.*

BARRETT. You may go.

ELIZABETH. Good night.

[HENRIETTA, *with a defiant look at her father, goes out.*

BARRETT *puts the tankard on the mantelpiece; then goes to the sofa*
and stands looking down at ELIZABETH. *She stares up at him with*
wide fearful eyes.

BARRETT (*in a gentle voice*). Elizabeth.

ELIZABETH (*in a whisper*). Yes?

BARRETT (*placing his hand on her head and bending it slightly back*).
Why do you look at me like that, child? . . . Are you frightened?

ELIZABETH (*as before*). No.

BARRETT. You're trembling. . . . Why?

ELIZABETH. I—I don't know.

BARRETT. You're not frightened of me? (ELIZABETH *is about to speak*
—*he goes on quickly*) No, no. You mustn't say it. I couldn't bear to think
that. (*He seats himself on the side of the sofa and takes her hands*) You're
everything in the world to me—you know that. Without you I should
be quite alone—you know that too. And you—if you love me, you can't
be afraid of me. For love casts out fear. . . . You love me, my darling?
You love your father?

ELIZABETH (*in a whisper*). Yes.

BARRETT (*eagerly*). And you'll prove your love by doing as I wish?

ELIZABETH. I don't understand. I was going to drink——

BARRETT (*quickly*). Yes—out of fear, not love. Listen, dear. I told
you just now that if you disobeyed me you would incur my displeasure.
I take that back. I shall never, in any way, reproach you. You shall never
know by deed or word, or hint, of mine how much you have grieved and
wounded your father by refusing to do the little thing he asked. . . .

ELIZABETH. Oh please, please, don't say any more. It's all so petty and
sordid. Please give me the tankard.

BARRETT (*rising*). You are acting of your own free will, and not——

ELIZABETH. Oh, Papa, let us get this over and forget it! I can't forgive
myself for having made the whole house miserable over a tankard of
porter.

[*He gives her the tankard. She drinks the porter straight off.* BARRETT
places the tankard back on the mantelpiece; then returns to the sofa
and looks yearningly down at ELIZABETH.

BARRETT. You're not feeling worse to-night, my darling?

ELIZABETH (*listlessly*). No, Papa.

BARRETT. Just tired?

ELIZABETH. Yes . . . just tired.

BARRETT. I'd better leave you now. . . . Shall I say a little prayer with you before I go?

ELIZABETH. Please, Papa.

[BARRETT *kneels down beside the sofa, clasps his hands, lifts his face, and shuts his eyes.* ELIZABETH *clasps her hands, but keeps her eyes wide open.*

BARRETT. Almighty and merciful God, hear me, I beseech Thee, and grant my humble prayer. In Thine inscrutable wisdom Thou hast seen good to lay on Thy daughter Elizabeth grievous and heavy afflictions. For years she hath languished in sickness; and for years, unless in Thy mercy Thou take her to Thyself, she may languish on. Give her to realise the blessed word that Thou chastisest those whom Thou lovest. Give her to bear her sufferings in patience. Give her to fix her heart and soul on Thee and on that Heavenly Eternity which may at any moment open out before her. Take her into Thy loving care tonight; purge her mind of all bitter and selfish and unkind thoughts; guard her and comfort her. These things I beseech Thee for the sake of Thy dear Son, Jesus Christ. Amen.

ELIZABETH. Amen.

BARRETT (*rising to his feet, and kissing her forehead*). Good night, my child.

ELIZABETH (*receiving his kiss impassively*). Good night, Papa. (BARRETT *goes out.* ELIZABETH *lies motionless, staring before her for a moment or two. A knock at the door*) Come in.

[WILSON *enters, carrying* FLUSH.

WILSON (*putting* FLUSH *in his basket*). Are you ready for your bed now, Miss Ba?

ELIZABETH. Oh, Wilson, I'm so tired—tired—tired of it all. . . . Will it never end?

WILSON. End, Miss?

ELIZABETH. This long, long, grey death in life.

WILSON. Oh, Miss Ba, you shouldn't say such things!

ELIZABETH. No, I suppose I shouldn't. . . . Did Flush enjoy his run?

WILSON. Oh, yes, Miss. (*A short pause*)

ELIZABETH. Is it a fine night, Wilson?

WILSON. Yes, Miss, and quite warm, and there's such a lovely moon.

ELIZABETH (*eagerly*). A moon! Oh, do you think I can see it from here?

WILSON. I don't know, I'm sure.

ELIZABETH. Draw back the curtains and raise the blind.

[WILSON *does so; and moonlight, tempered by the lamplight, streams on* ELIZABETH'S *face.*

WILSON. There you are, Miss! The moon's right above the chimleys. You can see it lovely!

ELIZABETH (*dreamily*). Yes. . . . Yes. . . . Please put out the lamp and leave me for a little. I don't want to go to bed quite yet.

WILSON. Very well, Miss Ba.

WILSON *extinguishes the lamp and goes out.*

ELIZABETH *is bathed in strong moonlight. She stares, for a while, with wide eyes at the moon. Then her quickened breathing becomes audible, and her whole body is shaken with sobs. She turns over on her side and buries her face in her arms. The only sound is her strangled weeping as the Scene closes.*

*   *   *

BARRETT. If returning health must bring with it such sad change of character I shall be driven to wish that you were once more lying helpless on that sofa. There is nothing more to be said.

[*He turns to the door.*

ELIZABETH (*with restrained anger*). But there is more to be said, and I must beg you to listen to me, Papa. How many years have I lain here? Five? Six? It's hard to remember—as each year has been like ten. And all that time I've had nothing to look forward to, or hope for, but death.

BARRETT. Death . . . ?

ELIZABETH. Yes, death. I was born with a large capacity for happiness—you remember me as a young girl?—and when life brought me little happiness and much pain, I was often impatient for the end, and——

BARRETT (*outraged*). Elizabeth! I'm shocked that——

ELIZABETH (*swiftly*). And now this miracle has happened! Day by day I am better able to take and enjoy such good things as every one has a right to—able to meet my friends, to breathe the open air and feel the sun, and see grass and flowers growing under the sky. . . . When Doctor Chambers first spoke to me of Italy I put the idea from me—it seemed too impossibly wonderful! But as I grew stronger, it came over me, like a revelation, that Italy wasn't an impossibility at all, that nothing really stood in the way of my going, that I had every right to go——

BARRETT. Right?

ELIZABETH. Yes! every right—if only I could get your consent. So I set about consulting my friends, meeting all obstacles, settling every detail, so as to have a perfectly arranged plan to put before you after the doctors had given you their opinion. In my eagerness I may have acted stupidly, mistakenly, tactlessly. But to call my conduct underhand and deceitful is more than unkind. It's unjust. It's cruel.

BARRETT (*more in sorrow than in anger*). Self! Self! Self! No thought, no consideration, for any one but yourself, or for anything but your pleasure.

ELIZABETH (*passionately*). But Papa——

BARRETT (*with a silencing gesture*). Didn't it even once occur to you that all through those long, dark months you proposed to enjoy yourself in Italy, your father would be left here utterly alone?

ELIZABETH. Alone?

BARRETT. Utterly alone. . . . Your brothers and sisters might as well be shadows for all the companionship they afford me. And you—oh, my child, don't think that I haven't noticed that you too, now that you are stronger and no longer wholly dependent on me, are slowly drawing away from your father. . . .

ELIZABETH. It's not true!

BARRETT. It is true—and, in your heart, you know it's true.

ELIZABETH. No!

BARRETT. New life, new interests, new pleasures, new friends—and little by little, I am being pushed into the background—I who used to be your whole world, I who love you—who love you——

ELIZABETH. But Papa——

BARRETT (*with a silencing gesture*). No. There is nothing more to be said. (*He crosses to the window, looks out, then turns*) You want my consent for this—Italian jaunt. I shall neither give it nor withhold it. To give it would be against my conscience as encouraging selfishness and self-indulgence. To withhold it would be a futile gesture. You are your own mistress. Even if I refused to pay your expenses, you have ample means of your own to carry out your intentions. You are at liberty to do as you wish. . . . And if you go, I hope you will sometimes spare a thought for your father. Think of him at night stealing into this room which once held all he loved. Think of him kneeling alone by the empty sofa and imploring the Good Shepherd to——(*A knock at the door*) Eh . . . ?

Obsessive-Compulsive Neurosis

II. The obsessional neurosis is characterized by psychological defenses against the expression or awareness of emotion. These defenses block feelings but frequently allow the related thoughts to become conscious. Thus the patient may, as will be illustrated in the chapter on neurotic symptoms, be plagued by unwanted ideas. Other obsessionals are apt to repeat compulsively certain numbers, or prayers, or ceremonies.

The obsessive compulsive is usually a careful person preoccupied with neatness and cleanliness. He plans everything in detail and every decision is a major crisis in which both sides must be weighed and reweighed in a cloud of doubt and confusion. Money is often a focus of concern. Nabokov portrays with insight the interesting fact that the obsessional, despite all his plans, more often than not does things in an inefficient and wasteful fashion.

Professor Pnin is an isolated man in a strange country. He is on his way to give a lecture; a typical obsessional, he has carefully, almost ritualistically, mapped out every aspect of his short trip. Like many an obsessional, his compulsive plans are in the end ineffective, and he meets one frustration after another. Finally, discovering that he has the wrong manuscript in his pocket, his defenses crumble and he has a full blown anxiety attack.

Pnin is a touching example of a man who protects himself from feelings by setting up a wall of ritual and routine.

PNIN

Vladimir Nabokov (1899–   )

. . . Pnin left the station, satisfied himself about the bus stop, and entered a coffee shop. He consumed a ham sandwich, ordered another, and consumed that too. At exactly five minutes to four, having paid for the food but not for an excellent toothpick which he carefully selected from a neat little cup in the shape of a pine cone near the cash register, Pnin walked back to the station for his bag.

A different man was now in charge. The first had been called home to drive his wife in all haste to the maternity hospital. He would be back in a few minutes.

"But I must obtain my valise!" cried Pnin.

The substitute was sorry but could not do a thing.

"It is there!" cried Pnin, leaning over and pointing.

This was unfortunate. He was still in the act of pointing when he realized that he was claiming the wrong bag. His index finger wavered. That hesitation was fatal.

"My bus to Cremona!" cried Pnin.

"There is another at eight," said the man.

What was our poor friend to do? Horrible situation! He glanced streetward. The bus had just come. The engagement meant an extra fifty dollars. His hand flew to his right side. *It* was there, *slava Bogu* (thank God)! Very well! He would not wear his black suit—*vot i vsyo* (that's all). He would retrieve it on his way back. He had lost, dumped, shed many more valuable things in his day. Energetically, almost lightheartedly, Pnin boarded the bus.

He had endured this new stage of his journey only for a few city blocks when an awful suspicion crossed his mind. Ever since he had been separated from his bag, the tip of his left forefinger had been alternating with the proximal edge of his right elbow in checking a precious presence in his inside coat pocket. All of a sudden he brutally yanked it out. It was Betty's paper.

Emitting what he thought were international exclamations of anxiety and entreaty, Pnin lurched out of his seat. Reeling, he reached the exit. With one hand the driver grimly milked out a handful of coins from his little machine, refunded him the price of the ticket, and stopped the bus. Poor Pnin landed in the middle of a strange town.

He was less strong than his powerfully puffed-out chest might imply, and the wave of hopeless fatigue that suddenly submerged his topheavy body, detaching him, as it were, from reality, was a sensation not utterly unknown to him. He found himself in a damp, green, purplish park, of the formal and funereal type, with the stress laid on somber rhododendrons, glossy laurels, sprayed shade trees and closely clipped lawns; and hardly had he turned into an alley of chestnut and oak, which the bus driver had curtly told him led back to the railway station, than that eerie feeling, that tingle of unreality overpowered him completely. Was it something he had eaten? That pickle with the ham? Was it a mysterious disease that none of his doctors had yet detected? My friend wondered, and I wonder, too.

I do not know if it has ever been noted before that one of the main characteristics of life is discreteness. Unless a film of flesh envelops us, we die. Man exists only insofar as he is separated from his surroundings. The cranium is a space-traveler's helmet. Stay inside or you perish. Death is divestment, death is communion. It may be wonderful to mix with the landscape, but to do so is the end of the tender ego. The sensation poor Pnin experienced was something very like that divestment, that communion. He felt porous and pregnable. He was sweating. He was terrified. A stone bench among the laurels saved him from collapsing on the sidewalk. Was his seizure a heart attack? I doubt it. For the nonce I am his physician, and let me repeat, I doubt it. My patient was one of those singular and unfortunate people who regard their heart ("a hollow, muscular organ," according to the gruesome definition in *Webster's New Collegiate Dictionary*, which Pnin's orphaned bag contained) with a queasy dread, a nervous repulsion, a sick hate, as if it were some strong slimy untouchable monster that one had to be parasitized with, alas. Occasionally, when puzzled by his tumbling and tottering pulse, doctors examined him more thoroughly, the cardiograph outlined fabulous mountain ranges and indicated a dozen fatal diseases that excluded one another. He was afraid of touching his own wrist. He never attempted to sleep on his left side, even in those dismal hours of the night when the insomniac longs for a third side after trying the two he has.

And now, in the park of Whitchurch, Pnin felt what he had felt already on August 10, 1942, and February 15 (his birthday), 1937, and May 18, 1929, and July 4, 1920—that the repulsive automaton he lodged had developed a consciousness of its own and not only was grossly alive but was causing him pain and panic. He pressed his poor bald head against the stone back of the bench and recalled all the past occasions of similar discomfort and despair. Could it be pneumonia this time? He had been chilled to the bone a couple of days before in one of those hearty American drafts that a host treats his guests to after the second round of drinks on a windy night. And suddenly Pnin (was he dying?) found himself sliding back into his own childhood. This sensation had the sharpness of retrospective detail that is said to be the dramatic privilege of drowning individuals, especially in the former Russian Navy—a phenomenon of suffocation that a veteran psychoanalyst, whose name escapes me, has explained as being the subconsciously evoked shock of one's baptism which causes an explosion of intervening recollections between the first immersion and the last. It all happened in a flash but there is no way of rendering it in less than so many consecutive words.

Pnin came from a respectable, fairly well-to-do, St. Petersburg family. His father, Dr. Pavel Pnin, an eye specialist of considerable repute, had once had the honor of treating Leo Tolstoy for a case of conjunctivitis. Timofey's mother, a frail, nervous little person with a waspy waist and bobbed hair, was the daughter of the once famous revolutionary Umov (rhymes with "zoom off") and of a German lady from Riga. Through his half swoon, he saw his mother's approaching eyes. It was a Sunday in midwinter. He was eleven. He had been preparing lessons for his Monday classes at the First Gymnasium when a strange chill pervaded his body. His mother took his temperature, looked at her child with a kind of stupefaction, and immediately called her husband's best friend, the pediatrician Belochkin. He was a small, beetle-browed man, with a short beard and cropped hair. Easing the skirts of his frock coat, he sat down on the edge of Timofey's bed. A race was run between the doctor's fat golden watch and Timofey's pulse (an easy winner). Then Timofey's torso was bared, and to it Belochkin pressed the icy nudity of his ear and the sandpapery side of his head. Like the flat sole of some monopode, the ear ambulated all over Timofey's back and chest, gluing itself to this or that patch of skin and stomping on to the next. No sooner had the doctor left than Timofey's mother and a robust servant girl with safety pins between her teeth encased the distressed little patient in a strait-jacket-like compress. It consisted of a layer of soaked linen, a thicker layer of absorbent cotton, and another of tight flannel, with a sticky diabolical oilcloth—the hue of urine and fever—coming between the clammy pang of the linen next to his skin and the excruciating squeak of the cotton around which the outer layer of flannel was wound. A poor cocooned pupa, Timosha (Tim) lay under a mass of additional blankets; they were of no avail against the branching chill that crept up his ribs from both sides of his frozen spine. He could not close his eyes because his eyelids stung so. Vision was but oval pain with oblique stabs of light; familiar shapes became the breeding places of evil delusions. Near his bed was a four-section screen of polished wood, with pyrographic designs representing a bridle path felted with fallen leaves, a lily pond, an old man hunched up on a bench, and a squirrel holding a reddish object in its front paws. Timosha, a methodical child, had often wondered what that object could be (a nut? a pine cone?), and now that he had nothing else to do, he set himself to solve this dreary riddle, but the fever that hummed in his head drowned every effort in pain and panic. Still more oppressive was his tussle with the wallpaper. He had always been able to see that in the vertical plane a combination made up of three different clusters of purple flowers and seven different oak leaves was repeated a number of times with soothing exactitude; but now he was bothered by the undismissable fact that he could not find what system of inclusion and circumscription governed the horizontal recurrence of the pattern; that such a recurrence existed was proved by his being able to pick out here and there, all along the wall from bed to wardrobe and from stove to door, the reappearance of this or that element of the series, but when he tried traveling right or left from any chosen set of three inflorescences and seven leaves, he forthwith lost himself in a meaningless tangle of rhododendron and oak. It stood to reason that if the evil designer—the destroyer of minds, the friend of fever—had concealed the key of the pattern with such monstrous care, that key must be as precious as life itself and, when found, would regain for Timofey Pnin his everyday health, his everyday world; and this lucid—alas, too lucid—thought forced him to persevere in the struggle.

A sense of being late for some appointment as odiously exact as school, dinner, or bedtime added the discomfort of awkward haste to the difficulties of a quest that was grading into delirium. The foliage and the flowers, with none of the intricacies of their warp disturbed, appeared to detach themselves in one undulating body from their pale-blue background which, in its turn, lost its papery flatness and dilated in depth till the spectator's heart almost burst in response to the expansion. He could still make out through the autonomous garlands certain parts of the nursery more tenacious of life than the rest, such as the lacquered screen, the gleam of a tumbler, the brass knobs of his bedstead, but these interfered even less with the oak leaves and rich blossoms than would the reflection of an inside object in a windowpane with the outside scenery perceived through the same glass. And although the witness and victim of these phantasms was tucked up in bed, he was, in accordance with the twofold nature of his surroundings, simultaneously seated on a bench in a green and purple park. During one melting moment, he had the sensation of holding at last the key he had sought; but, coming from very far, a rustling wind, its soft volume increasing as it ruffled the rhododendrons —now blossomless, blind—confused whatever rational pattern Timofey Pnin's surroundings had once had. He was alive and that was sufficient. The back of the bench against which he still sprawled felt as real as his clothes, or his wallet, or the date of the Great Moscow Fire—1812.

A gray squirrel sitting on comfortable haunches on the ground before him was sampling a peach stone. The wind paused, and presently stirred the foliage again.

The seizure had left him a little frightened and shaky, but he argued that had it been a real heart attack, he would have surely felt a good deal more unsettled and concerned, and this roundabout piece of reasoning completely dispelled his fear. It was now four-twenty. He blew his nose and trudged to the station.

The initial employee was back. "Here's your bag," he said cheerfully. "Sorry you missed the Cremona bus."

"At least"—and what dignified irony our unfortunate friend tried to inject into that "at least"—"I hope everything is good with your wife?"

"She'll be all right. Have to wait till tomorrow, I guess."

"And now," said Pnin, "where is located the public telephone?"

The man pointed with his pencil as far out and sideways as he could without leaving his lair. Pnin, bag in hand, started to go, but he was called back. The pencil was now directed streetward.

"Say, see those two guys loading that truck? They're going to Cremona right now. Just tell them Bob Horn sent you. They'll take you." . . .

Phobias

III. Many situations in real life are dangerous, and fear can be a useful emotion, warning the individual to take steps to deal with the dangers. A phobia develops when a relatively harmless situation is reacted to as though it were dangerous or when the danger is grossly overestimated. Countless objects and situations can therefore become the center for the formation of a phobia. The common ones have been

given names such as acrophobia, fear of heights; agoraphobia,
fear of open places, particularly the downtown areas;
claustrophobia, fear of closed-in places; zoophobia, fear of
animals. Children quite frequently develop phobias, particularly
zoophobia. These are transient and probably common enough
to be considered a normal phase of development. The strange
irony of the neurotic phobia is in the sustained intense dread
of the harmless. Nowhere is this more dramatically portrayed
than in Graham Greene's "The End of the Party."

THE END OF THE PARTY

Graham Greene (1904–   )

Peter Morton woke with a start to face the first light.
Through the window he could see a bare bough dropping across a frame
of silver. Rain tapped against the glass. It was January the fifth.

He looked across a table, on which a night-light had guttered into a
pool of water, at the other bed. Francis Morton was still asleep, and Peter
lay down again with his eyes on his brother. It amused him to imagine that
it was himself whom he watched, the same hair, the same eyes, the same
lips and line of cheek. But the thought soon palled, and the mind went
back to the fact which lent the day importance. It was the fifth of January. He could hardly believe that a year had passed since Mrs. Henne-
Falcon had given her last children's party.

Francis turned suddenly upon his back and threw an arm across his
face, blocking his mouth. Peter's heart began to beat fast, not with pleasure
now but with uneasiness. He sat up and called across the table, "Wake
up." Francis's shoulders shook and he waved a clenched fist in the air, but
his eyes remained closed. To Peter Morton the whole room seemed suddenly to darken, and he had the impression of a great bird swooping. He
cried again, "Wake up," and once more there was silver light and the
touch of rain on the windows. Francis rubbed his eyes. "Did you call
out?" he asked.

"You are having a bad dream," Peter said with confidence. Already
experience had taught him how far their minds reflected each other. But
he was the elder, by a matter of minutes, and that brief extra interval of
light, while his brother still struggled in pain and darkness, had given him
self-reliance and an instinct of protection towards the other who was
afraid of so many things.

From *Twenty-One Stories* by Graham Greene. Copyright 1947 by Graham Greene.
Reprinted by permission of The Viking Press, Inc.

"I dreamed that I was dead," Francis said.

"What was it like?" Peter asked with curiosity.

"I can't remember," Francis said, and his eyes turned with relief to the silver of day, as he allowed the fragmentary memories to fade.

"You dreamed of a big bird."

"Did I?" Francis accepted his brother's knowledge without question, and for a little the two lay silent in bed facing each other, the same green eyes, the same nose tilting at the tip, the same firm lips parted, and the same premature modelling of the chin. The fifth of January, Peter thought again, his mind drifting idly from the image of cakes to the prizes which might be won. Egg-and-spoon races, spearing apples in basins of water, blind-man's buff.

"I don't want to go," Francis said suddenly. "I suppose Joyce will be there . . . Mabel Warren." Hateful to him, the thought of a party shared with those two. They were older than he. Joyce was eleven and Mabel Warren thirteen. Their long pigtails swung superciliously to a masculine stride. Their sex humiliated him, as they watched him fumble with his egg, from under lowered scornful lids. And last year . . . he turned his face away from Peter, his cheeks scarlet.

"What's the matter?" Peter asked.

"Oh, nothing. I don't think I'm well. I've got a cold. I oughtn't to go to the party."

Peter was puzzled. "But, Francis, is it a bad cold?"

"It will be a bad cold if I go to the party. Perhaps I shall die."

"Then you mustn't go," Peter said with decision, prepared to solve all difficulties with one plain sentence, and Francis let his nerves relax in a delicious relief, ready to leave everything to Peter. But though he was grateful he did not turn his face towards his brother. His cheeks still bore the badge of a shameful memory, of the game of hide-and-seek last year in the darkened house, and of how he had screamed when Mabel Warren put her hand suddenly upon his arm. He had not heard her coming. Girls were like that. Their shoes never squeaked. No boards whined under their tread. They slunk like cats on padded claws. When the nurse came in with hot water Francis lay tranquil, leaving everything to Peter. Peter said, "Nurse, Francis has got a cold."

The tall starched woman laid the towels across the cans and said, without turning, "The washing won't be back till tomorrow. You must lend him some of your handkerchiefs."

"But, Nurse," Peter asked, "hadn't he better stay in bed?"

"We'll take him for a good walk this morning," the nurse said. "Wind'll blow away the germs. Get up now, both of you," and she closed the door behind her.

"I'm sorry," Peter said, and then, worried at the sight of a face creased again by misery and foreboding, "Why don't you just stay in bed?

I'll tell mother you felt too ill to get up." But such a rebellion against destiny was not in Francis's power. Besides, if he stayed in bed they would come up and tap his chest and put a thermometer in his mouth and look at his tongue, and they would discover that he was malingering. It was true that he felt ill, a sick empty sensation in his stomach and a rapidly beating heart, but he knew that the cause was only fear, fear of the party, fear of being made to hide by himself in the dark, uncompanioned by Peter and with no nightlight to make a blessed breach.

"No, I'll get up," he said, and then with sudden desperation, "but I won't go to Mrs. Henne-Falcon's party. I swear on the Bible I won't." Now surely all would be well, he thought. God would not allow him to break so solemn an oath. He would show him a way. There was all the morning before him and all the afternoon until four o'clock. No need to worry now when the grass was still crisp with the early frost. Anything might happen. He might cut himself or break his leg or really catch a bad cold. God would manage somehow.

He had such confidence in God that when at breakfast his mother said, "I hear you have a cold, Francis," he made light of it. "We should have heard more about it," his mother said with irony, "if there was not a party this evening," and Francis smiled uneasily, amazed and daunted by her ignorance of him. His happiness would have lasted longer if, out for a walk that morning, he had not met Joyce. He was alone with his nurse, for Peter had leave to finish a rabbit-hutch in the woodshed. If Peter had been there he would have cared less; the nurse was Peter's nurse also, but now it was as though she were employed only for his sake, because he could not be trusted to go for a walk alone. Joyce was only two years older and she was by herself.

She came striding towards them, pigtails flapping. She glanced scornfully at Francis and spoke with ostentation to the nurse. "Hello, Nurse. Are you bringing Francis to the party this evening? Mabel and I are coming." And she was off again down the street in the direction of Mabel Warren's home, consciously alone and self-sufficient in the long empty road. "Such a nice girl," the nurse said. But Francis was silent, feeling again the jump-jump of his heart, realizing how soon the hour of the party would arrive. God had done nothing for him, and the minutes flew.

They flew too quickly to plan any evasion, or even to prepare his heart for the coming ordeal. Panic nearly overcame him when, all unready, he found himself standing on the door-step, with coat-collar turned up against a cold wind, and the nurse's electric torch making a short luminous trail through the darkness. Behind him were the lights of the hall and the sound of a servant laying the table for dinner, which his mother and father would eat alone. He was nearly overcome by a desire to run back into the house and call out to his mother that he would not go to the party, that he dared not go. They could not make him go. He could almost hear himself saying those final words, breaking down for ever, as he knew instinctively, the barrier of ignorance that saved his mind from his parents' knowledge. "I'm afraid of going. I won't go. I daren't go. They'll make me hide in the dark, and I'm afraid of the dark. I'll scream and scream and scream." He could see the expression of amazement on his mother's face, and then the cold confidence of a grown-up's retort. "Don't be silly. You must go. We've accepted Mrs. Henne-Falcon's invitation."

But they couldn't make him go; hesitating on the door-step while the nurse's feet crunched across the frost-covered grass to the gate, he knew that. He would answer, "You can say I'm ill. I won't go. I'm afraid of the dark." And his mother, "Don't be silly. You know there's nothing to be afraid of in the dark." But he knew the falsity of that reasoning; he knew how they taught also that there was nothing to fear in death, and how fearfully they avoided the idea of it. But they couldn't make him go to the party. "I'll scream. I'll scream."

"Francis, come along." He heard the nurse's voice across the dimly phosphorescent lawn and saw the small yellow circle of her torch wheel from tree to shrub and back to tree again. "I'm coming," he called with despair, leaving the lighted doorway of the house; he couldn't bring himself to lay bare his last secrets and end reserve between his mother and himself, for there was still in the last resort a further appeal possible to Mrs. Henne-Falcon. He comforted himself with that, as he advanced steadily across the hall, very small, towards her enormous bulk. His heart beat unevenly, but he had control now over his voice, as he said with meticulous accent, "Good evening, Mrs. Henne-Falcon. It was very good of you to ask me to your party." With his strained face lifted towards the curve of her breasts, and his polite set speech, he was like an old withered man. For Francis mixed very little with other children. As a twin he was in many ways an only child. To address Peter was to speak to his own image in a mirror, an image a little altered by a flaw in the glass, so as to throw back less a likeness of what he was than of what he wished to be, what he would be without his unreasoning fear of darkness, footsteps of strangers, the flight of bats in dusk-filled gardens.

"Sweet child," said Mrs. Henne-Falcon absent-mindedly, before, with a wave of her arms, as though the children were a flock of chickens, she whirled them into her set programme of entertainments: egg-and-spoon races, three-legged races, the spearing of apples, games which held for Francis nothing worse than humiliation. And in the frequent intervals when nothing was required of him and he could stand alone in corners as far removed as possible from Mabel Warren's scornful gaze, he was able to plan how he might avoid the approaching terror of the dark. He knew there was nothing to fear until after tea, and not until he was sitting down in a pool of yellow radiance cast by the ten candles on Colin Henne-

Falcon's birthday cake did he become fully conscious of the imminence of what he feared. Through the confusion of his brain, now assailed suddenly by a dozen contradictory plans, he heard Joyce's high voice down the table. "After tea we are going to play hide-and-seek in the dark."

"Oh, no," Peter said, watching Francis's troubled face with pity and an imperfect understanding, "don't let's. We play that every year."

"But it's in the programme," cried Mabel Warren. "I saw it myself. I looked over Mrs. Henne-Falcon's shoulder. Five o'clock, tea. A quarter to six to half-past, hide-and-seek in the dark. It's all written down in the programme."

Peter did not argue, for if hide-and-seek had been inserted in Mrs. Henne-Falcon's programme, nothing which he could say could avert it. He asked for another piece of birthday cake and sipped his tea slowly. Perhaps it might be possible to delay the game for a quarter of an hour, allow Francis at least a few extra minutes to form a plan, but even in that Peter failed, for children were already leaving the table in twos and threes. It was his third failure, and again, the reflection of an image in another's mind, he saw a great bird darken his brother's face with its wings. But he upbraided himself silently for his folly, and finished his cake encouraged by the memory of that adult refrain, "There's nothing to fear in the dark." The last to leave the table, the brothers came together to the hall to meet the mustering and impatient eyes of Mrs. Henne-Falcon.

"And now," she said, "we will play hide-and-seek in the dark."

Peter watched his brother and saw, as he had expected, the lips tighten. Francis, he knew, had feared this moment from the beginning of the party, had tried to meet it with courage and had abandoned the attempt. He must have prayed desperately for cunning to evade the game, which was now welcomed with cries of excitement by all the other children. "Oh, do let's." "We must pick sides." "Is any of the house out of bounds?" "Where shall home be?"

"I think," said Francis Morton, approaching Mrs. Henne-Falcon, his eyes focused unwaveringly on her exuberant breasts, "it will be no use my playing. My nurse will be calling for me very soon."

"Oh, but your nurse can wait, Francis," said Mrs. Henne-Falcon absent-mindedly, while she clapped her hands together to summon to her side a few children who were already straying up the wide staircase to upper floors. "Your mother will never mind."

That had been the limit of Francis's cunning. He had refused to believe that so well prepared an excuse could fail. All that he could say now, still in the precise tone which other children hated, thinking it a symbol of conceit, was, "I think I had better not play." He stood motionless, retaining, though afraid, unmoved features. But the knowledge of his terror, or the reflection of the terror itself, reached his brother's brain. For the moment, Peter Morton could have cried aloud with the fear of bright lights going out, leaving him alone in an island of dark surrounded by the gentle lapping of strange footsteps. Then he remembered that the fear was not his own, but his brother's. He said impulsively to Mrs. Henne-Falcon, "Please. I don't think Francis should play. The dark makes him jump so." They were the wrong words. Six children began to sing, "Cowardly, cowardly custard," turning torturing faces with the vacancy of wide sunflowers towards Francis Morton.

Without looking at his brother, Francis said, "Of course I will play. I am not afraid. I only thought. . . ." But he was already forgotten by his human tormentors and was able in loneliness to contemplate the approach of the spiritual, the more unbounded, torture. The children scrambled round Mrs. Henne-Falcon, their shrill voices pecking at her with questions and suggestions. "Yes, anywhere in the house. We will turn out all the lights. Yes, you can hide in the cupboards. You must stay hidden as long as you can. There will be no home."

Peter, too, stood apart, ashamed of the clumsy manner in which he had tried to help his brother. Now he could feel, creeping in at the corners of his brain, all Francis's resentment of his championing. Several children ran upstairs, and the lights on the top floor went out. Then darkness came down like the wings of a bat and settled on the landing. Others began to put out the lights at the edge of the hall, till the children were all gathered in the central radiance of the chandelier, while the bats squatted round on hooded wings and waited for that, too, to be extinguished.

"You and Francis are on the hiding side," a tall girl said, and then the light was gone, and the carpet wavered under his feet with the sibilance of footfalls, like small cold draughts, creeping away into corners.

"Where's Francis?" he wondered. "If I join him he'll be less frightened of all these sounds." "These sounds" were the casing of silence. The squeak of a loose board, the cautious closing of a cupboard door, the whine of a finger drawn along polished wood.

Peter stood in the centre of the dark deserted floor, not listening but waiting for the idea of his brother's whereabouts to enter his brain. But Francis crouched with fingers on his ears, eyes uselessly closed, mind numbed against impressions, and only a sense of strain could cross the gap of dark. Then a voice called "Coming," and as though his brother's self-possession had been shattered by the sudden cry, Peter Morton jumped with his fear. But it was not his own fear. What in his brother was a burning panic, admitting no ideas except those which added to the flame, was in him an altruistic emotion that left the reason unimpaired. "Where, if I were Francis, should I hide?" Such, roughly, was his thought. And because he was, if not Francis himself, at least a mirror to him, the answer was immediate. "Between the oak bookcase on the left of the study door and the leather settee." Peter Morton was unsurprised by the swiftness of the response. Between the twins there could be no jargon of telepathy. They had been together in the womb, and they could not be parted.

Peter Morton tiptoed towards Francis's hiding place. Occasionally a board rattled, and because he feared to be caught by one of the soft questers through the dark, he bent and untied his laces. A tag struck the floor and the metallic sound set a host of cautious feet moving in his direction. But by that time he was in his stockings and would have laughed inwardly at the pursuit had not the noise of someone stumbling on his abandoned shoes made his heart trip in the reflection of another's surprise. No more boards revealed Peter Morton's progress. On stockinged feet he moved silently and unerringly towards his object. Instinct told him that he was near the wall, and, extending a hand, he laid the fingers across his brother's face.

Francis did not cry out, but the leap of his own heart revealed to Peter a proportion of Francis's terror. "It's all right," he whispered, feeling down the squatting figure until he captured a clenched hand. "It's only me. I'll stay with you." And grasping the other tightly, he listened to the cascade of whispers his utterance had caused to fall. A hand touched the bookcase close to Peter's head and he was aware of how Francis's fear continued in spite of his presence. It was less intense, more bearable, he hoped, but it remained. He knew that it was his brother's fear and not his own that he experienced. The dark to him was only an absence of light; the groping hand that of a familiar child. Patiently he waited to be found.

He did not speak again, for between Francis and himself touch was the most intimate communion. By way of joined hands thought could flow more swiftly than lips could shape themselves round words. He could experience the whole progress of his brother's emotion, from the leap of panic at the unexpected contact to the steady pulse of fear, which now went on and on with the regularity of a heartbeat. Peter Morton thought with intensity, "I am here. You needn't be afraid. The lights will go on again soon. That rustle, that movement is nothing to fear. Only Joyce, only Mabel Warren." He bombarded the drooping form with thoughts of safety, but he was conscious that the fear continued. "They are beginning to whisper together. They are tired of looking for us. The lights will go on soon. We shall have won. Don't be afraid. That was only someone on the stairs. I believe it's Mrs. Henne-Falcon. Listen. They are feeling for the lights." Feet moving on a carpet, hands brushing a wall, a curtain pulled apart, a clicking handle, the opening of a cupboard door. In the case above their heads a loose book shifted under a touch. "Only Joyce, only Mabel Warren, only Mrs. Henne-Falcon," a crescendo of reassuring thought before the chandelier burst, like a fruit tree, into bloom.

The voices of the children rose shrilly into the radiance. "Where's

Peter?" "Have you looked upstairs?" "Where's Francis?" but they were
silenced again by Mrs. Henne-Falcon's scream. But she was not the first to
notice Francis Morton's stillness, where he had collapsed against the wall
at the touch of his brother's hand. Peter continued to hold the clenched
fingers in an arid and puzzled grief. It was not merely that his brother was
dead. His brain, too young to realize the full paradox, yet wondered with
an obscure self-pity why it was that the pulse of his brother's fear went
on and on, when Francis was now where he had been always told there
was no more terror and no more darkness.

Neurotic Depression

IV. The neurotic depression is often precipitated by
current circumstance. The predominance of depressed mood,
however, is maintained, and usually the person cannot mobilize
himself to alter it. Loneliness and feelings of worthlessness
and inferiority are prominent, but not so severe as in a
psychotic depression. Colette, in "The Vagabond," captures
this mood of chronic neurotic depression.

THE VAGABOND

Colette   (1873–1954)

. . . As always, I give a great sigh when I close the door
of my ground-floor flat behind me. Is it a sigh of weariness, or relaxation,
or relief? Or does it spring from the bitterness of solitude? Better not
think of it, far better not!

But what on earth is the matter with me tonight? It must be this icy
December fog, like particles of frost hanging in the air, quivering in an
iridescent halo round the gas lamps and melting on one's lips with a taste
of creosote. And besides, this new quarter where I live, looming up all
white behind Les Ternes, is enough to discourage both one's eyes and
one's spirit.

My street, under the greenish gas at this hour, is a morass of toffee-
like, creamy mud—coffee-coloured, maroon and caramel yellow—a sort of
crumbling, slushy trifle in which the floating bits of meringue are lumps
of concrete. Even my house, the only one in the street, has a sort of "it
can't be true" look. But its new walls and thin partitions offer, at a modest

rent, a shelter sufficiently comfortable for "ladies on their own" like me.

When you are a "lady on your own," in other words the landlords' abomination, outcast and terror all rolled into one, you take what you find, lodge where you may and put up with newly plastered walls.

The house where I live compassionately shelters quite a colony of "ladies on their own." On the mezzanine floor we have the acknowledged mistress of Young, of Young-Automobiles; above, the girl-friend, very much "kept," of the Comte de Bravailles; higher up are two fair-haired sisters, both of whom are visited every day by the same man, a very-correct-gentleman-in-industry; higher still a terrible little tart makes as much of a racket night and day as an unleashed fox-terrier, screaming, playing the piano, singing and throwing empty bottles out of the window.

"She's a disgrace to the house," Madame Young-Automobiles said one day.

Finally, on the ground floor, there is myself who neither screams, nor plays the piano, nor ever receives gentlemen and still less ladies. The little tart on the fourth floor makes too much noise and I not enough, as the concierge does not fail to remark to me. "It's funny, one never knows whether Madame is there because one doesn't hear her. One would never think she was an artiste!"

What an ugly December night it is! The radiator smells of iodoform, Blandine has forgotten to put my hot-water bottle in my bed, and even my dog is in a bad mood. Grumpy and shivering, she merely casts one black and white glance at me, without leaving her basket. I must say! I don't expect triumphal arches and illuminations, but all the same. . . .

No need to search the place, to peer in the corners or look under the bed, there is no one here, no one but myself. What I see in the big looking-glass in my bedroom is no longer the painted image of an itinerant music-hall artiste. It reflects only—myself.

Behold me then, just as I am! This evening I shall not be able to escape the meeting in the long mirror, the soliloquy which I have a hundred times avoided, accepted, fled from, taken up again and broken off. I feel in advance, alas, the uselessness of trying to change the subject. This evening I shall not feel sleepy, and the spell of a book—even a brand-new book with that smell of printers' ink and paper fresh from the press that makes you think of coal and trains and departures!—even that spell will not be able to distract me from myself.

Behold me then, just as I am! Alone, alone, and for the rest of my life, no doubt. Already alone; it's early for that. When I turned thirty I did not feel cast down because mine is a face that depends on the expression which animates it, the colour of my eyes, and the defiant smile that plays over it—what Marinetti calls my *gaiezza volpina*. But if I look like a fox, it's a fox without guile, which a hen could catch! And a fox without rapacity, one that remembers only the trap and the cage. A gay-looking fox, if you like, but only because the corners of its mouth and eyes look as if they were smiling. A captive fox, tired of dancing to the sound of music.

It is true enough that I do look like a fox. But a slender, pretty fox is not an ugly thing, is it? Brague says too that I look like a rat when I purse my lips and blink my eyelids so as to see better. I see nothing to mind in that.

But how I dislike seeing myself with that drooping mouth and those slack shoulders, the weight of my whole sad body slumped on one leg! My hair hangs dank and lank and in a little while I shall have to brush it for a long time to give it back its shining beaver brown. My eyes are still faintly ringed with blue eye-shadow and there's a wavering trace of red on my nails. It will take me at least fifty good minutes of bathing and grooming to get rid of all that.

It is one o'clock already. What am I waiting for? A smart little lash with the whip to make the obstinate creature go on again. But no one will give it me because . . . because I am alone. How clearly one sees, in that long frame which holds my reflection, that I'm used already to living alone!

No matter what visitor, for a mere tradesman, or even for my char-woman Blandine, I should raise this drooping neck, straighten that slouch-ing hip and clasp those empty hands. But tonight I am so alone.

Alone! Really one might think I was pitying myself for it!

"If you live all alone," said Brague, "it's because you really want to, isn't it?"

Certainly I "really" want to, and in fact I *want* to, quite simply. Only, well . . . there are days when solitude, for someone of my age, is a heady wine which intoxicates you with freedom, others when it is a bitter tonic, and still others when it is a poison which makes you beat your head against the wall.

This evening I would much prefer not to say which it is; all I want is to remain undecided, and not to be able to say whether the shiver which will seize me when I slip between the cold sheets comes from fear or con-tentment.

Alone . . . and for a long time past. The proof is that I am giving way to the habit of talking to myself and of holding conversations with my dog, and the fire, and my own reflection. It is an idiosyncracy which recluses and old prisoners fall into; but I'm not like them, I'm free. And if I talk to myself it is because I have a writer's need to express my thoughts in rhythmical language.

Facing me from the other side of the looking-glass, in that mysterious reflected room, is the image of "a woman of letters who has turned out badly." They also say of me that I'm "on the stage," but they never call me an actress. Why? The nuance is subtle, but there is certainly a polite refusal, on the part both of the public and my friends themselves, to accord me any standing in this career which I have nevertheless adopted. A woman of letters who has turned out badly: that is what I must remain for everyone, I who no longer write, who deny myself the pleasure, the luxury of writing.

To write, to be able to write, what does it mean? It means spending long hours dreaming before a white page, scribing unconsciously, letting your pen play round a blot of ink and nibble at a half-formed word, scratching it, making it bristle with darts and adorning it with antennae and paws until it loses all resemblance to a legible word and turns into a fantastic insect or a fluttering creature half butterfly, half fairy.

To write is to sit and stare, hypnotised, at the reflection of the window in the silver ink-stand, to feel the divine fever mounting to one's cheeks and forehead while the hand that writes grows blissfully numb upon the paper. It also means idle hours curled up in the hollow of the divan, and then the orgy of inspiration from which one emerges stupefied and aching all over, but already recompensed and laden with treasures that one unloads slowly on to the virgin page in the little round pool of light under the lamp.

To write is to pour one's innermost self passionately upon the tempting paper, at such frantic speed that sometimes one's hand struggles and rebels, overdriven by the impatient god who guides it—and to find, next day, in place of the golden bough that bloomed miraculously in that dazzling hour, a withered bramble and a stunted flower.

To write is the joy and torment of the idle. Oh to write! From time to time I feel a need, sharp as thirst in summer, to note and to describe. And then I take up my pen again and attempt the perilous and elusive task of seizing and pinning down, under its flexible double-pointed nib, the many-hued, fugitive, thrilling adjective. . . . The attack does not last long; it is but the itching of an old scar.

It takes up too much time to write. And the trouble is, I am no Balzac! The fragile story I am constructing crumbles away when the tradesman rings, or the shoemaker sends in his bill, when the solicitor, or one's counsel, telephones, or when the theatrical agent summons me to his office for "a social engagement at the house of some people of very good position but not in the habit of paying large fees."

The problem is, since I have been living alone, that I have had first to live, then to divorce, and then to go on living. To do all that demands incredible activity and persistence. And to get where? Is there, for me, no other haven than this commonplace room done up in gimcrack Louis XVI? Must I stay for ever before this impenetrable mirror where I come up against myself, face to face?

Tomorrow is Sunday: that means afternoon and evening performances at the *Empyrée-Clichy*. Two o'clock already! High time for a woman of letters who has turned out badly to go to sleep. . . .

The Traumatic Neurosis

V. During the first world war every variety of acute emotional disturbance occurring at or near the front was lumped under the rubric: *shell shock*. This group of conditions is now called traumatic neurosis.* The diagnosis has been broadened to designate a neurotic symptom that has an acute onset in a setting of a life-and-death stress. With its sudden onset and its direct relationship to external factors, the traumatic neurosis is the most dramatic of neurotic disturbances. The overpowering emotions that surround the acute trauma are preserved in the symptoms and played out over and over again. This sequence is depicted in a story by Somerset Maugham. The first excerpt contains a description of the "tics," the pathological muscular movements which are often part of the outward form of this neurosis. The second excerpt describes the traumatic events which precipitated the neurosis.

* *Some psychiatrists use this term only when there is an accompanying head injury.*

FLOTSAM AND JETSAM

W. Somerset Maugham   (1874–   )

. . . She wore a blue cotton dress, simple enough, but more suited to a young girl than to a woman of her age; her short hair was tousled, as though on getting out of bed she had scarcely troubled to pass a comb through it, and dyed a vivid yellow, but badly, and the roots showed white. Her skin was raddled and dry, and there was a great dab of rouge on each cheek-bone, put on however so clumsily that you could not for a moment take it for a natural colour, and a smear of lipstick on her mouth. But the strangest thing about her was a tic she had that made her jerk her head as though she were beckoning you to an inner room. It seemed to come at regular intervals, perhaps three times a minute, and her left hand was in almost constant movement; it was not quite a tremble, it was a rapid twirl as though she wanted to draw your attention to something behind her back. Skelton was startled by her appearance and embarrassed by her tic. . . .

. . . Living this lonely life Mrs. Grange got into the habit of talking out loud to herself. Shut up in her room she could be heard chattering away hour after hour; and now, dipping the puff in her powder and plastering her face with it, she addressed her reflection in the mirror exactly as though she were talking to another person.

"That ought to have warned me. I should have insisted on going by myself, and who knows, I might have got a job when I got to London. With all the experience I had and everything. Then I'd have written to him and said I wasn't coming back." Her thoughts turned to Skelton. "Pity I didn't tell him," she continued. "I had half a mind to. P'raps he was right, p'raps it would have eased me mind. I wonder what he'd have said." She imitated his Oxford accent. "I'm so terribly sorry, Mrs. Grange. I wish I could help you." She gave a chuckle which was almost a sob. "I'd have liked to tell him about Jack. Oh, Jack."

It was when they had been married for two years that they got a neighbour. The price of rubber at that time was so high that new estates were being put under cultivation and one of the big companies had bought a great tract of land on the opposite bank of the river. It was a rich company and everything was done on a lavish scale. The manager they had put in had a launch at his disposal so that it was no trouble for him to pop over and have a drink whenever he felt inclined. Jack Carr his name was. He was quite a different sort of chap from Norman; for one thing he was a gentleman, he'd been to a public school and a university; he was about thirty-five, tall, not beefy like Norman, but slight, he had the sort of figure that looked lovely in evening dress; and he had crisply curling hair and a laughing look in his eyes. Just her type. She took to him at once. It was a treat, having someone you could talk about London to, and the theatre. He was gay and easy. He made the sort of jokes you could understand. In a week or two she felt more at home with him than she did with her husband after two years. There had always been something about Norman that she hadn't quite been able to get to the bottom of. He was crazy about her, of course, and he'd told her a lot about himself, but she had a funny feeling that there was something he kept from her, not because he wanted to, but—well, you couldn't hardly explain it, because it was so alien, you might say, that he couldn't put it into words. Later, when she knew Jack better, she mentioned it to him, and Jack said it was because he was country-born; even though he hadn't a drop of native blood in his veins, something of the country had gone to the making of him so that he wasn't white really; he had an Eastern streak in him. However hard he tried he could never be quite English.

She chattered away aloud, in that empty house, for the two boys, the cook and the house boy, were in their own quarters, and the sound of her voice, ringing along the wooden floors, piercing the wooden walls, was like the uncanny, unhuman gibber of new wine fermenting in a vat. She spoke just as though Skelton were there, but so incoherently that if he had been, he would have had difficulty in following the story she told. It did not take her long to discover that Jack Carr wanted her. She was excited. She'd never been promiscuous, but in all those years she'd been on the stage naturally there'd been episodes. You couldn't hardly have put up with being on tour month after month if you didn't have a bit of fun sometimes. Of course now she wasn't going to give in too easily, she didn't want to make herself cheap, but what with the life she led, she'd be a fool if she missed the chance; and as far as Norman was concerned, well, what the eye didn't see the heart didn't grieve over. They understood one another all right, Jack and her; they knew it was bound to happen sooner or later, it was only a matter of waiting for the opportunity; and the opportunity came. But then something happened that they hadn't bargained for: they fell madly in love with one another. If Mrs. Grange really had been telling the story to Skelton it might have seemed as unlikely to him as it did to them. They were two very ordinary people, he a jolly, good-natured, commonplace planter, and she a small-part actress far from clever, not even very young, with nothing to recommend her but a neat figure and a prettyish face. What started as a casual affair turned without warning into a devastating passion, and neither of them was of a texture to sustain its exorbitant compulsion. They longed to be with one another; they were restless and miserable apart. She'd been finding Norman a bore for some time, but she'd put up with him because he was her husband; now he irritated her to frenzy because he stood between her and Jack. There was no question of their going off together, Jack Carr had nothing but his salary, and he couldn't throw up a job he'd been only too glad to get. It was difficult for them to meet. They had to run awful risks. Perhaps the chances they had to take, the obstacles they had to surmount, were fuel to their love; a year passed and it was as overwhelming as at the beginning; it was a year of agony and bliss, of fear and thrill. Then she discovered that she was pregnant. She had no doubt that Jack Carr was the father and she was wildly happy. It was true life was difficult, so difficult sometimes that she felt she just couldn't cope with it, but there'd be a baby, his baby, and that would make everything easy. She was going to Kuching for her confinement. It happened about then that Jack Carr had to go to Singapore on business and was to be away for several weeks; but he promised to get back before she left and he said he'd send word by a native the moment he arrived. When at last the message came she felt sick with the anguish of her joy. She had never wanted him so badly.

"I hear that Jack is back," she told her husband at dinner. "I shall go over to-morrow morning and get the things he promised to bring me."

"I wouldn't do that. He's pretty sure to drop in towards sundown and he'll bring them himself."

"I can't wait. I'm crazy to have them."

"All right. Have it your own way."

She couldn't help talking about him. For some time now they had seemed to have little to say to one another, Norman and she, but that night, in high spirits, she chattered away as she had done during the first months of their marriage. She always rose early, at six, and next morning she went down to the river and had a bathe. There was a little dent in the bank just there, with a tiny sandy beach, and it was delicious to splash about in the cool, transparent water. A kingfisher stood on the branch of a tree overhanging the pool and its reflection was brilliantly blue in the water. Lovely. She had a cup of tea and then stepped into a dug-out. A boy paddled her across the river. It took a good half-hour. As they got near she scanned the bank; Jack knew she would come at the earliest opportunity; he must be on the lookout. Ah, there he was. The delicious pain in her heart was almost unbearable. He came down to the landing-stage and helped her to get out of the boat. They walked hand in hand up the pathway and when they were out of sight of the boy who had paddled her over and of prying eyes from the house, they stopped. He put his arms round her and she yielded with ecstasy to his embrace. She clung to him. His mouth sought hers. In that kiss was all the agony of their separation and all the bliss of their reunion. The miracle of love transfused them so that they were unconscious of time and place. They were not human any more, but two spirits united by a divine fire. No thought passed through their minds. No words issued from their lips. Suddenly there was a brutal shock, like a blow, and immediately, almost simultaneously, a deafening noise. Horrified, not understanding, she clung to Jack more tightly and his grip on her was spasmodic, so that she gasped; then she felt that he was bearing her over.

"Jack."

She tried to hold him up. His weight was too great for her and as he fell to the ground she fell with him. Then she gave a great cry, for she felt a gush of heat, and his blood sputtered over her. She began to scream. A rough hand seized her and dragged her to her feet. It was Norman. She was distraught. She could not understand.

"Norman, what have you done?"

"I've killed him."

She stared at him stupidly. She pushed him aside.

"Jack. Jack."

"Shut up. I'll go and get help. It was an accident."

He walked quickly up the pathway. She fell to her knees and took Jack's head in her arms.

"Darling," she moaned. "Oh, my darling."

Norman came back with some coolies and they carried him up to the house. That night she had a miscarriage and was so ill that for days it looked as if she would die. When she recovered she had the nervous tic that she'd had ever since. She expected that Norman would send her away; but he didn't, he had to keep her to allay suspicion. There was some talk among the natives, and after a while the District Officer came up and asked a lot of questions; but the natives were frightened of Norman, and the D.O. could get nothing out of them. The Dyak boy who paddled her over had vanished. Norman said something had gone wrong with his gun and Jack was looking at it to see what was the matter and it went off. They bury people quickly in that country and by the time they might have dug him up there wouldn't have been much left to show that Norman's story wasn't true. The D.O. hadn't been satisfied.

"It all looks damned fishy to me," he said, "but in the absence of any evidence, I suppose I must accept your version."

She would have given anything to get away, but with that nervous affliction she had no ghost of a chance any longer of earning a living. She had to stay—or starve; and Norman had to keep her—or hang. Nothing had happened since then and now nothing ever would happen. The endless years one after another dragged out their weary length.

Mrs. Grange on a sudden stopped talking. Her sharp ears had caught the sound of a footstep on the path and she knew that Norman was back from his round. Her head twitching furiously, her hand agitated by that sinister, uncontrollable gesture, she looked in the untidy mess of her dressing-table for her precious lipstick. She smeared it on her lips, and then, she didn't know why, on a freakish impulse daubed it all over her nose till she looked like a red-nose comedian in a music-hall. She looked at herself in the glass and burst out laughing.

"To hell with life!" she shouted.

CHAPTER six

Neurotic Symptoms

The symptoms of neurosis are protean; they may affect thought, character, emotion, or behavior. Examples of some of the typical forms are presented in this chapter.

Anxiety Attacks

I. One of the major symptoms of emotional disorder is anxiety. It is a symptom that occurs in all human beings at some time during their lives, be they sick or not. There are many explanations of anxiety, but the exact causes and the differences in intensity from person to person have never been adequately explained. Dynamic psychiatrists believe that a major cause of anxiety is conflict, and that one major source of conflict occurs when some unacceptable impulse, idea, or wish threatens to force its way into awareness.

Whatever the causes are, typical anxiety attacks occur and can be described. The elements of such an attack are brilliantly captured by John Updike.

Pigeon Feathers

John Updike   (1932–   )

. . . He had to go to the bathroom, and took a flashlight
down through the wet grass to the outhouse. For once, his fear of spiders
there felt trivial. He set the flashlight, burning, beside him, and an insect
alighted on its lens, a tiny insect, a mosquito or flea, made so fine that the
weak light projected its X-ray onto the wall boards; the faint rim of its
wings, the blurred strokes, magnified, of its long hinged legs, the dark
cone at the heart of its anatomy. The tremor must be its heart beating.
Without warning, David was visited by an exact vision of death: a long
hole in the ground, no wider than your body, down which you are drawn
while the white faces above recede. You try to reach them but your arms
are pinned. Shovels pour dirt into your face. There you will be forever,
in an upright position (blind and silent, and in time no one will remember
you, and you will never be called. As strata of rock shift, your fingers
elongate, and your teeth are distended sideways in a great underground
grimace indistinguishable from a strip of chalk. And the earth tumbles on,
and the sun expires, and unaltering darkness reigns where once there were
stars.

Sweat broke out on his back. His mind seemed to rebound off a
solidness. Such extinction was not another threat, a graver sort of danger,
a kind of pain; it was qualitatively different. It was not even a conception
that could be voluntarily pictured; it entered him from outside. His protesting nerves swarmed on its surface like lichen on a meteor. The skin of
his chest was soaked with the effort of rejection. At the same time that the
fear was dense and internal, it was dense and all around him; a tide of clay
had swept up to the stars; space was crushed into a mass. When he stood
up, automatically hunching his shoulders to keep his head away from the
spider webs, it was with a numb sense of being cramped between two
huge volumes of rigidity. That he had even this small freedom to move
surprised him. In the narrow shelter of that rank shack, adjusting his pants,
he felt—his first spark of comfort—too small to be crushed.

But in the open, as the beam of the flashlight skidded with frightened
quickness across the remote surfaces of the barn and the grape arbor and
the giant pine that stood by the path to the woods, the terror descended.
He raced up through the clinging grass pursued, not by one of the wild
animals the woods might hold, or one of the goblins his superstitious
grandmother had communicated to his childhood, but by spectres out of

science fiction, where gigantic cinder moons fill half the turquoise sky. As David ran, a gray planet rolled inches behind his neck. If he looked back, he would be buried. And in the momentum of his terror, hideous possibilities—the dilation of the sun, the triumph of the insects, the crabs on the shore in *The Time Machine*—wheeled out of the vacuum of make-believe and added their weight to his impending oblivion. . . .

Obsessions

II. It is not uncommon for neurotics to develop a special concern about some minor danger or problem. These exaggerated concerns may become very intense and are then called obsessions. For example, it may be necessary for someone to get out of bed countless times at night to check the gas valves on the stove, or to be concerned about the slightest contact with dirt and need to wash his hands constantly. Neurotic obsessions are thought to conceal some wish, often of a destructive or sexual nature. For example, the mother who gets out of bed every ten minutes to make sure her baby is breathing may in fact be struggling with her own hostile wishes toward the infant.

a. The wish is quite obscure in many obsessions and hidden in symbolic distortion, as the following brief example from Rilke will illustrate.

THE NOTEBOOKS OF MALTE LAURIDS BRIGGE
Rainer Maria Rilke (1875–1926)

. . . At the time when she no longer wanted to see anyone and when she always, even on a journey, carried with her the small fine, silver sieve, through which she filtered everything she drank. Solid food she no longer took, save for some biscuit or bread, which, when she was alone, she broke into bits and ate crumb by crumb, as children eat crumbs. Her fear of needles already dominated her completely at that time. To others she simply said by way of excuse, "I really cannot digest anything any more, but don't let that trouble you, I feel very well in-

Reprinted from *The Notebooks of Malte Laurids Brigge* by Rainer Maria Rilke. Translated by M. D. Herter Norton. By permission of W. W. Norton & Company, Inc. Copyright 1949 by W. W. Norton & Company, Inc.

deed." But to me she would suddenly turn (for I was already a little bit grown-up) and say, with a smile that cost her a severe effort, "What a lot of needles there are, Malte, and how they lie about everywhere, and when you think how easily they fall out. . . ." She tried to say this playfully; but terror shook her at the thought of all the insecurely fastened needles that might at any instant, anywhere, fall into something. . . .

b. A second example, from Melville, is less dramatic but quite typical. Nippers, a scrivener, can never leave off trying to find the right height for his writing desk. Melville, a man of insight, hints at the reason for this obsession.

BARTLEBY THE SCRIVENER
Herman Melville (*1819–1891*)

. . . Nippers, the second on my list, was a whiskered, sallow, and, upon the whole, rather piratical-looking young man of about five and twenty. I always deemed him the victim of two evil powers— ambition and indigestion. The ambition was evinced by a certain impatience of the duties of a mere copyist—an unwarrantable usurpation of strictly professional affairs, such as the original drawing up of legal documents. The indigestion seemed betokened in an occasional nervous testiness and grinning irritability, causing the teeth to audibly grind together over mistakes committed in copying; unnecessary maledictions, hissed, rather than spoken, in the heat of business; and especially by a continual discontent with the height of the table where he worked. Though of a very ingenious mechanical turn, Nippers could never get this table to suit him. He put chips under it, blocks of various sorts, bits of pasteboard, and at last went so far as to attempt an exquisite adjustment by final pieces of folded blotting-paper. But no invention would answer. If, for the sake of easing his back, he brought the table lid at a sharp angle well up toward his chin, and wrote there like a man using the steep roof of a Dutch house for his desk—then he declared that it stopped the circulation in his arms. If now he lowered the table to his waistbands, and stooped over it in writing, then there was a sore aching in his back. In short, the truth of the matter was, Nippers knew not what he wanted. Or, if he wanted anything, it was to be rid of a scrivener's table altogether. . . .

From "Bartleby the Scrivener" by Herman Melville.

Compulsive Thoughts

III. One common neurotic symptom is the sudden
entry into awareness of a thought that the person would
ordinarily violently repudiate. Typically, these thoughts have
a sexual or aggressive component. A mother suddenly has the
thought of taking a knife and stabbing her baby. She is shocked
and horrified and instantly repudiates the idea, but the
experience leaves its mark with anxiety and discomfort.
Hawthorne shows us this symptom in the minister in his
famous novel, *The Scarlet Letter*.

THE SCARLET LETTER
Nathaniel Hawthorne (*1804–1864*)

. . . Before Mr. Dimmesdale reached home, his inner
man gave him other evidences of a revolution in the sphere of thought
and feeling. In truth, nothing short of a total change of dynasty and moral
code in that interior kingdom was adequate to account for the impulses
now communicated to the unfortunate and startled minister. At every
step he was incited to do some strange, wild, wicked thing or other, with
a sense that it would be at once involuntary and intentional; in spite of
himself, yet growing out of a profounder self than that which opposed
the impulse. For instance, he met one of his own deacons. The good old
man addressed him with the paternal affection and patriarchal privilege,
which his venerable age, his upright and holy character, and his station in
the Church entitled him to use, and, conjoined with this, the deep, almost
worshipping respect which the minister's professional and private claims
alike demanded. Never was there a more beautiful example of how the
majesty of age and wisdom may comport with the obeisance and respect
enjoined upon it, as from a lower social rank and inferior order of endowment, towards a higher. Now, during a conversation of some two or three
moments between the Reverend Mr. Dimmesdale and this excellent and
hoary-bearded deacon, it was only by the most careful self-control that
the former could refrain from uttering certain blasphemous suggestions
that rose into his mind, respecting the communion supper. He absolutely
trembled and turned pale as ashes, lest his tongue should wag itself, in
utterance of these horrible matters, and plead his own consent for so do-

From *The Scarlet Letter* by Nathaniel Hawthorne.

ing without his having fairly given it. And, even with this terror in his heart, he could hardly avoid laughing, to imagine how the sanctified old patriarchal deacon would have been petrified by his minister's impiety!

Again, another incident of the same nature. Hurrying along the street, the Reverend Mr. Dimmesdale encountered the eldest female member of his church, a most pious and exemplary old dame; poor, widowed, lonely, and with a heart as full of reminiscences about her dead husband and children and her dead friends of long ago as a burial ground is full of storied gravestones. Yet all this, which would else have been such heavy sorrow, was made almost a solemn joy to her devout old soul by religious consolations and the truths of Scripture, wherewith she had fed herself continually for more than thirty years. And, since Mr. Dimmesdale had taken her in charge, the good grandam's chief earthly comfort—which, unless it had been likewise a heavenly comfort, could have been none at all—was to meet her pastor, whether casually, or of set purpose, and be refreshed with a word of warm, fragrant, heaven-breathing Gospel truth, from his beloved lips into her dulled but rapturously attentive ear. But on this occasion, up to the moment of putting his lips to the old woman's ear, Mr. Dimmesdale, as the great enemy of souls would have it, could recall no text of Scripture, nor aught else, except a brief, pithy, and, as it then appeared to him, unanswerable argument against the immortality of the human soul. The instilment thereof into her mind would probably have caused this aged sister to drop down dead at once, as by the effect of an intensely poisonous infusion. What he really did whisper, the minister could never afterwards recollect. There was, perhaps, a fortunate disorder in his utterance, which failed to impart any distinct idea to the good widow's comprehension, or which Providence interpreted after a method of its own. Assuredly, as the minister looked back, he beheld an expression of divine gratitude and ecstasy that seemed like the shine of the celestial city on her face, so wrinkled and ashy pale.

Again, a third instance. After parting from the old church member, he met the youngest sister of them all. It was a maiden newly won—and won by the Reverend Mr. Dimmesdale's own sermon, on the Sabbath after his vigil—to barter the transitory pleasures of the world for the heavenly hope that was to assume brighter substance as life grew dark around her, and which would gild the utter gloom with final glory. She was fair and pure as a lily that had bloomed in Paradise. The minister knew well that he was himself enshrined within the stainless sanctity of her heart, which hung its snowy curtains about his image, imparting to religion the warmth of love, and to love a religious purity. Satan, that afternoon, had surely led the poor young girl away from her mother's side, and thrown her into the pathway of this sorely tempted, or—shall we not rather say?—this lost and desperate man. As she drew nigh, the archfiend whispered him to condense into small compass and drop into her tender bosom a germ of evil that would be sure to blossom darkly soon, and bear black fruit betimes. Such was his sense of power over this virgin soul, trusting him as she did, that the minister felt potent to blight all the field of innocence with but one wicked look, and develop all its opposite with but a word. So—with a mightier struggle than he had yet sustained—he held his Geneva cloak before his face, and hurried onward, making no sign of recognition, and leaving the young sister to digest his rudeness as she might. She ransacked her conscience—which was full of harmless little matters, like her pocket or her workbag—and took herself to task, poor thing! for a thousand imaginary faults; and went about her household duties with swollen eyelids the next morning.

Before the minister had time to celebrate his victory over this last temptation, he was conscious of another impulse, more ludicrous and almost as horrible. It was—we blush to tell it—it was to stop short in the road, and teach some very wicked words to a knot of little Puritan children who were playing there, and had but just begun to talk. Denying himself this freak as unworthy of his cloth, he met a drunken seaman, one of the ship's crew from the Spanish Main. And, here, since he had so valiantly forborne all other wickedness, poor Mr. Dimmesdale longed, at least, to shake hands with the tarry blackguard, and recreate himself with a few improper jests, such as dissolute sailors so abound with, and a volley of good, round, solid, satisfactory, and heaven-defying oaths! It was not so much a better principle, as partly his natural good taste, and still more his buckramed habit of clerical decorum, that carried him safely through the latter crisis.

"What is it that haunts and tempts me thus?" cried the minister to himself, at length, pausing in the street, and striking his hand against his forehead. "Am I mad? or am I given over utterly to the fiend? Did I make a contract with him in the forest, and sign it with my blood? And does he now summon me to its fulfilment, by suggesting the performance of every wickedness which his most foul imagination can conceive?" . . .

Depression

IV. The symptoms of neurotic depression often focus on a preoccupation with death. Dread is more central than fear. Loneliness and emptiness pervade the feelings of the person. Emily Dickinson illustrates these feelings in her two poems.

Two Poems

Emily Dickinson (*1830–1886*)

I felt a funeral in my brain,
    And mourners, to and fro,
Kept treading, treading, till it seemed
    That sense was breaking through.

And when they all were seated,
    A service like a drum
Kept beating, beating, till I thought
    My mind was going numb.

And then I heard them lift a box,
    And creak across my soul
With those same boots of lead, again.
    Then space began to toll

As all the heavens were a bell.
    And Being but an ear,
And I and silence some strange race,
    Wrecked, solitary, here.

Bereaved of all, I went abroad,
    No less bereaved to be
Upon a new peninsula,—
    The grave preceded me,

Obtained my lodgings ere myself,
    And when I sought my bed,
The grave it was, reposed upon
    The pillow for my head.

I waked to find it first awake,
    I rose,—it followed me;
I tried to drop it in the crowd,
    To lose it in the sea,

In cups of artificial drowse
    To sleep its shape away,—
The grave was finished, but the spade
    Remained in memory.

Reaction Formation

V. One of the more common neurotic defenses against
an unacceptable impulse is the development of a completely
antithetical type of behavior. For example, a person with
intense sexual curiosity becomes prudish and modest to an
extreme. The outward behavior is a constant denial and
repudiation of the unconscious motive. This defense, called
reaction formation, is particularly common in the
obsessive-compulsive neurosis and the compulsive character.
When the defense is extensively developed, it has a profound
effect on character, and the whole outward personality may
seem to be related to it.

Thomas Mann has dramatically depicted this in his story of
"Tobias Mindernickel." Tobias is one of those incredibly meek
persons who are cruelly scapegoated in life. He seems willing
to accept any indignity without anger. Painful humility seems
to be the central substance of his personality. The secret
impulses that lie behind this neurotic character trait are
terrifyingly revealed in Mann's story.

Tobias Mindernickel

Thomas Mann (1875–1955)

One of the streets running steeply up from the docks to
the middle town was named Grey's Road. At about the middle of it, on the
right, stood Number 47, a narrow, dingy-looking building no different
from its neighbours. On the ground floor was a chandler's shop where you
could buy overshoes and castor oil. Crossing the entry along a courtyard
full of cats and mounting the mean and shabby, musty-smelling stair, you
arrived at the upper storeys. In the first, on the left, lived a cabinet-maker;
on the right a midwife. In the second, on the left a cobbler, on the right a
lady who began to sing loudly whenever she heard steps on the stair. In the
third on the left, nobody; but on the right a man named Mindernickel—
and Tobias to boot. There was a story about this man; I tell it, because it is
both puzzling and sinister, to an extraordinary degree.

Mindernickel's exterior was odd, striking, and provoking to laughter. When he took a walk, his meagre form moving up the street supported by a cane, he would be dressed in black from head to heels. He wore a shabby old-fashioned top hat with a curved brim, a frock-coat shining with age, and equally shabby trousers, fringed round the bottoms and so short that you could see the elastic sides to his boots. True, these garments were all most carefully brushed. His scrawny neck seemed longer because it rose out of a low turn-down collar. His hair had gone grey and he wore it brushed down smooth on the temples. His wide hatbrim shaded a smooth-shaven sallow face with sunken cheeks, red-rimmed eyes which were usually directed at the floor, and two deep, fretful furrows running from the nose to the drooping corners of the mouth.

Mindernickel seldom left his house—and this for a very good reason. For whenever he appeared in the street a mob of children would collect and sally behind him, laughing, mocking, singing—"Ho, ho, Tobias!" they would cry, tugging at his coat-tails, while people came to their doors to laugh. He made no defence; glancing timidly round, with shoulders drawn up and head stuck out, he continued on his way, like a man hurrying through a driving rain without an umbrella. Even while they were laughing in his face he would bow politely and humbly to people as he passed. Further on, when the children had stopped behind and he was not known, and scarcely noted, his manner did not change. He still hurried on, still stooped, as though a thousand mocking eyes were on him. If it chanced that he lifted his timid, irresolute gaze from the ground, you would see that, strangely enough, he was not able to fix it steadily upon anyone or anything. It may sound strange, but there seemed to be missing in him the natural superiority with which the normal, perceptive individual looks out upon the phenomenal world. He seemed to measure himself against each phenomenon, and find himself wanting; his gaze shifted and fell, it grovelled before men and things.

What was the matter with this man, who was always alone and unhappy even beyond the common lot? His clothing belonged to the middle class; a certain slow gesture he had, of his hand across his chin, betrayed that he was not of the common people among whom he lived. How had fate been playing with him? God only knows. His face looked as though life had hit him between the eyes, with a scornful laugh. On the other hand, perhaps it was a question of no cruel blow but simply that he was not up to it. The painful shrinking and humility expressed in his whole figure did indeed suggest that nature had denied him the measure of strength, equilibrium, and backbone which a man requires if he is to live with his head erect.

When he had taken a turn up into the town and come back to Grey's Road, where the children welcomed him with lusty bawlings, he went into the house and up the stuffy stair into his own bare room. It had but one piece of furniture worthy the name, a solid Empire chest of drawers with brass handles, a thing of dignity and beauty. The view from the window was hopelessly cut off by the heavy side wall of the next house; a flower-pot full of earth stood on the ledge, but there was nothing growing in it. Tobias Mindernickel went up to it sometimes and smelled at the earth. Next to this room was a dark little bedchamber. Tobias on coming in would lay hat and stick on the table, sit down on the dusty green-covered sofa, prop his chin with his hand, and stare at the floor with his eyebrows raised. He seemed to have nothing else to do.

As for Tobias Mindernickel's character, it is hard to judge of that. Some favourable light seems to be cast by the following episode. One day this strange man left his house and was pounced upon by a troop of children who followed him with laughter and jeers. One of them, a lad of ten years, tripped over another child's foot and fell so heavily to the pavement that blood burst from his nose and ran from his forehead. He lay there and wept. Tobias turned at once, went up to the lad, and began to console him in a mild and quavering voice. "You poor child," said he, "have you hurt yourself? You are bleeding—look how the blood is running down from his forehead. Yes, yes, you do look miserable, you weep because it hurts you so. I pity you. Of course, you did it yourself, but I will tie my handkerchief round your head. There, there! Now pull yourself together and get up." And actually with the words he bound his own handkerchief round the bruise and helped the lad to his feet. Then he went away. But he looked a different man. He held himself erect and stepped out firmly, drawing longer breaths under his narrow coat. His eyes looked larger and brighter, he looked squarely at people and things, while an expression of joy so strong as to be almost painful tightened the corners of his mouth.

After this for a while there was less tendency to jeer at him among the denizens of Grey's Road. But they forgot his astonishing behaviour with the lapse of time, and once more the cruel cries resounded from dozens of lusty throats behind the bent and infirm man: "Ho, ho, Tobias!"

One sunny morning at eleven o'clock Mindernickel left the house and betook himself through the town to the Lerchenberg, a long ridge which constitutes the afternoon walk of good society. Today the spring weather was so fine that even in the forenoon there were some carriages as well as pedestrians moving about. On the main road, under a tree, stood a man with a young hound on a leash, exhibiting it for sale. It was a muscular little animal about four months old, with black ears and black rings round its eyes.

Tobias at a distance of ten paces noticed this; he stood still, rubbed his chin with his hand, and considered the man, and the hound alertly wagging its tail. He went forward, circling three times round the tree, with the crook of his stick pressed against his lips. Then he stepped up to the man, and keeping his eye fixed on the dog, he said in a low, hurried tone: "What are you asking for the dog?"

"Ten marks," answered the man.

Tobias kept still a moment, then he said with some hesitation: "Ten marks?"

"Yes," said the man.

Tobias drew a black leather purse from his pocket, took out a note for five marks, one three-mark and one two-mark piece, and quickly handed them to the man. Then he seized the leash, and two or three people who had been watching the bargain laughed to see him as he gave a quick, frightened look about him and, with his shoulders stooped, dragged away the whimpering and protesting beast. It struggled the whole of the way, bracing its forefeet and looking up pathetically in its new master's face. But Tobias pulled, in silence, with energy and succeeded in getting through the town.

An outcry arose among the urchins of Grey's Road when Tobias appeared with the dog. He lifted it in his arms, while they danced round, pulling at his coat and jeering; carried it up the stair and bore it into his own room, where he set it on the floor, still whimpering. Stooping over and patting it with kindly condescension he told it:

"There, there, little man, you need not be afraid of me; that is quite unnecessary."

He took a plate of cooked meat and potatoes out of a drawer and tossed the dog a part of it, whereat it ceased to whine and ate the food with loud relish, wagging its tail.

"And I will call you Esau," said Tobias. "Do you understand? That will be easy for you to remember." Pointing to the floor in front of him he said, in a tone of command:

"Esau!"

And the dog, probably in the hope of getting more to eat, did come up to him. Tobias clapped him gently on the flank and said:

"That's right, good doggy, good doggy!"

He stepped back a few paces, pointed to the floor again, and commanded:

"Esau!"

And the dog sprang to him quite blithely, wagging its tail, and licked its master's boots.

Tobias repeated the performance with unflagging zest, some twelve or fourteen times. Then the dog got tired, it wanted to rest and digest its meal. It lay down, in the sagacious and charming attitude of a hunting dog, with both long, slender forelegs stretched before it, close together.

"Once more," said Tobias. "Esau!"

But Esau turned his head aside and stopped where he was.

"Esau!" Tobias's voice was raised, his tone more dictatorial still. "You've got to come, even if you are tired."

But Esau laid his head on his paws and came not at all.

"Listen to me," said Tobias, and his voice was now low and threatening; "you'd best obey or you will find out what I do when I am angry."

But the dog hardly moved his tail.

Then Mindernickel was seized by a mad and extravagant fit of anger. He clutched his black stick, lifted up Esau by the nape of the neck, and in a frenzy of rage he beat the yelping animal, repeating over and over in a horrible, hissing voice:

"What, you do not obey me? You dare to disobey me?"

At last he flung the stick from him, set down the crying animal, and with his hands upon his back began to pace the room, his breast heaving, and flinging upon Esau an occasional proud and angry look. When this had gone on for some time, he stopped in front of the dog as it lay on its back, moving its fore-paws imploringly. He crossed his arms on his chest and spoke with a frightful hardness and coldness of look and tone—like Napoleon, when he stood before a company that had lost its standard in battle:

"May I ask you what you think of your conduct?"

And the dog, delighted at this condescension, crawled closer, nestled against its master's leg, and looked up at him brighteyed.

For a while Tobias gazed at the humble creature with silent contempt. Then as the touching warmth of Esau's body communicated itself to his leg he lifted Esau up.

"Well, I will have pity on you," he said. But when the good beast essayed to lick his face his voice suddenly broke with melancholy emotion. He pressed the dog passionately to his breast, his eyes filling with tears, unable to go on. Chokingly he said:

"You see, you are my only . . . my only. . . ." He put Esau to bed, with great care, on the sofa, supported his own chin with his hand, and gazed at him with mild eyes, speechlessly.

Tobias Mindernickel left his room now even less often than before; he had no wish to show himself with Esau in public. He gave his whole time to the dog, from morning to night; feeding him, washing his eyes, teaching him commands, scolding him, and talking to him as though he were human. Esau, alas, did not always behave to his master's satisfaction. When he lay beside Tobias on the sofa, dull with lack of air and exercise, and gazed at him with soft, melancholy eyes, Tobias was pleased. He sat content and quiet, tenderly stroking Esau's back as he said:

"Poor fellow, how sadly you look at me! Yes, yes, life is sad, that you will learn before you are much older."

But sometimes Esau was wild, beside himself with the urge to exercise his hunting instincts; he would dash about the room, worry a slipper, leap on the chairs, or roll over and over with sheer excess of spirits. Then Tobias followed his motions from afar with a helpless, disapproving, wandering air and a hateful, peevish smile. At last he would brusquely call Esau to him and say:

"That's enough now, stop dashing about like that—there is no reason for such high spirits."

Once it even happened that Esau got out of the room and bounced down the stairs to the street, where he at once began to chase a cat, to eat dung in the road, and jump up at the children frantic with joy. But when the distressed Tobias appeared with his wry face, half the street roared with laughter to see him, and it was painful to behold the dog bounding away in the other direction from his master. That day Tobias in his anger beat him for a long time.

One day, when he had had the dog for some weeks, Tobias took a loaf of bread out of the chest of drawers and began stooping over to cut off little pieces with his big bone-handled knife and let them drop on the floor for Esau to eat. The dog was frantic with hunger and playfulness; it jumped up at the bread, and the long-handled knife in the clumsy hands of Tobias ran into its right shoulder-blade. It fell bleeding to the ground.

In great alarm Tobias flung bread and knife aside and bent over the injured animal. Then the expression of his face changed, actually a gleam of relief and happiness passed over it. With the greatest care he lifted the wounded animal to the sofa—and then with what inexhaustible care and devotion he began to tend the invalid. He did not stir all day from its side, he took it to sleep on his own bed, he washed and bandaged, stroked and caressed and consoled it with unwearying solicitude.

"Does it hurt so much?" he asked. "Yes, you are suffering a good deal, my poor friend. But we must be quiet, we must try to bear it." And the look on his face was one of gentle and melancholy happiness.

But as Esau got better and the wound healed, so the spirits of Tobias sank again. He paid no more attention to the wound, confining his sympathy to words and caresses. But it had gone on well, Esau's constitution was sound; he began to move about once more. One day after he had finished off a whole plate of milk and white bread he seemed quite right again; jumped down from the sofa to rush about the room, barking joyously, with all his former lack of restraint. He tugged at the bed-covers, chased a potato round the room, and rolled over and over in his excitement.

Tobias stood by the flower-pot in the window. His arms stuck out long and lean from the ragged sleeves and he mechanically twisted the hair that hung down from his temples. His figure stood out black and uncanny against the grey wall of the next building. His face was pale and drawn with suffering and he followed Esau's pranks unmoving, with a sidelong, jealous, wicked look. But suddenly he pulled himself together, approached the dog, and made it stop jumping about; he took it slowly in his arms.

"Now, poor creature," he began, in a lachrymose tone—but Esau was not minded to be pitied, his spirits were too high. He gave a brisk snap at the hand which would have stroked him; he escaped from the arms to the floor, where he jumped mockingly aside and ran off, with a joyous bark.

That which now happened was so shocking, so inconceivable, that I simply cannot tell it in any detail. Tobias Mindernickel stood leaning a little forward, his arms hanging down; his lips were compressed, the balls of his eyes vibrated uncannily in their sockets. Suddenly with a sort of frantic leap, he seized the animal, a large bright object gleamed in his hand—and then he flung Esau to the ground with a cut which ran from the right shoulder deep into the chest. The dog made no sound, he simply fell on his side, bleeding and quivering.

The next minute he was on the sofa with Tobias kneeling before him, pressing a cloth on the wound and stammering:

"My poor brute, my poor dog! How sad everything is! How sad it is for both of us! You suffer—yes, yes, I know. You lie there so pathetic—but I am with you, I will console you—here is my best handkerchief—"

But Esau lay there and rattled in his throat. His clouded, questioning eyes were directed upon his master, with a look of complaining, innocence, and incomprehension—and then he stretched out his legs a little and died.

But Tobias stood there motionless, as he was. He had laid his face against Esau's body and he wept bitter tears.

Repression

VI. In the course of emotional maturation, many psychological devices are developed to regulate and cope with painful feelings. One of the most common mechanisms is simply to wall off intense feelings so that they cannot enter awareness. Repression is the name given to this walling-off process. Stronger personalities can cope with feelings, and have less need for repression. All human beings, however, are in childhood subjected to intense emotional surges, and mastery over this challenge universally involves some repression of emotions and the memories connected with them. This repression of childhood memory and feeling is not simple forgetting, because under certain circumstances in psychotherapy they can be recalled. Psychoanalysts refer to this aspect of childhood repression as infantile amnesia, and George Eliot, one of the first "psychological novelists," has described this with unusual skill and considerable feminine intuition.

THE MILL ON THE FLOSS

George Eliot   (1819–1880)

. . . Tom followed Maggie upstairs into her mother's room, and saw her go at once to a drawer from which she took out a large pair of scissors.

"What are they for, Maggie?" said Tom, feeling his curiosity awakened.

Maggie answered by seizing her front locks and cutting them straight across the middle of her forehead.

"O, my buttons, Maggie, you'll catch it!" exclaimed Tom, "you'd better not cut any more off."

Snip! went the great scissors again while Tom was speaking, and he couldn't help feeling it was rather good fun; Maggie would look so queer.

"Here, Tom, cut it behind for me," said Maggie, excited by her own daring, and anxious to finish the deed.

"You'll catch it, you know," said Tom, nodding his head in an admonitory manner, and hesitating a little as he took the scissors.

"Never mind—make haste!" said Maggie, giving a little stamp with her foot. Her cheeks were quite flushed.

The black locks were so thick—nothing could be more tempting to a lad who had already tasted the forbidden pleasure of cutting the pony's mane. I speak to those who know the satisfaction of making a pair of shears meet through a duly resisting mass of hair. One delicious grinding snip, and then another and another, and the hinderlocks fell heavily on the floor, and Maggie stood cropped in a jagged, uneven manner, but with a sense of clearness and freedom, as if she had emerged from a wood into the open plain.

"O, Maggie," said Tom, jumping round her, and slapping his knees as he laughed, "O, my buttons, what a queer thing you look! Look at yourself in the glass—you look like the idiot we throw out nut-shells to at school."

Maggie felt an unexpected pang. She had thought beforehand chiefly

From *The Mill on the Floss* by George Eliot.

of her own deliverance from her teasing hair and teasing remarks about it, and something also of the triumph she should have over her mother and her aunts by this very decided course of action: she didn't want her hair to look pretty—that was out of the question—she only wanted people to think her a clever little girl, and not to find fault with her. But now, when Tom began to laugh at her and say she was like the idiot, the affair had quite a new aspect. She looked in the glass, and still Tom laughed and clapped his hands, and Maggie's flushed cheeks began to pale, and her lips to tremble a little.

"O Maggie, you'll have to go down to dinner directly," said Tom. "O my!"

"Don't laugh at me, Tom," said Maggie, in a passionate tone, with an outburst of angry tears, stamping, and giving him a push.

"Now, then, spitfire!" said Tom. "What did you cut it off for, then? I shall go down: I can smell the dinner going in."

He hurried downstairs and left poor Maggie to that bitter sense of the irrevocable which was almost an everyday experience of her small soul. She could see clearly enough, now the thing was done, that it was very foolish, and that she should have to hear and think more about her hair than ever, for Maggie rushed to her deeds with passionate impulse, and then saw not only their consequences but what would have happened if they had not been done, with all the detail and exaggerated circumstance of an active imagination. Tom never did the same sort of foolish things as Maggie, having a wonderful instinctive discernment of what would turn to his advantage or disadvantage, and so it happened, that though he was much more wilful and inflexible than Maggie, his mother hardly ever called him naughty. But if Tom did make a mistake of that sort, he espoused it, and stood by it: he "didn't mind." If he broke the lash of his father's gig-whip by lashing the gate, he couldn't help it—the whip shouldn't have got caught in the hinge. If Tom Tulliver whipped a gate, he was convinced, not that the whipping of gates by all boys was a justifiable act, but that he, Tom Tulliver, was justifiable in whipping that particular gate, and he wasn't going to be sorry. But Maggie, as she stood crying before the glass, felt it impossible that she should go down to dinner and endure the severe eyes and severe words of her aunts, while Tom, and Lucy, and Martha, who waited at table, and perhaps her father and her uncles, would laugh at her, for if Tom had laughed at her, of course everyone else would, and if she had only let her hair alone, she could have sat with Tom and Lucy, and had the apricot pudding and the custard! What could she do but sob? She sat as helpless and despairing among her black locks as Ajax among the slaughtered sheep. Very trivial, perhaps, this anguish seems to weather-worn mortals who have to think of Christmas bills, dead loves, and broken friendships, but it was not less bitter to Maggie—perhaps it was even more bitter—than what we are fond of calling antithetically the real troubles of mature life. "Ah, my child, you will have real troubles to fret about by-and-by," is the consolation we have almost all of us administered to us in our childhood, and have repeated to other children since we have been grown up. We have all of us sobbed so piteously, standing with tiny bare legs above our little socks, when we lost sight of our mother or nurse in some strange place, but we can no longer recall the poignancy of that moment and weep over it, as we do over the remembered sufferings of five or ten years ago. Every one of those keen moments has left its trace, and lives in us still, but such traces have blent themselves irrecoverably with the firmer texture of our youth and manhood, and so it comes that we can look on at the troubles of our children with a smiling disbelief in the reality of their pain. Is there any-one who can recover the experience of his childhood, not merely with a memory of what he did and what happened to him, of what he liked and disliked when he was in frock and trousers, but with an intimate penetra-tion, a revived consciousness of what he felt then—when it was so long from one Midsummer to another? What he felt when his schoolfellows shut him out of their game because he would pitch the ball wrong out of mere wilfulness; or on a rainy day in the holidays, when he didn't know how to amuse himself, and fell from idleness into mischief, from mischief into defiance, and from defiance into sulkiness; or when his mother ab-solutely refused to let him have a tailed coat that "half," although every other boy of his age had gone into tails already? Surely if we could recall that early bitterness, and the dim guesses, the strangely perspectiveless conception of that life that gave the bitterness its intensity, we should not pooh-pooh the griefs of our children. . . .

Hypomania

VII. Mania was exemplified in the story of *Foma Gordayev*, by Gorky. The exaggerated activity illustrated there is thought to be superimposed on a denial of the underlying emotional reality; namely, depression and a sense of loss. Hypomania is a more moderate instance of the same form of pathology, and is usually, therefore, considered a neurotic phenomenon. At the time of a loss, rather than a normal grief reaction ensuing, there is an effort to avoid the grief that is perhaps too painful. The hypomanic response is one of exaggerated activity and a sense of good cheer, which to the onlooker seems thin and unreal.

A touching instance of such behavior is described by Pirandello, who captures the effort of a grieving widower to cope with his loss and his encroaching sense of the emptiness of life. His effort to regain a youthful sense of enjoyment is fragile and results in an encounter that plunges him back into the depression he had sought to escape.

THE SOFT TOUCH OF GRASS
Luigi Pirandello   (1867–1936)

They went into the next room, where he was sleeping in a big chair, to ask if he wanted to look at her for the last time before the lid was put on the coffin.

"It's dark. What time is it?" he asked.

It was nine-thirty in the morning, but the day was overcast and the light dim. The funeral had been set for ten o'clock.

Signor Pardi stared up at them with dull eyes. It hardly seemed possible that he could have slept so long and well all night. He was still numb with sleep and the sorrow of these last days. He would have liked to cover his face with his hands to shut out the faces of his neighbors grouped about his chair in the thin light; but sleep had weighted his body like lead, and although there was a tingling in his toes urging him to rise, it quickly went away. Should he still give way to his grief? He happened to say aloud, "Always . . ." but he said it like someone settling himself under the covers to go back to sleep. They all looked at him questioningly. Always what?

Always dark, even in the daytime, he had wanted to say, but it made no sense. The day after her death, the day of her funeral, he would always remember this wan light and his deep sleep, too, with her lying dead in the next room. Perhaps the windows. . . .

"The windows?"

Yes, they were still closed. They had not been opened during the night, and the warm glow of those big dripping candles lingered. The bed had been taken away, and she was there in her padded casket, rigid and ashen against the creamy satin.

No. Enough. He had seen her.

He closed his eyes, for they burned from all the crying he had done these past few days. Enough. He had slept, and everything had been washed away with that sleep. Now he was relaxed, with a sense of sorrowful emptiness. Let the casket be closed and carried away with all it held of his past life.

But since she was still there. . . .

He jumped to his feet and tottered. They caught him, and with eyes still closed he allowed himself to be led to the open casket. When he opened his eyes and saw her, he called her by name, her name that lived for him alone, the name in which he saw her and knew her in all the fullness of the life they had shared together. He glared resentfully at the others daring to stare at her lying still in death. What did they know about her? They could not even imagine what it meant to him to be deprived of her. He felt like screaming, and it must have been apparent, for his son hurried over to take him away. He was quick to see the meaning of this and felt a chill as though he were stripped bare. For shame—those foolish ideas up to the very last, even after his night-long sleep. Now they must hurry so as not to keep the friends waiting who had come to follow the coffin to the church.

"Come on, Papa. Be reasonable."

With angry, piteous eyes, the bereaved man turned back to his big chair.

Reasonable, yes; it was useless to cry out the anguish that welled within him and that could never be expressed by words or deeds. For a husband who is left a widower at a certain age, a man still yearning for his wife, can the loss be the same as that of a son for whom—at a certain point —it is almost timely to be left an orphan? Timely, since he was on the point of getting married and would, as soon as the three months' mourning were passed, now that he had the added excuse that it was better for both of them to have a woman to look after the house.

"Pardi! Pardi!" they shouted from the entrance hall.

His chill became more intense when he understood clearly for the first time that they were not calling him but his son. From now on their surname would belong more to his son than to him. And he, like a fool, had gone in there to cry out the living name of his mate, like a profanation. For shame! Yes, useless, foolish ideas, he now realized, after that long sleep which had washed him clean of everything.

Now the one vital thing to keep him going was his curiosity as to how their new home would be arranged. Where, for example, were they going to have him sleep? The big double bed had been removed. Would he have a small bed? he wondered. Yes, probably his son's single bed. Now he would have the small bed. And his son would soon be lying in a big bed, his wife beside him within arm's reach. He, alone, in his little bed, would stretch out his arms into thin air.

He felt torpid, perplexed, with a sensation of emptiness inside and all around him. His body was numb from sitting so long. If he tried now to get up, he felt sure that he would rise light as a feather in all that emptiness, now that his life was reduced to nothing. There was hardly any difference between himself and the big chair. Yet that chair appeared secure on its four legs, whereas he no longer knew where his feet and legs belonged nor what to do with his hands. What did he care about his life? He did not care particularly about the lives of others, either. Yet, as he was still alive, he must go on. Begin again—some sort of life which he could not yet conceive and which he certainly would never have contemplated if things had not changed in his own world. Now, deposed like this all of a sudden, not old and yet no longer young. . . .

He smiled and shrugged his shoulders. For his son, all at once, he had become a child. But after all, as everyone knows, fathers are children to their grown sons who are full of worldly ambition and have successfully outdistanced them in positions of importance. They keep their fathers in idleness to repay all they have received when they themselves were small, and their fathers in turn become young again.

The single bed. . . .

But they did not even give him the little room where his son had slept. Instead, they said, he would feel more independent in another, almost hidden on the courtyard; he would feel free there to do as he liked. They refurnished it with all the best pieces, so it would not occur to anyone that it had once been a servant's room. After the marriage, all the front rooms were pretentiously decorated and newly furnished, even to the luxury of carpets. Not a trace remained of the way the old house had looked. Even with his own furniture relegated to that little dark room, out of the mainstream of the young people's existence, he did not feel at home. Yet, oddly enough, he did not resent the disregard he seemed to have reaped along with the old furniture, because he admired the new rooms and was satisfied with his son's success.

But there was another deeper reason, not too clear as yet, a promise of another life, all shining and colorful, which was erasing the memory of the old one. He even drew a secret hope from it that a new life might begin for him, too. Unconsciously, he sensed the luminous opening of a door at his back whence he might escape at the right moment, easy enough now that no one bothered about him, leaving him as if on holiday in the sanctuary of his little room "to do as he pleased." He felt lighter than air. His eyes had a gleam in them that colored everything, leading him from marvel to marvel, as though he really were a child again. He had the eyes of a child—lively and open wide on a world which was still new.

He took the habit of going out early in the morning to begin his holiday which was to last as long as his life lasted. Relieved of all responsibilities, he agreed to pay his son so much every month out of his pension for his maintenance. It was very little. Though he needed nothing, his son thought he should keep some money for himself to satisfy any need he might have. But need for what? He was satisfied now just to look on at life.

Having shaken off the weight of experience, he no longer knew how to get along with oldsters. He avoided them. And the younger people considered him too old, so he went to the park where the children played.

That was how he started his new life—in the meadow among the children in the grass. What an exhilarating scent the grass had, and so fresh where it grew thick and high. The children played hide-and-seek there. The constant trickle of some hidden stream outpurled the rustle of the leaves. Forgetting their game, the children pulled off their shoes and stockings. What a delicious feeling to sink into all that freshness of soft new grass with bare feet!

He took off one shoe and was stealthily removing the other when a young girl appeared before him, her face flaming. "You pig!" she cried, her eyes flashing.

Her dress was caught up in front on a bush, and she quickly pulled it down over her legs, because he was looking up at her from where he sat on the ground.

He was stunned. What had she imagined? Already she had disappeared. He had wanted to enjoy the children's innocent fun. Bending down, he put his two hands over his hard, bare feet. What had she seen wrong? Was he too old to share a child's delight in going barefoot in the grass? Must one immediately think evil because he was old? Ah, he knew that he could change in a flash from being a child to becoming a man again, if he must. He was still a man, after all, but he didn't want to think about it. He refused to think about it. It was really as a child that he had taken off his shoes. How wrong it was of that wretched girl to insult him like that! He threw himself face down on the grass. All his grief, his loss, his daily loneliness had brought about this gesture, interpreted now in the light of vulgar malice. His gorge rose in disgust and bitterness. Stupid girl! If he had wanted that—even his son admitted he might have "some desires"—he had plenty of money in his pocket for such needs.

Indignant, he pulled himself upright. Shamefacedly, with trembling hands, he put on his shoes again. All the blood had gone to his head, and the pulse now beat hot behind his eyes. Yes, he knew where to go for that. He knew.

Calmer now, he got up and went back to the house. In the welter of furniture which seemed to have been placed there on purpose to drive him mad, he threw himself on the bed and turned his face to the wall.

Displacement

VIII. A typical neurotic device is unconsciously to direct emotion from a significant figure onto a person who has neither inspired nor caused the feeling. Displacement is ubiquitous in human beings and can be seen in normal and psychotic individuals. James Joyce's example is unforgettable in its pathos.

COUNTERPARTS

James Joyce   (1882–1941)

. . . A very sullen-faced man stood at the corner of O'Connell Bridge waiting for the little Sandymount tram to take him home. He was full of smouldering anger and revengefulness. He felt humiliated and discontented; he did not even feel drunk; and he had only twopence in his pocket. He cursed everything. He had done for himself in the office, pawned his watch, spent all his money; and he had not even got drunk. He began to feel thirsty again and he longed to be back again in the hot reeking public-house. He had lost his reputation as a strong man, having been defeated twice by a mere boy. His heart swelled with fury and, when he thought of the woman in the big hat who had brushed against him and said *Pardon!* his fury nearly choked him.

His tram let him down at Shelbourne Road and he steered his great body along in the shadow of the wall of the barracks. He loathed returning to his home. When he went in by the side-door he found the kitchen empty and the kitchen fire nearly out. He bawled upstairs:

"Ada! Ada!"

His wife was a little sharp-faced woman who bullied her husband when he was sober and was bullied by him when he was drunk. They had five children. A little boy came running down the stairs.

"Who is that?" said the man, peering through the darkness.

"Me, pa."

"Who are you? Charlie?"

"No, pa. Tom."

"Where's your mother?"

"She's out at the chapel."

"That's right. . . . Did she think of leaving any dinner for me?"

"Yes, pa. I——"

"Light the lamp. What do you mean by having the place in darkness? Are the other children in bed?"

The man sat down heavily on one of the chairs while the little boy lit the lamp. He began to mimic his son's flat accent, saying half to himself: "*At the chapel. At the chapel, if you please!*" When the lamp was lit he banged his fist on the table and shouted:

"What's for my dinner?"

"I'm going . . . to cook it, pa," said the little boy.

The man jumped up furiously and pointed to the fire.

"On that fire! You let the fire out! By God, I'll teach you to do that again!"

He took a step to the door and seized the walking-stick which was standing behind it.

"I'll teach you to let the fire out!" he said, rolling up his sleeve in order to give his arm free play.

The little boy cried "*O, pa!*" and ran whimpering round the table, but the man followed him and caught him by the coat. The little boy looked about him wildly but, seeing no way of escape, fell upon his knees.

"Now, you'll let the fire out the next time!" said the man, striking at him vigorously with the stick. "Take that, you little whelp!"

The boy uttered a squeal of pain as the stick cut his thigh. He clasped his hands together in the air and his voice shook with fright.

"O, pa!" he cried. "Don't beat me, pa! And I'll . . . I'll say a *Hail Mary* for you. . . . I'll say a *Hail Mary* for you, pa, if you don't beat me. . . . I'll say a *Hail Mary*. . . ."

Depersonalization

IX. During the past twenty years the symptom of depersonalization has received increasing attention in the literature of abnormal personality. Depersonalization is found in all personality disturbances; in its most extreme form it occurs in schizophrenia, and in a less intense manner is found in neurotics and even normal individuals. Depersonalization is ordinarily a frightening state of mind in which an individual suddenly loses track of who he is. His continuity as an individual identifiable to himself is disrupted. His relatedness to the reality around him loses perspective, and the world recedes from him. As one might expect, depersonalization occurs frequently when there are disruptions of the continuity of self; for example, in falling asleep or awakening.

a. Proust describes brilliantly the phenomenon of depersonalization as it may occur on awakening. Such sensations may occur throughout the day in acute psychoses.

SWANN'S WAY

Marcel Proust   (1871–1922)

. . . I would fall asleep, and often I would be awake again for short snatches only, just long enough to hear the regular creaking of the wainscot or to open my eyes to settle the shifting kaleidoscope of the darkness, to savor, in an instantaneous flash of perception, the sleep which lay heavy upon the furniture, the room, the whole surroundings of which I formed but an insignificant part and whose unconsciousness I should very soon return to share. Or, perhaps, while I was asleep I have returned without the least effort to an earlier stage in my life, now forever outgrown, and had come under the thrall of one of my childish terrors, such as that old terror of my great-uncle's pulling my curls, which was effectually dispelled on the day—the dawn of a new era to me—on which they were finally cropped from my head. I had forgotten that event during my sleep; I remembered it again immediately I had succeeded in making myself wake up to escape my great-uncle's fingers; still, as a measure of precaution, I would bury the whole of my head in the pillow before returning to the world of dreams.

Sometimes, too, just as Eve was created from a rib of Adam, so a woman would come into existence while I was sleeping, conceived from some strain in the position of my limbs. Formed by the appetite that I was on the point of gratifying, she it was, I imagined, who offered me that gratification. My body, conscious that its own warmth was permeating hers, would strive to become one with her, and I would awake. The rest of humanity seemed very remote in comparison with this woman whose company I had left but a moment ago: my cheek was still warm with her kiss, my body bent beneath the weight of hers. If, as would sometimes happen, she had the appearance of some woman whom I had known in waking hours, I would abandon myself altogether to the sole quest of her, like people who set out on a journey to see with their own eyes some city that they have always longed to visit, and imagine that they can taste in reality what has charmed their fancy. And then, gradually, the memory of her would dissolve and vanish until I had forgotten the maiden of my dream.

When a man is asleep, he has in a circle round him the chain of the hours, the sequence of the years, the order of the heavenly host. Instinctively, when he awakes, he looks to these and in an instant reads off his own position on the earth's surface and the amount of time that has elapsed during his slumbers; but this ordered procession is apt to grow confused and to break its ranks. Suppose that toward morning, after a night of insomnia, sleep descends upon him while he is reading, in quite a different position from that in which he normally goes to sleep; he has only to lift his arm to arrest the sun and turn it back in its course, and at the moment of waking he will have no idea of the time but will conclude that he has just gone to bed. Or suppose that he gets drowsy in some even more abnormal position—sitting in an armchair, say, after dinner; then the world will fall topsy-turvy from its orbit, the magic chair will carry him at full speed through time and space, and when he opens his eyes again he will imagine that he went to sleep months earlier and in some far distant country. But for me it was enough if, in my own bed, my sleep was so heavy as completely to relax my consciousness; for then I lost all sense of the place in which I had gone to sleep, and when I awoke at midnight, not knowing where I was, I could not be sure at first who I was; I had only the most rudimentary sense of existence, such as may lurk and flicker in the depths of an animal's consciousness; I was more destitute of human qualities than the cave dweller; but then the memory, not yet of the place in which I was but of various other places where I had lived and might now very possibly be, would come like a rope let down from heaven to draw me up out of the abyss of not-being, from which I could never have escaped by myself: in a flash I would traverse and surmount centuries of civilization, and out of a half-visualized succession of oil lamps, followed by shirts with turned-down collars, would put together by degrees the component parts of my ego.

Perhaps the immobility of the things that surround us is forced upon them by our conviction that they are themselves and not anything else and by the immobility of our conceptions of them. For it always happened that when I awoke like this and my mind struggled in an unsuccessful attempt to discover where I was, everything would be moving round me through the darkness: things, places, years. My body, still too heavy with sleep to move, would make an effort to construe the form which its tiredness took as an orientation of its various members, so as to induce from that where the wall lay and the furniture stood, to piece together and to give a name to the house in which it must be living. Its memory, the composite memory of its ribs, knees, and shoulder blades, offered it a whole series of rooms in which it had at one time or another slept, while the unseen walls kept changing, adapting themselves to the shape of each successive room that it remembered, whirling madly through the darkness. And even before my brain, lingering in consideration of when things had happened and of what they had looked like, had collected sufficient impressions to enable it to identify the room, it, my body, would recall from each room in succession what the bed was like, where the doors were, how daylight came in at the windows, whether there was a passage outside, what I had had in my mind when I went to sleep and had found there

when I awoke. The stiffened side underneath my body would, for instance, in trying to fix its position, imagine itself to be lying, face to the
wall, in a big bed with a canopy; and at once I would say to myself:
"Why, I must have gone to sleep after all, and Mamma never came to say
good night!" . . .

b. Depersonalization is also thought to occur as the
result of an intense emotion, particularly rage, forcing its way
towards awareness. A brief excerpt from Updike clearly
illustrates this phenomenon.

FLIGHT

John Updike (1932–   )

. . . After I returned her to her house—she told me not
to worry, her mother enjoyed shouting—I went to the all-night diner just
beyond the Olinger town line and ate three hamburgers, ordering them
one at a time, and drank two glasses of milk. It was close to two o'clock
when I got home, but my mother was still awake. She lay on the sofa in
the dark, with the radio sitting on the floor murmuring Dixieland piped
up from New Orleans by way of Philadelphia. Radio music was a steady
feature of her insomniac life; not only did it help drown out the noise of
her father upstairs but she seemed to enjoy it in itself. She would resist my
father's pleas to come to bed by saying that the New Orleans program
was not over yet. The radio was an old Philco we had always had; I had
once drawn a fish on the orange disc of its celluloid dial, which looked to
my child's eyes like a fishbowl.

Her loneliness caught at me; I went into the living room and sat on a
chair with my back to the window. For a long time she looked at me
tensely out of the darkness. "Well," she said at last, "how was little hot-
pants?" The vulgarity this affair had brought out in her language appalled
me.

"I made her cry," I told her.

"Why do you torment the girl?"

"To please you."

"It doesn't please me."

"Well, then, stop nagging me."

"I'll stop nagging you if you'll solemnly tell me you're willing to
marry her."

I said nothing to this, and after waiting she went on in a different voice, "Isn't it funny, that you should show this weakness?"

"Weakness is a funny way to put it when it's the only thing that gives me strength."

"Does it really, Allen? Well. It may be. I forget, you were born here."

Upstairs, close to our heads, my grandfather, in a voice frail but still melodious, began to sing, "There is a happy land, far, far away, where saints in glory stand, bright, bright as day." We listened; and his voice broke into coughing, a terrible rending cough growing in fury, struggling to escape, and loud with fear he called my mother's name. She didn't stir. His voice grew enormous, a bully's voice, as he repeated, "Lillian! Lillian!" and I saw my mother's shape quiver with the force coming down the stairs into her; she was like a dam; and then the power, as my grandfather fell momentarily silent, flowed toward me in the darkness, and I felt intensely angry, and hated that black mass of suffering, even while I realized, with a rapid, light calculation, that I was too weak to withstand it.

In a dry tone of certainty and dislike—how hard my heart had become!—I told her, "All right. You'll win this one, Mother; but it'll be the last one you'll win."

My pang of fright following this unprecedentedly cold insolence seemed to blot my senses; the chair ceased to be felt under me, and the walls and furniture of the room fell away—there was only the dim orange glow of the radio dial down below. In a husky voice that seemed to come across a great distance my mother said, with typical melodrama, "Goodbye, Allen." . . .

Repetition Compulsion

X. As psychiatrists and psychologists study the life histories of neurotics they are impressed with the frequency of recurrent patterns or themes. The neurotic somehow time and again gets himself into the same sort of difficult situation. There is little or no awareness of this tendency, and it seems to be mediated by unconscious forces. Often the neurotic insists that these odd coincidences are entirely accidental.

Although the term was originally applied to much more limited phenomena, repetition compulsion is now clinically applied to recurrent themes of many varieties. The importance of this symptom is that it indicates how unconscious factors can influence behavior and affect the most important life situations.

Chekhov brilliantly illustrates this in his delightful story
of "An Enigmatic Nature."

An Enigmatic Nature

Anton Chekhov   (1860–1904)

On the red velvet seat of a first-class railway carriage a
pretty lady sits half reclining. An expensive fluffy fan trembles in her
tightly closed fingers, a pince-nez keeps dropping off her pretty little
nose, the brooch heaves and falls on her bosom, like a boat on the ocean.
She is greatly agitated.

On the seat opposite sits the Provincial Secretary of Special Commissions, a budding young author, who from time to time publishes long
stories of high life, or "Novelli" as he calls them, in the leading paper of
the province. He is gazing into her face, gazing intently, with the eyes of
a connoisseur. He is watching, studying, catching every shade of this ex-
ceptional, enigmatic nature. He understands it, he fathoms it. Her soul,
her whole psychology lies open before him.

"Oh, I understand, I understand you to your inmost depths!" says
the Secretary of Special Commissions, kissing her hand near the bracelet.
"Your sensitive, responsive soul is seeking to escape from the maze of——
Yes, the struggle is terrific, titanic. But do not lose heart, you will be
triumphant! Yes!"

"Write about me, Voldemar!" says the pretty lady, with a mournful
smile. "My life has been so full, so varied, so chequered. Above all, I am
unhappy. I am a suffering soul in some page of Dostoevsky. Reveal my
soul to the world, Voldemar. Reveal that hapless soul. You are a psychologist. We have not been in the train an hour together, and you have already fathomed my heart."

"Tell me! I beseech you, tell me!"

"Listen. My father was a poor clerk in the Service. He had a good
heart and was not without intelligence; but the spirit of the age—of his
environment—vous comprenez?—I do not blame my poor father. He
drank, gambled, took bribes. My mother—but why say more? Poverty,
the struggle for daily bread, the consciousness of insignificance—ah, do
not force me to recall it! I had to make my own way. You know the
monstrous education at a boarding-school, foolish novel-reading, the
errors of early youth, the first timid flutter of love. It was awful!
The vacillation! And the agonies of losing faith in life, in oneself! Ah, you

are an author. You know us women. You will understand. Unhappily I have an intense nature. I looked for happiness—and what happiness! I longed to set my soul free. Yes. In that I saw my happiness!"

"Exquisite creature!" murmured the author, kissing her hand close to the bracelet. "It's not you I am kissing, but the suffering of humanity. Do you remember Raskolnikov and his kiss?"

"Oh, Voldemar, I longed for glory, renown, success, like every—why affect modesty?—every nature above the commonplace. I yearned for something extraordinary, above the common lot of woman! And then— and then—there crossed my path—an old general—very well off. Understand me, Voldemar! It was self-sacrifice, renunciation! You must see that! I could do nothing else. I restored the family fortunes, was able to travel, to do good. Yet how I suffered, how revolting, how loathsome to me were his embraces—though I will be fair to him—he had fought nobly in his day. There were moments—terrible moments—but I was kept up by the thought that from day to day the old man might die, that then I would begin to live as I liked, to give myself to the man I adore—be happy. There is such a man, Voldemar, indeed there is!"

The pretty lady flutters her fan more violently. Her face takes a lachrymose expression. She goes on:

"But at last the old man died. He left me something. I was free as a bird of the air. Now is the moment for me to be happy, isn't it, Voldemar? Happiness comes tapping at my window, I had only to let it in—but —Voldemar, listen, I implore you! Now is the time for me to give myself to the man I love, to become the partner of his life, to help, to uphold his ideals, to be happy—to find rest—but—how ignoble, repulsive, and senseless all our life is! How mean it all is, Voldemar. I am wretched, wretched, wretched! Again there is an obstacle in my path! Again I feel that my happiness is far, far away! Ah, what anguish!—if only you knew what anguish!"

"But what—what stands in your way? I implore you tell me! What is it?"

"Another old general, very well off——"

The broken fan conceals the pretty little face. The author props on his fist his thought-heavy brow and ponders with the air of a master in psychology. The engine is whistling and hissing while the window curtains flush red with the glow of the setting sun.

Action as Symptom

XI. During the past fifty years there seems to have been a gradual shift in the manifest quality of neurotic symptoms. The nature of this change is that more patients behave or act in ways that are impulsive or "antisocial."

Apparently at times of anxiety or conflict, rather than
developing "old fashioned symptoms," these people "act out,"
often impulsively, but usually knowing the nature of
their actions.

Action as a symptom creates special problems for the
community and the community reacts often by imprisonment;
less often by hospitalization; and still less often by adequate
treatment. Not all symptomatic actions are obviously antisocial.
The young woman who gets pregnant—impulsively—to cope
with sexual conflict and the young man who sabotages his
career, are not openly attacking the community, they are
attacking themselves. In reality, most symptomatic action has a
profound element of self-destructiveness, which will be
illustrated in our first example.

a. Pirandello's vignette of a depressed and anxious
man is a brilliant illustration of action as symptom. It captures
both the underlying conflicts and the "escapist,"
self-destructive features of impulsive behavior.

ESCAPE

Luigi Pirandello (1867–1936)

          This fog is the last straw! Bareggi thought as its icy
needles stung his face and neck. Tomorrow I'll feel it in all my bones—
head heavy as lead, eyes swollen shut between watery bags. It's enough to
drive a man out of his mind.

Signor Bareggi, worn out by nephritis at fifty-two, squelched along
the avenue with his cheap cloth shoes oozing as if there had been a down-
pour. His feet were so swollen that if a finger were pressed to them, it
took a full minute for the skin to come smooth again, and the pain in his
kidneys never let up.

Morning and evening, wearing the same cloth shoes, Signor Bareggi
trudged from home to office and from his office, home. (Hadn't his
doctor told him to exercise "within reason"?) As he dragged himself
along, moving slowly because of those tender, aching feet, he nursed a
dream: he would run away some day, run away to hide from it all, run
away forever.

His home life drove him to desperation, too. The thought of having to go back day after day to that house—on its remote cross street off the long avenue where he was now walking—had become unbearable. It was not the distance he minded, though with his feet it was no small matter. Nor was it the isolation, which, in fact, he cherished. The cross streets were little more than lanes with no streetlamps, and as yet there were few signs of "civilization." There were only three small houses to the left, and, on the right, a country hedgerow shielded vast truck gardens. In the middle of the hedge was a weatherbeaten sign reading LOTS FOR SALE.

His was the third little house, with four dark rooms on the ground floor. There were shutters at the windows. In addition the glass panes had been screened to shield them from the stones thrown by the hoodlums in the neighborhood. But on the upper floor there were three small cheerful bedrooms and a little veranda with a view over the truck gardens, which was his delight in good weather.

As soon as he entered the house he was plagued by the anxious attentions of his wife and daughters, a fluttering hen followed by two peeping chicks. They ran here, flew there, getting his slippers or his cup of milk with the egg yolk in it. One of them would be down on all fours untying his shoes, another asking, in a whining voice, whether he was soaked from rain or sweat, according to the season—as if he could be dry when he had walked all the way home without an umbrella, or as if in mid-August he would not be bathed in perspiration!

All this coddling would be the ruination of his stomach. They only treat me this way so I can't give free rein to my feelings, he thought ruefully. How could he complain before those eyes melting with pity, before those eternally ministering hands?

And how he yearned to complain—about so many things! He had only to turn his head to the left or right to find a reason for complaint, a reason they never even dreamed of. Take the big old kitchen table, for instance. They all ate there, and with his diet of bread and milk, its smell of good raw meat and beautiful onions in their golden skins was a downright offense! Could he chide his daughters because they ate meat which their mother prepared deliciously with those onions? Or could he reproach them because they did the laundry at home to save money and threw the water, reeking of strong soap, out the door, thus spoiling that breath of fresh green from the vegetable gardens he so enjoyed in the evenings?

How unjustified such a reproof would seem to them who drudged all day long, stuck away there like exiles, little dreaming that, in other circumstances, each of them might have led a far different life.

Fortunately, his daughters were a little simple-minded, like their mother. He pitied them, but, seeing them reduce themselves to the state of old dish rags, his pity turned to sour vexation.

For he was not good-natured. No, no. He was not even good, as those poor women—and for that matter most everybody else—seemed to

think. He was bad. At certain times the bitterness he felt deep inside must
have burned in his eyes. It would come out as he sat alone at his desk in
the office, unconsciously toying, perhaps, with the blade of his penknife.
Insane impulses, like slashing the canvas sheathing of his desk top or the
leather of his armchair, would almost overcome him. Instead, he would
spread out his swollen hand, fingers splayed on the desk, and look at it
while tears welled up in his eyes. With the other hand he would pluck
furiously at the reddish hairs on the backs of his distended fingers.

He was bad, yes, but he was desperate, too, for he would probably
wind up one of these days in a wheelchair, paralyzed down one side, completely at the mercy of those three tiresome women. It was this longing to
escape while there was yet time that drove him wild.

That evening, as he was nearing the house, the longing suddenly
rushed into his hands and one foot before it reached his head. His foot
rose automatically to the step of the milkman's cart and his hands went to
the seat, as it stood there untended at the corner of his lane.

What! Signor Bareggi, a serious man, sedate, respectable, a professional man, on a milkman's cart?

The impulse came over him when he had spied the cart through the
thickening fog as he had turned off the avenue into the cross street; when
his nostrils had caught that fresh odor of hay in the feedbag and the goaty
smell of the milkman's coat thrown across the seat; when smells of the
distant countryside far, far beyond Casal dei Pazzi—vast and free—had
assailed him.

The horse, stretching his neck and cropping grass at the roadside,
wandered a step at a time away from the three little houses at the end of
the lane. The milkman tarried, as usual, to chat with the women, well
knowing that his horse would wait patiently before their door. Tonight,
when he came out, empty bottles in hand, and didn't find the horse in its
usual place, he started to run toward the corner.

Bareggi's eyes were fever-bright. He tingled all over with pleasure
and apprehension. Whatever happened, he no longer cared about the consequences for himself, the milkman, or his womenfolk. In the confusion of
his troubled mind, all was dismissed as he seized the reins in one hand,
the whip in the other, gave the horse a mighty slash on the rump—and
they were off.

The startled horse looked old, but he wasn't. Bareggi had not counted
on the beast's flying leap, which set up a din of clattering cans and jugs,
racks and bottles, in back of him. The reins flew out of his hands when he
tried to brace himself after the jolt, and his feet were knocked off the
shaft as he was thrown backward. He scrambled to his feet again and recovered the reins, but scarcely was one danger over when another loomed.
He held his breath as the maddened beast launched out on a wild race
through the fog which had closed in with the coming night.

No one ran up to head them off or called out to anyone else to way-lay them, even though all those milk cans banging around must have made a frightful racket. Perhaps there were no longer any people on the avenue or, if there were, their cries were not heard above the din. The street-lights must certainly have been lit by now, but Bareggi could not see them through the dense fog.

He let go of the whip and reins to hang onto the seat with both hands. The horse was either as fear-crazed as himself or not accustomed to the whip. Then again it might have been joy at the quick end of his evening's rounds that set him off, or his relief at no longer feeling the restraining reins. He neighed and neighed. Signor Bareggi was terrified by the violent backward thrust of his flanks in that race that seemed to gain momentum with every lunge.

The risk of crashing into something as they turned off the avenue crossed his mind, and he tried to retrieve the reins, but when he let go of the seat to stretch out a hand, he was thrown forward and banged his nose. Blood now spurted over his mouth, chin, and hands, but he had no time to stanch it. He could only clutch the seat and hang on for dear life. God, O God, how that milk was swishing and sloshing around in those over-turned cans, spattering all over his back! Blood before and milk behind! Signor Bareggi laughed aloud as his bowels twisted in terror. He was laughing wildly at his own fear, instinctively rejecting the certainty of imminent disaster and hoping that, after all, this might turn out to be a magnificent joke—a mad prank to tell at the office tomorrow. He went on laughing desperately as he tried to recall the calm of the farmers watering their vegetable gardens while he watched them from his little balcony across the street. He thought next of things like the patches peasants wear on their clothes, as if to say, Yes, poverty covers my buttocks, knees, and elbows, as bright and defiant as a flag. Meanwhile, beneath such thoughts, the threat of turning over at any moment lay vivid and terrifying. At any moment the cart would surely crash into something and scatter all over the place.

They flew past the Nomentana gate, past the Casal dei Pazzi, on and on into the open country, dimly visible through the fog.

When the horse finally stopped in front of a small farmhouse, the cart was battered and not a can or jug was left inside.

Hearing the horse pull up unusually early, the milkman's wife called out a greeting. When no one replied, she went to the door with an oil lamp and saw the wreck. Again she called her husband's name. Where could he be? What had happened?

But these were questions which the horse, still panting and happy after his wonderful gallop, was unable to answer. Snorting and stamping, his eyes bloodshot, he could only shake his head.

b. The meaning of an impulsive act can sometimes
be understood in a careful analysis of a person's life history.
Often there is a symbolic meaning, and occasionally the impulsive
behavior may be seen to reflect an attempt to identify or be
reunited with some figure in the past. John Cheever gives us an
insight into this in his brief characterization of Mr. Wryson.
At times of depression, Mr. Wryson swings into action; in this
case there is no antisocial aspect. Rather, he is attempting to
recreate the feelings of comfort and security that once warded
off loneliness and boredom. Mr. Wryson's story is
tragicomic, but it is real.

THE WRYSONS

John Cheever   (1912–   )

. . . Donald Wryson's oddness could be traced easily
enough to his childhood. He had been raised in a small town in the Middle
West that couldn't have had much to recommend it, and his father, an old-
fashioned commercial traveler, with a hothouse rose in his buttonhole and
buff-colored spats, had abandoned his wife and his son when the boy was
young. Mrs. Wryson had few friends and no family. With her husband
gone, she got a job as a clerk in an insurance office, and took up, with her
son, a life of unmitigated melancholy and need. She never forgot the
horror of her abandonment, and she leaned so heavily for support on her
son that she seemed to threaten his animal spirits. Her life was a Calvary,
as she often said, and the most she could do was to keep body and soul
together.

She had been young and fair and happy once, and the only way she
had of evoking these lost times was by giving her son baking lessons.
When the nights were long and cold and the wind whistled around the
four-family house where they lived, she would light a fire in the kitchen
range and drop an apple peel onto the stove lid for the fragrance. Then
Donald would put on an apron and scurry around, getting out the necessary bowls and pans, measuring out flour and sugar, separating eggs. He
learned the contents of every cupboard. He knew where the spices and
the sugar were kept, the nut meats and the citron, and when the work was
done, he enjoyed washing the bowls and pans and putting them back

where they belonged. Donald loved these hours himself, mostly because they seemed to dispel the oppression that stood unlifted over those years of his mother's life—and was there any reason why a lonely boy should rebel against the feeling of security that he found in the kitchen on a stormy night? She taught him how to make cookies and muffins and banana bread and, finally, a Lady Baltimore cake. It was sometimes after eleven o'clock when their work was done. "We do have a good time together, don't we, son?" Mrs. Wryson would ask. "We have a lovely time together, don't we, you and me. Oh, hear that wind howling! Think of the poor sailors at sea." Then she would embrace him, she would run her fingers through his light hair, and sometimes, although he was much too big, she would draw him onto her lap.

All of that was long ago. Mrs. Wryson was dead, and when Donald stood at the edge of her grave he had not felt any very great grief. She had been reconciled to dying years before she did die, and her conversation had been full of gallant references to the grave. Years later, when Donald was living alone in New York, he had been overtaken suddenly, one spring evening, by a depression as keen as any in his adolescence. He did not drink, he did not enjoy books or movies or the theatre, and, like his mother, he had few friends. Searching desperately for some way to take himself out of this misery, he hit on the idea of baking a Lady Baltimore cake. He went out and bought the ingredients—deeply ashamed of himself—and sifted the flour and chopped the nuts and citron in the kitchen of the little walk-up apartment where he lived. As he stirred the cake batter, he felt his depression vanish. It was not until he had put the cake in the oven and sat down to wipe his hands on his apron that he realized how successful he had been in summoning the ghost of his mother and the sense of security he had experienced as a child in her kitchen on stormy nights. When the cake was done he iced it, ate a slice, and dumped the rest into the garbage.

The next time he felt troubled, he resisted the temptation to bake a cake, but he was not always able to do this, and during the eight or nine years he had been married to Irene he must have baked eight or nine cakes. He took extraordinary precautions, and she knew nothing of this. She believed him to be a complete stranger to the kitchen. And how could he at the breakfast table—all two hundred and sixteen pounds of him—explain that he looked sleepy because he had been up until three baking a Lady Baltimore cake, which he had hidden in the garage?

CHAPTER seven

Character Disorders

Psychologists, psychiatrists, and psychoanalysts have all struggled with the problem of classifying human character, but none has developed a simple and workable scheme that has the merits of theoretical clarity and clinical validity. This is in part due to the unique nature and breadth of human personality and human aberrance, factors that resist ready-made pigeonholes.

Despite the inherent problems, psychiatrists have groped for categories in which to include those forms of psychopathology that manifest themselves not by "symptoms," but by aberrant patterns of character. Clinical psychiatrists have compromised on three major categories:

Disturbances of Personality Pattern

I. This group is generally distinguished by a longstanding and inflexible deviation in personality structure. There are four subtypes: the inadequate, the schizoid, the cyclothymic, and the paranoid personalities.

1. The inadequate personality is illustrated by one of the unique heroes of Russian literature, Goncharov's *Oblomov*. Ilya Ilyitch Oblomov, a man of breeding and promise, settles into a life, ineffective, unconcerned, improvident. He lacks emotional or physical stamina, satisfied with the next meal and the next nap. His life is without goals, and he settles into an existence without real human relations or values.

OBLOMOV

Ivan Goncharov (*1812–1891*)

. . . Ilya Ilyitch was worn out with fear and misery serving under a kind and easy-going chief; Heaven only knows what would have become of him had he had a stern and exacting one! Oblomov managed to stay in the service for two years; he might have endured it for a third and obtained a rank had not a special incident caused him to resign. He once sent an important paper to Archangel instead of to Astrakhan. This was found out; a search was made for the culprit. All the others were waiting with interest for the chief to call Oblomov and ask him coldly and deliberately "whether he had sent the paper to Archangel," and everyone wondered in what sort of voice Ilya Ilyitch would reply. Some thought he would not reply at all—would not be able to. The general atmosphere infected Ilya Ilyitch; he was frightened, too, although he knew that the chief would do nothing worse than reprimand him. His own conscience, however, was much sterner than any reprimand; he did not wait for the punishment he deserved, but went home and sent in a medical certificate.

The certificate was as follows: "I, the undersigned, certify and append my seal thereto that the collegiate secretary, Ilya Oblomov, suffers from an enlarged heart and a dilation of its left ventricle (*Hypertrophia cordis cum dilatione ejus ventriculi sinistri*), and also from a chronic pain in the liver (*hepatitis*), which may endanger the patient's health and life, the attacks being due, it is to be surmised, to his going daily to the office. Therefore, to prevent the repetition and increase of these painful attacks, I find it necessary to forbid Mr. Oblomov to go to the office and insist that he should altogether abstain from intellectual pursuits and any sort of activity."

But this helped for a time only: sooner or later he had to recover and then there was the prospect of daily going to the office again. Oblomov could not endure it and sent in his resignation. So ended, never to be resumed again, his work for the State.

His social career was at first more successful. During his early years in Petersburg his placid features were more frequently animated; his eyes often glowed with the fire of life and shone with light, hope, energy. He was stirred to excitement like other people, hoped and rejoiced at trifles, and suffered from trifles too. But that was long ago, at that tender age when one regards every man as a sincere friend, falls in love with almost every woman and is ready to offer her one's hand and heart—which some, indeed, succeed in doing, often to their profound regret for the rest of their lives. In those blissful days Ilya Ilyitch, too, had received not a few tender, soft, and even passionate glances from the crowd of beauties, a number of promising smiles, two or three stolen kisses, and many friendly handclasps that hurt to tears.

He was never held captive by the beauties, however, never was their slave or even a very assiduous admirer, if only because intimacy with a woman involves a lot of exertion. For the most part, Oblomov confined himself to admiring them from a respectful distance. Very seldom did fate throw him so much together with a woman that he could catch fire for a few days and believe that he was in love. His sentimental feelings never developed into love affairs; they stopped short at the very beginning, and were as innocent, pure, and simple as the loves of a schoolgirl.

He particularly avoided the pale, melancholy maidens, generally with black eyes reflecting "bitter days and sinful nights"; hollow-eyed maidens with mysterious joys and sorrows, who always want to confide in their friend, to tell him something, and, when it comes to telling, shudder, burst into tears, throw their arms round his neck, gaze into his eyes, then at the sky, say that the curse of destiny is upon them, and sometimes fall down in a faint. Oblomov feared them and kept away. His soul was still pure and virginal; it may have been waiting for the right moment, for real love, for ecstatic passion, and then with years it seemed to have despaired of waiting.

Ilya Ilyitch parted still more coldly with the crowd of his friends. After the first letter from his bailiff about arrears and failure of crops, he replaced his chief friend, the chef, by a female cook, then sold his horses, and at last dismissed his other "friends."

Hardly any outside attractions existed for him, and every day he grew more firmly rooted in his flat.

At first he found it irksome to remain dressed all day, then he felt lazy about dining out except with intimate bachelor friends, at whose houses he could take off his tie, unbutton his waistcoat, and even lie down and have an hour's sleep. Evening-parties soon wearied him also: one had to put on a dress-coat, to shave every day. Having read somewhere that only the morning dew was good for one and the evening dew was bad, he began to fear the damp. In spite of all these fancies his friend Stolz succeeded in making him go and see people; but Stolz often left Petersburg for Moscow, Nizhni, the Crimea, and foreign parts, and without him Oblomov again wholly abandoned himself to solitude and seclusion that could only be disturbed by something unusual, out of the ordinary routine of life; but nothing of the sort happened or was likely to happen.

Besides, as Oblomov grew older he reverted to a kind of childish timidity, expecting harm and danger from everything that was beyond the range of his everyday life—the result of losing touch with external events.

He was not afraid of the crack in his bedroom ceiling—he was used to it; it did not occur to him that stuffy atmosphere and perpetual sitting indoors might be more perilous for his health than night dampness, or that continual overfeeding was a kind of slow suicide: he was used to it and was not afraid. He was not used to movement, to life, to seeing many people, to bustling about. He felt stifled in a dense crowd; he stepped into a boat feeling uncertain of reaching the other bank; he drove in a carriage expecting the horses to bolt and smash it. Sometimes he had an attack of purely nervous fear: he was afraid of the stillness around him or he did not know himself of what—a cold shiver ran down his body. He nervously peeped at a dark corner, expecting his imagination to trick him into seeing some supernatural apparition.

This was the end to which his social life had come. With a lazy wave of his hand he dismissed all the youthful hopes that had betrayed him or been betrayed by him, all the tender, melancholy, and bright memories that make some people's hearts beat faster even in their old age. . . .

. . . And Oblomov himself? Oblomov was the complete and natural embodiment and expression of the unruffled peace, quiet, and plenty around him. Thinking about his way of living and growing more and more used to it, he decided at last that there was nothing further for him to aim at, nothing further to seek, that he had attained his ideal of life, though it had not the poetic setting and radiance with which his imagination had once clothed his ideas of an easy and care-free existence in his native village among the peasants and house serfs. He considered his present life a continuation of that same Oblomovka existence, though the setting was different because of the place and the time. Here, too, as at Oblomovka, he succeeded in getting off cheaply, in making a good bargain with life and ensuring for himself undisturbed peace. He triumphed inwardly at having escaped life's persistent, painful claims and storms raging under the wide expanse of sky lit up by the lightnings of great joys and resounding with the thunder of great sorrows; where false hopes and magnificent phantoms of happiness are at play and man's own thought consumes and devours him; where passion destroys him and intellect triumphs or is defeated; where man is engaged in a continuous combat and leaves the battlefield wounded and exhausted, but still insatiate and discontented. Not having experienced the delights won by struggle, Oblomov mentally renounced them and felt at peace only in his out-of-the-way corner where there was no movement, struggle, or life. And if his imagination caught fire once more, if forgotten memories and unfulfilled dreams rose before him, if his conscience suddenly reproached him for the way he had spent his life—he slept badly, woke up in the night, jumped out of bed, and sometimes wept hopeless tears for his bright ideal of life,

now gone forever, as one weeps for the beloved dead with the bitter
consciousness of not having done enough for them while they lived. Then
he looked at his surroundings, tasted the transitory sweets of life, calmed
down, watching dreamily the evening sun melt in the fiery afterglow;
finally, he came to the conclusion that his life had not merely happened
to be so simple and uneventful, but had been created and designed to be
such, in order to demonstrate the ideally restful aspect of human existence. It was other people's lot, he thought, to express its tempestuous aspects, to set in motion the creative and destructive forces; everyone had
his own appointed task! Such was the philosophy that the Plato from
Oblomovka had arrived at and that lulled him to rest in the midst of the
stern demands of duty and problems of human destiny! He had been born
and brought up, not as a gladiator for the arena, but as a peaceful spectator
of the battle; his timid and indolent soul would not have stood either the
anxieties of happiness or the blows of Fate—therefore he was the expression just of one particular aspect of life, and it was no use struggling for
something else, changing anything, or repenting. With years, agitation
and remorse visited him less and less often, and he settled down slowly
and gradually in the plain and wide coffin he had made of his existence,
like ancient hermits who, turning away from life, dig their own
graves. . . .

2.   The schizoid personality is a cold, aloof, and distant
person living in his fantasies, unsociable, sensitive, and unable
to relate as a person to other persons. The fantasies are often
grandiose, but always more gratifying than the rough
give-and-take of everyday life. Willa Cather has given us a
window into the mind of such a person in her story,
"Paul's Case."

Paul's Case
Willa Cather   (1876–1947)

It was Paul's afternoon to appear before the faculty of
the Pittsburgh High School to account for his various misdemeanors. He
had been suspended a week ago, and his father had called at the Principal's
office and confessed his perplexity about his son. Paul entered the faculty-
room suave and smiling. His clothes were a trifle outgrown, and the tan
velvet on the collar of his open overcoat was frayed and worn; but for

"Paul's Case" by Willa Cather.

all that there was something of the dandy about him, and he wore an opal pin in his neatly knotted black four-in-hand, and a red carnation in his buttonhole. This latter adornment the faculty somehow felt was not properly significant of the contrite spirit befitting a boy under the ban of suspension.

Paul was tall for his age and very thin, with high, cramped shoulders and a narrow chest. His eyes were remarkable for a certain hysterical brilliancy, and he continually used them in a conscious, theatrical sort of way, peculiarly offensive in a boy. The pupils were abnormally large, as though he were addicted to belladonna, but there was a glassy glitter about them which that drug does not produce.

When questioned by the Principal as to why he was there, Paul stated, politely enough, that he wanted to come back to school. This was a lie, but Paul was quite accustomed to lying; found it, indeed, indispensable for overcoming friction. His teachers were asked to state their respective charges against him, which they did with such a rancor and aggrievedness as evinced that this was not a usual case. Disorder and impertinence were among the offenses named, yet each of his instructors felt that it was scarcely possible to put into words the real cause of the trouble, which lay in a sort of hysterically defiant manner of the boy's; in the contempt which they all knew he felt for them, and which he seemingly made not the least effort to conceal. Once, when he had been making a synopsis of a paragraph at the blackboard, his English teacher had stepped to his side and attempted to guide his hand. Paul had started back with a shudder and thrust his hands violently behind him. The astonished woman could scarcely have been more hurt and embarrassed had he struck at her. The insult was so involuntary and definitely personal as to be unforgettable. In one way and another, he had made all his teachers, men and women alike, conscious of the same feeling of physical aversion. In one class he habitually sat with his hand shading his eyes; in another he always looked out of the window during the recitation; in another he made a running commentary on the lecture, with humorous intent.

His teachers felt this afternoon that his whole attitude was symbolized by his shrug and his flippantly red carnation flower, and they fell upon him without mercy, his English teacher leading the pack. He stood through it smiling, his pale lips parted over his white teeth. (His lips were continually twitching, and he had a habit of raising his eyebrows that was contemptuous and irritating to the last degree.) Older boys than Paul had broken down and shed tears under that ordeal, but his set smile did not once desert him, and his only sign of discomfort was the nervous trembling of the fingers that toyed with the buttons of his overcoat, and an occasional jerking of the other hand which held his hat. Paul was always smiling, always glancing about him, seeming to feel that people might be watching him and trying to detect something. This conscious expression, since it was so far as possible from boyish mirthfulness, was usually attributed to insolence or "smartness."

As the inquisition proceeded, one of his instructors repeated an impertinent remark of the boy's, and the Principal asked him whether he thought that a courteous speech to make to a woman. Paul shrugged his shoulders slightly and his eyebrows twitched.

"I don't know," he replied. "I didn't mean to be polite or impolite, either. I guess it's a sort of way I have, of saying things regardless."

The Principal asked him whether he didn't think that a way it would be well to get rid of. Paul grinned and said he guessed so. When he was told that he could go, he bowed gracefully and went out. His bow was like a repetition of the scandalous red carnation.

His teachers were in despair, and his drawing master voiced the feeling of them all when he declared there was something about the boy which none of them understood. He added: "I don't really believe that smile of his comes altogether from insolence; there's something sort of haunted about it. The boy is not strong, for one thing. There is something wrong about the fellow."

The drawing master had come to realize that, in looking at Paul, one saw only his white teeth and the forced animation of his eyes. One warm afternoon the boy had gone to sleep at his drawing-board, and his master had noted with amazement what a white, blue-veined face it was; drawn and wrinkled like an old man's about the eyes, the lips twitching even in his sleep.

His teachers left the building dissatisfied and unhappy; humiliated to have felt so vindictive towards a mere boy, to have uttered this feeling in cutting terms, and to have set each other on, as it were, in the gruesome game of intemperate reproach. One of them remembered having seen a miserable street cat set at bay by a ring of tormentors.

As for Paul, he ran down the hill whistling the Soldiers Chorus from *Faust*, looking wildly behind him now and then to see whether some of his teachers were not there to witness his light-heartedness. As it was now late in the afternoon and Paul was on duty that evening as usher at Carnegie Hall, he decided that he would not go home to supper.

When he reached the concert hall the doors were not yet open. It was chilly outside, and he decided to go up into the picture gallery—always deserted at this hour—where there were some of Raffelli's gay studies of Paris streets and an airy blue Venetian scene or two that always exhilarated him. He was delighted to find no one in the gallery but the old guard, who sat in the corner, a newspaper on his knee, a black patch over one eye and the other closed. Paul possessed himself of the place and walked confidently up and down, whistling under his breath. After a while he sat down before a blue Rico and lost himself. When he bethought him to look at his watch, it was after seven o'clock, and he rose with a start and ran downstairs, making a face at Augustus Cæsar, peering out from the east-room, and an evil gesture at the Venus of Milo as he passed her on the stairway.

When Paul reached the ushers' dressing-room half-a-dozen boys were there already, and he began excitedly to tumble into his uniform. It was one of the few that at all approached fitting, and Paul thought it very becoming—though he knew the tight, straight coat accentuated his narrow chest, about which he was exceedingly sensitive. He was always excited while he dressed, twanging all over to the tuning of the strings and the preliminary flourishes of the horns in the music-room; but tonight he seemed quite beside himself, and he teased and plagued the boys until, telling him that he was crazy, they put him down on the floor and sat on him.

Somewhat calmed by his suppression, Paul dashed out to the front of the house to seat the early comers. He was a model usher. Gracious and smiling he ran up and down the aisles. Nothing was too much trouble for him; he carried messages and brought programs as though it were his greatest pleasure in life, and all the people in his section thought him a charming boy, feeling that he remembered and admired them. As the house filled, he grew more and more vivacious and animated, and the color came to his cheeks and lips. It was very much as though this were a great reception and Paul were the host. Just as the musicians came out to take their place, his English teacher arrived with checks for the seats which a prominent manufacturer had taken for the season. She betrayed some embarrassment when she handed Paul the tickets, and a *hauteur* which subsequently made her feel very foolish. Paul was startled for a moment, and had the feeling of wanting to put her out; what business had she here among all these fine people and gay colors? He looked her over and decided that she was not appropriately dressed and must be a fool to sit downstairs in such togs. The tickets had probably been sent her out of kindness, he reflected, as he put down a seat for her, and she had about as much right to sit there as he had.

When the symphony began Paul sank into one of the rear seats with a long sigh of relief, and lost himself as he had done before the Rico. It was not that symphonies, as such, meant anything in particular to Paul, but the first sigh of the instruments seemed to free some hilarious spirit within him; something that struggled there like the Genius in the bottle found by the Arab fisherman. He felt a sudden zest of life; the lights danced before his eyes and the concert hall blazed into unimaginable splendor. When the soprano soloist came on, Paul forgot even the nastiness of his teacher's being there, and gave himself up to the peculiar intoxication such personages always had for him. The soloist chanced to be a German woman, by no means in her first youth, and the mother of many children; but she wore a satin gown and a tiara, and she had that indefinable air of achievement, that world-shine upon her, which always blinded Paul to any possible defects.

After a concert was over, Paul was often irritable and wretched until he got to sleep,—and tonight he was even more than usually restless. He had the feeling of not being able to let down; of its being impossible to give up this delicious excitement which was the only thing that could be called living at all. During the last number he withdrew and, after hastily changing his clothes in the dressing-room, slipped out to the side door where the singer's carriage stood. Here he began pacing rapidly up and down the walk, waiting to see her come out.

Over yonder the Schenley, in its vacant stretch, loomed big and square through the fine rain, the windows of its twelve stories glowing like those of a lighted cardboard house under a Christmas tree. All the actors and singers of any importance stayed there when they were in the city, and a number of the big manufacturers of the place lived there in the winter. Paul had often hung about the hotel, watching the people go in and out, longing to enter and leave schoolmasters and dull care behind him forever.

At last the singer came out, accompanied by the conductor, who helped her into her carriage and closed the door with a cordial *auf wiedersehen*,—which set Paul to wondering whether she were not an old sweetheart of his. Paul followed the carriage over to the hotel, walking so rapidly as not to be far from the entrance when the singer alighted and disappeared behind the swinging glass doors which were opened by a Negro in a tall hat and a long coat. In the moment that the door was ajar, it seemed to Paul that he, too, entered. He seemed to feel himself go after her up the steps, into the warm, lighted building, into an exotic, a tropical world of shiny, glistening surfaces and basking ease. He reflected upon the mysterious dishes that were brought into the dining-room, the green bottles in buckets of ice, as he had seen them in the supper party pictures of the Sunday supplement. A quick gust of wind brought the rain down with sudden vehemence, and Paul was startled to find that he was still outside in the slush of the gravel driveway; that his boots were letting in the water and his scanty overcoat was clinging wet about him; that the lights in front of the concert hall were out, and that the rain was driving in sheets between him and the orange glow of the windows above him. There it was, what he wanted—tangibly before him, like the fairy world of a Christmas pantomime; as the rain beat in his face, Paul wondered whether he were destined always to shiver in the black night outside, looking up at it.

He turned and walked reluctantly towards the car tracks. The end had to come sometime; his father in his night-clothes at the top of the stairs, explanations that did not explain, hastily improvised fictions that were forever tripping him up, his upstairs room and its horrible yellow wall-paper, the creaking bureau with the greasy plush collar-box, and over his painted wooden bed the pictures of George Washington and John Calvin, and the framed motto, "Feed my Lambs," which had been worked in red worsted by his mother, whom Paul could not remember.

Half an hour later, Paul alighted from the Negley Avenue car and went slowly down one of the side streets off the main thoroughfare. It was a highly respectable street, where all the houses were exactly alike, and where business men of moderate means begot and reared large families of children, all of whom went to Sabbath-school and learned the shorter catechism, and were interested in arithmetic; all of whom were as exactly alike as their homes, and of a piece with the monotony in which they lived. Paul never went up Cordelia Street without a shudder of loathing. His home was next the house of the Cumberland minister. He approached it tonight with the nerveless sense of defeat, the hopeless feeling of sinking back forever into ugliness and commonness that he had always had when he came home. The moment he turned into Cordelia Street he felt the waters close above his head. After each of these orgies of living, he experienced all the physical depression which follows a debauch; the loathing of respectable beds, of common food, of a house permeated by kitchen odors; a shuddering repulsion for the flavorless, colorless mass of everyday existence; a morbid desire for cool things and soft lights and fresh flowers.

The nearer he approached the house, the more absolutely unequal Paul felt to the sight of it all; his ugly sleeping chamber; the cold bathroom with the grimy zinc tub, the cracked mirror, the dripping spiggots; his father, at the top of the stairs, his hairy legs sticking out from his nightshirt, his feet thrust into carpet slippers. He was so much later than usual that there would certainly be inquiries and reproaches. Paul stopped short before the door. He felt that he could not be accosted by his father tonight; that he could not toss again on that miserable bed. He would not go in. He would tell his father that he had no car-fare, and it was raining so hard that he had gone home with one of the boys and stayed all night.

Meanwhile, he was wet and cold. He went around to the back of the house and tried one of the basement windows, found it open, raised it cautiously, and scrambled down the cellar wall to the floor. There he stood, holding his breath, terrified by the noise he had made; but the floor above him was silent, and there was no creak on the stairs. He found a soap-box, and carried it over to the soft ring of light that streamed from the furnace door, and sat down. He was terribly afraid of rats, so he did not try to sleep, but sat looking distrustfully at the dark, still terrified lest he might have awakened his father. In such reactions, after one of the experiences which made days and nights out of the dreary blanks of the calendar, when his senses were deadened, Paul's head was always singularly clear. Suppose his father had heard him getting in at the window and had come down and shot him for a burglar? Then, again, suppose his father had come down, pistol in hand, and he had cried out in time to save himself, and his father had been horrified to think how nearly he had killed him? Then, again, suppose a day should come when his father would remember that night, and wish there had been no warning cry to stay his hand? With this last supposition Paul entertained himself until daybreak.

The following Sunday was fine; the sodden November chill was broken by the last flash of autumnal summer. In the morning Paul had to go to church and Sabbath-school, as always. On seasonable Sunday afternoons the burghers of Cordelia Street usually sat out on their front "stoops," and talked to their neighbors on the next stoop, or called to those across the street in neighborly fashion. The men sat placidly on gay cushions upon the steps that led down to the sidewalk, while the women, in their Sunday "waists," sat in rockers on the cramped porches, pretending to be greatly at their ease. The children played in the streets; there were so many of them that the place resembled the recreation grounds of a kindergarten. The men on the steps—all in their shirt sleeves, their vests unbuttoned—sat with their legs well apart, their stomachs comfortably protruding, and talked of the prices of things, or told anecdotes of the sagacity of their various chiefs and overlords. They occasionally looked over the multitude of squabbling children, listened affectionately to their high-pitched, nasal voices, smiling to see their own proclivities reproduced in their offspring, and interspersed their legends of the iron kings with remarks about their sons' progress at school, their grades in arithmetic, and the amounts they had saved in their toy banks.

On this last Sunday of November, Paul sat all the afternoon on the lowest step of his "stoop," staring into the street, while his sisters, in their rockers, were talking to the minister's daughters next door about how many shirtwaists they had made in the last week, and how many waffles some one had eaten at the last church supper. When the weather was warm, and his father was in a particularly jovial frame of mind, the girls made lemonade, which was always brought out in a red-glass pitcher, ornamented with forget-me-nots in blue enamel. This the girls thought very fine, and the neighbors joked about the suspicious color of the pitcher.

Today Paul's father, on the top step, was talking to a young man who shifted a restless baby from knee to knee. He happened to be the young man who was daily held up to Paul as a model, and after whom it was his father's dearest hope that he would pattern. This young man was of a ruddy complexion, with a compressed, red mouth, and faded, near-sighted eyes, over which he wore thick spectacles, with gold bows that curved about his ears. He was clerk to one of the magnates of a great steel corporation, and was looked upon in Cordelia Street as a young man with a future. There was a story that, some five years ago—he was now barely twenty-six—he had been a trifle "dissipated," but in order to curb his appetites and save the loss of time and strength that a sowing of wild oats might have entailed, he had taken his chief's advice, oft reiterated to his employees, and at twenty-one had married the first woman whom he could persuade to share his fortunes. She happened to be an angular school mistress, much older than he, who also wore thick glasses, and who had now borne him four children, all near-sighted, like herself.

The young man was relating how his chief, now cruising in the Mediterranean, kept in touch with all the details of the business, arranging his office hours on his yacht just as though he were at home, and "knocking off work enough to keep two stenographers busy." His father told, in turn, the plan his corporation was considering, of putting in an electric railway plant at Cairo. Paul snapped his teeth; he had an awful apprehension that they might spoil it all before he got there. Yet he rather liked to hear these legends of the iron kings, that were told and retold on Sundays and holidays; these stories of palaces in Venice, yachts on the Mediterranean, and high play at Monte Carlo appealed to his fancy, and he was interested in the triumphs of cash boys who had become famous, though he had no mind for the cash-boy stage.

After supper was over, and he had helped to dry the dishes, Paul nervously asked his father whether he could go to George's to get some help in his geometry, and still more nervously asked for car-fare. This latter request he had to repeat, as his father, on principle, did not like to hear requests for money whether much or little. He asked Paul whether he could not go to some boy who lived nearer, and told him that he ought not to leave his school work until Sunday; but he gave him the dime. He was not a poor man, but he had a worthy ambition to come up in the world. His only reason for allowing Paul to usher was that he thought a boy ought to be earning a little.

Paul bounded upstairs, scrubbed the greasy odor of the dish-water from his hands with the ill-smelling soap he hated, and then shook over his fingers a few drops of violet water from the bottle he kept hidden in his drawer. He left the house with his geometry conspicuously under his arm, and the moment he got out of Cordelia Street and boarded a downtown car, he shook off the lethargy of two deadening days, and began to live again.

The leading juvenile of the permanent stock company which played at one of the downtown theaters was an acquaintance of Paul's, and the boy had been invited to drop in at the Sunday-night rehearsals whenever he could. For more than a year Paul had spent every available moment loitering about Charley Edwards's dressing-room. He had won a place among Edwards's following not only because the young actor, who could not afford to employ a dresser, often found him useful, but because he recognized in Paul something akin to what churchmen term "vocation."

It was at the theater and at Carnegie Hall that Paul really lived; the rest was but a sleep and a forgetting. This was Paul's fairy tale, and it had for him all the allurement of a secret love. The moment he inhaled the gassy, painty, dusty odor behind the scenes, he breathed like a prisoner set free, and felt within him the possibility of doing or saying splendid, brilliant things. The moment the cracked orchestra beat out the overture from *Martha*, or jerked at the serenade from *Rigoletto*, all stupid and ugly things slid from him, and his senses were deliciously, yet delicately fired.

Perhaps it was because, in Paul's world, the natural nearly always wore the guise of ugliness, that a certain element of artificiality seemed to him necessary in beauty. Perhaps it was because his experience of life elsewhere was so full of Sabbath-school picnics, petty economies, wholesome advice as to how to succeed in life, and the unescapable odors of cooking, that he found this existence so alluring, these smartly clad men and women so attractive, that he was so moved by these starry apple orchards that bloomed perennially under the lime-light.

It would be difficult to put it strongly enough how convincingly the stage entrance of that theater was for Paul the actual portal of Romance. Certainly none of the company ever suspected it, least of all Charley Edwards. It was very like the old stories that used to float about London of fabulously rich Jews, who had subterranean halls, with palms, and fountains, and soft lamps and richly appareled women who never saw the disenchanting light of London day. So, in the midst of that smoke-palled city enamored of figures and grimy toil, Paul had his secret temple, his wishing-carpet, his bit of blue-and-white Mediterranean shore bathed in perpetual sunshine.

Several of Paul's teachers had a theory that his imagination had been perverted by garish fiction; but the truth was, he scarcely ever read at all. The books at home were not such as would either tempt or corrupt a youthful mind, and as for reading the novels that some of his friends urged upon him—well, he got what he wanted much more quickly from music; any sort of music, from an orchestra to a barrel organ. He needed only the spark, the indescribable thrill that made his imagination master of his senses, and he could make plots and pictures enough of his own. It was equally true that he was not stagestruck—not, at any rate, in the usual acceptance of that expression. He had no desire to become an actor, any more than he had to become a musician. He felt no necessity to do any of these things; what he wanted was to see, to be in the atmosphere, float on the wave of it, to be carried out, blue league after blue league, away from everything.

After a night behind the scenes, Paul found the schoolroom more than ever repulsive; the bare floors and naked walls; the prosy men who never wore frock coats, or violets in their buttonholes; the women with their dull gowns, shrill voices, and pitiful seriousness about prepositions that govern the dative. He could not bear to have the other pupils think, for a moment, that he took these people seriously; he must convey to them that he considered it all trivial, and was there only by way of a joke, anyway. He had autograph pictures of all the members of the stock company which he showed his classmates, telling them the most incredible stories of his familiarity with these people, of his acquaintance with the soloists who came to Carnegie Hall, his suppers with them and the flowers he sent them. When these stories lost their effect, and his audience grew listless, he would bid all the boys good-by, announcing that he was going to travel for a while; going to Naples, to California, to Egypt. Then, next Monday, he would slip back, conscious and nervously smiling; his sister was ill, and he would have to defer his voyage until spring.

Matters went steadily worse with Paul at school. In the itch to let his instructors know how heartily he despised them, and how thoroughly he was appreciated elsewhere, he mentioned once or twice that he had no time to fool with theorems; adding—with a twitch of the eyebrows and a touch of that nervous bravado which so perplexed them—that he was helping the people down at the stock company; they were old friends of his.

The upshot of the matter was that the Principal went to Paul's father, and Paul was taken out of school and put to work. The manager at Carnegie Hall was told to get another usher in his stead; the doorkeeper at the theater was warned not to admit him to the house; and Charley Edwards remorsefully promised the boy's father not to see him again.

The members of the stock company were vastly amused when some of Paul's stories reached them—especially the women. They were hard-working women, most of them supporting indolent husbands or brothers, and they laughed rather bitterly at having stirred the boy to such fervid and florid inventions. They agreed with the faculty and with his father that Paul's was a bad case.

The east-bound train was plowing through a January snowstorm; the dull dawn was beginning to show gray when the engine whistled a mile out of Newark. Paul started up from the seat where he had lain curled in uneasy slumber, rubbed the breath-misted window glass with his hand, and peered out. The snow was whirling in curling eddies above the white bottom lands, and the drifts lay already deep in the fields and along the fences, while here and there the long dead grass and dried weed stalks protruded black above it. Lights shone from the scattered houses, and a gang of laborers who stood beside the track waved their lanterns.

Paul had slept very little, and he felt grimy and uncomfortable. He had made the all-night journey in a day coach because he was afraid if he took a Pullman he might be seen by some Pittsburgh business man who had noticed him in Denny & Carson's office. When the whistle woke him, he clutched quickly at his breast pocket, glancing about him with an uncertain smile. But the little, clay bespattered Italians were still sleeping, the slatternly women across the aisle were in open-mouthed oblivion, and even the crumby, crying babies were for the nonce stilled. Paul settled back to struggle with his impatience as best he could.

When he arrived at the Jersey City station, he hurried through his breakfast, manifestly ill at ease and keeping a sharp eye about him. After he reached the Twenty-third Street station, he consulted a cabman, and had himself driven to a men's furnishing establishment which was just opening for the day. He spent upward of two hours there, buying with endless reconsidering and great care. His new street suit he put on in the fitting-room; the frock coat and dress clothes he had bundled into the cab with his new shirts. Then he drove to a hatter's and a shoe house. His next errand was at Tiffany's, where he selected silver mounted brushes and a scarf-pin. He would not wait to have his silver marked, he said. Lastly, he stopped at a trunk shop on Broadway, and had his purchases packed into various traveling bags.

It was a little after one o'clock when he drove up to the Waldorf, and, after settling with the cabman, went into the office. He registered from Washington; said his mother and father had been abroad, and that he had come down to await the arrival of their steamer. He told his story plausibly and had no trouble, since he offered to pay for them in advance, in engaging his rooms; a sleeping-room, sitting-room and bath.

Not once, but a hundred times Paul had planned this entry into New York. He had gone over every detail of it with Charley Edwards, and in his scrapbook at home there were pages of description about New York hotels, cut from the Sunday papers.

When he was shown to his sitting-room on the eighth floor, he saw at a glance that everything was as it should be; there was but one detail in his mental picture that the place did not realize, so he rang for the bell boy and sent him down for flowers. He moved about nervously until the boy returned, putting away his new linen and fingering it delightedly as he did so. When the flowers came, he put them hastily into water, and then tumbled into a hot bath. Presently he came out of his white bath-room, resplendent in his new silk underwear, and playing with the tassels of his red robe. The snow was whirling so fiercely outside his windows that he could scarcely see across the street; but within, the air was deliciously soft and fragrant. He put the violets and jonquils on the tabouret beside the couch, and threw himself down with a long sigh, covering himself with a Roman blanket. He was thoroughly tired; he had been in such haste, he had stood up to such a strain, covered so much ground in the last twenty-four hours, that he wanted to think how it had all come about. Lulled by the sound of the wind, the warm air, and the cool fragrance of the flowers, he sank into deep, drowsy retrospection.

It had been wonderfully simple; when they had shut him out of the theater and concert hall, when they had taken away his bone, the whole thing was virtually determined. The rest was a mere matter of opportunity. The only thing that at all surprised him was his own courage—for he realized well enough that he had always been tormented by fear, a sort of apprehensive dread that, of late years, as the meshes of the lies he had told closed about him, had been pulling the muscles of his body tighter and tighter. Until now, he could not remember a time when he had not been dreading something. Even when he was a little boy, it was always there—behind him, or before, or on either side. There had always been the shadowed corner, the dark place into which he dared not look, but from which something seemed always to be watching him—and Paul had done things that were not pretty to watch, he knew.

But now he had a curious sense of relief, as though he had at last thrown down the gauntlet to the thing in the corner.

Yet it was but a day since he had been sulking in the traces; but yesterday afternoon that he had been sent to the bank with Denny & Carson's deposit as usual—but this time he was instructed to leave the book to be balanced. There was above two thousand dollars in checks, and nearly a thousand in the bank notes which he had taken from the book and quietly transferred to his pocket. At the bank he had made out a new deposit slip. His nerves had been steady enough to permit of his returning to the office, where he had finished his work and asked for a full day's holiday to-morrow, Saturday, giving a perfectly reasonable pretext. The bank book, he knew, would not be returned before Monday or Tuesday, and his father would be out of town for the next week. From the time he slipped the bank notes into his pocket until he boarded the night train for New York, he had not known a moment's hesitation.

How astonishingly easy it had all been; here he was, the thing done; and this time there would be no awakening, no figure at the top of the stairs. He watched the snow flakes whirling by his window until he fell asleep.

When he awoke, it was four o'clock in the afternoon. He bounded up with a start; one of his precious days gone already! He spent nearly an hour in dressing, watching every stage of his toilet carefully in the mirror. Everything was quite perfect; he was exactly the kind of boy he had always wanted to be.

When he went downstairs, Paul took a carriage and drove up Fifth Avenue toward the Park. The snow had somewhat abated; carriages and tradesmen's wagons were hurrying soundlessly to and fro in the winter twilight; boys in woolen mufflers were shoveling off the doorsteps; the avenue stages made fine spots of color against the white street. Here and there on the corners whole flower gardens blooming behind glass windows, against which the snow flakes stuck and melted; violets, roses, carnations, lilies of the valley—somehow vastly more lovely and alluring that they blossomed thus unnaturally in the snow. The Park itself was a wonderful stage winter-piece.

When he returned, the pause of the twilight had ceased, and the tune of the streets had changed. The snow was falling faster, lights streamed from the hotels that reared their many stories fearlessly up into the storm, defying the raging Atlantic winds. A long, black stream of carriages poured down the avenue, intersected here and there by other streams, tending horizontally. There were a score of cabs about the entrance of his hotel, and his driver had to wait. Boys in livery were running in and out of the awning stretched across the sidewalk, up and down the red velvet carpet laid from the door to the street. Above, about, within it all, was the rumble and roar, the hurry and toss of thousands of human beings as hot for pleasure as himself, and on every side of him towered the glaring affirmation of the omnipotence of wealth.

The boy set his teeth and drew his shoulders together in a spasm of realization; the plot of all dramas, the text of all romances, the nerve-stuff of all sensations was whirling about him like the snow flakes. He burnt like a faggot in a tempest.

When Paul came down to dinner, the music of the orchestra floated up the elevator shaft to greet him. As he stepped into the thronged corridor, he sank back into one of the chairs against the wall to get his breath. The lights, the chatter, the perfumes, the bewildering medley of color—he had, for a moment, the feeling of not being able to stand it. But only for a moment; these were his own people, he told himself. He went slowly about the corridors, through the writing-rooms, smoking-rooms, reception-rooms, as though he were exploring the chambers of an enchanted palace, built and peopled for him alone.

When he reached the dining-room he sat down at a table near a window. The flowers, the white linen, the many-colored wine glasses, the gay toilets of the women, the low popping of corks, the undulating repetitions of the *Blue Danube* from the orchestra, all flooded Paul's dream with bewildering radiance. When the roseate tinge of his champagne was added—that cold, precious, bubbling stuff that creamed and foamed in his glass—Paul wondered that there were honest men in the world at all. This was what all the world was fighting for, he reflected; this was what all the struggle was about. He doubted the reality of his past. Had he ever known a place called Cordelia Street, a place where fagged looking business men boarded the early car? Mere rivets in a machine they seemed to Paul,—sickening men, with combings of children's hair always hanging to their coats, and the smell of cooking in their clothes. Cordelia Street—Ah, that belonged to another time and country! Had he not always been thus, had he not sat here night after night, from as far back as he could remember, looking pensively over just such shimmering textures, and slowly twirling the stem of a glass like this one between his thumb and middle finger? He rather thought he had.

He was not in the least abashed or lonely. He had no especial desire to meet or to know any of these people; all he demanded was the right to look on and conjecture, to watch the pageant. The mere stage properties were all he contended for. Nor was he lonely later in the evening, in his loge at the Opera. He was entirely rid of his nervous misgivings, of his forced aggressiveness, of the imperative desire to show himself different from his surroundings. He felt now that his surroundings explained him. Nobody questioned the purple; he had only to wear it passively. He had only to glance down at his dress coat to reassure himself that here it would be impossible for any one to humiliate him.

He found it hard to leave his beautiful sitting-room to go to bed that night, and sat long watching the raging storm from his turret window. When he went to sleep, it was with the lights turned on in his bedroom; partly because of his old timidity, and partly so that, if he should wake in the night, there would be no wretched moment of doubt, no horrible suspicion of yellow wall-paper, or of Washington and Calvin above his bed.

On Sunday morning the city was practically snowbound. Paul breakfasted late, and in the afternoon, he fell in with a wild San Francisco boy, a freshman at Yale, who said he had run down for a "little flyer" over Sunday. The young man offered to show Paul the night side of the town, and the two boys went off together after dinner, not returning to the hotel until seven o'clock the next morning. They had started out in the confiding warmth of a champagne friendship, but their parting in the elevator was singularly cool. The freshman pulled himself together to make his train, and Paul went to bed. He awoke at two o'clock in the afternoon, very thirsty and dizzy, and rang for ice-water, coffee, and the Pittsburgh papers.

On the part of the hotel management, Paul excited no suspicion. There was this to be said for him, that he wore his spoils with dignity and in no way made himself conspicuous. His chief greediness lay in his ears and eyes, and his excesses were not offensive ones. His dearest pleasures were the gray winter twilights in his sitting-room; his quiet enjoyment of his flowers, his clothes, his wide divan, his cigarette and his sense of power. He could not remember a time when he had felt so at peace with himself. The mere release from the necessity of petty lying, lying every day and every day, restored his self-respect. He had never lied for pleasure, even at school; but to make himself noticed and admired, to assert his difference from other Cordelia Street boys; and he felt a good deal more manly, more honest, even, now that he had no need for boastful pretensions, now that he could, as his actor friends used to say, "dress the part." It was characteristic that remorse did not occur to him. His golden days went by without a shadow, and he made each as perfect as he could.

On the eighth day after his arrival in New York, he found the whole affair exploited in the Pittsburgh papers, exploited with a wealth of detail which indicated that local news of a sensational nature was at a low ebb. The firm of Denny & Carson announced that the boy's father had refunded the full amount of his theft, and that they had no intention of prosecuting. The Cumberland minister had been interviewed, and expressed his hope of yet reclaiming the motherless lad, and Paul's Sabbath-school teacher declared that she would spare no effort to that end. The rumor had reached Pittsburgh that the boy had been seen in a New York hotel, and his father had gone East to find him and bring him home.

Paul had just come in to dress for dinner; he sank into a chair, weak in the knees, and clasped his head in his hands. It was to be worse than jail, even; the tepid waters of Cordelia Street were to close over him finally and forever. The gray monotony stretched before him in hopeless, unrelieved years; Sabbath-school, Young People's Meeting, the yellow-papered room, the damp dish-towels; it all rushed back upon him with sickening vividness. He had the old feeling that the orchestra had suddenly stopped, the sinking sensation that the play was over. The sweat broke out on his face, and he sprang to his feet, looked about him with his white, conscious smile, and winked at himself in the mirror. With something of the childish belief in miracles with which he had so often gone to class, all his lessons unlearned, Paul dressed and dashed whistling down the corridor to the elevator.

He had no sooner entered the dining-room and caught the measure of the music, than his remembrance was lightened by his old elastic power of claiming the moment, mounting with it, and finding it all sufficient. The glare and glitter about him, the mere scenic accessories had again, and for the last time, their old potency. He would show himself that he was game, he would finish the thing splendidly. He doubted, more than ever, the existence of Cordelia Street, and for the first time he drank his wine recklessly. Was he not, after all, one of these fortunate beings? Was he not still himself, and in his own place? He drummed a nervous accompaniment to the music and looked about him, telling himself over and over that it had paid.

He reflected drowsily, to the swell of the violin and the chill sweetness of his wine, that he might have done it more wisely. He might have caught an outbound steamer and been well out of their clutches before now. But the other side of the world had seemed too far away and too uncertain then; he could not have waited for it; his need had been too sharp. If he had to choose over again, he would do the same thing tomorrow. He looked affectionately about the dining-room, now gilded with a soft mist. Ah, it had paid indeed!

Paul was awakened next morning by a painful throbbing in his head and feet. He had thrown himself across the bed without undressing, and had slept with his shoes on. His limbs and hands were lead heavy, and his tongue and throat were parched. There came upon him one of those fateful attacks of clear-headedness that never occurred except when he was physically exhausted and his nerves hung loose. He lay still and closed his eyes and let the tide of realities wash over him.

His father was in New York; "stopping at some joint or other," he told himself. The memory of successive summers on the front stoop fell upon him like a weight of black water. He had not a hundred dollars left; and he knew now, more than ever, that money was everything, the wall that stood between all he loathed and all he wanted. The thing was winding itself up; he had thought of that on his first glorious day in New York, and had even provided a way to snap the thread. It lay on his dressing-table now; he had got it out last night when he came blindly up from dinner,—but the shiny metal hurt his eyes, and he disliked the look of it, anyway.

He rose and moved about with a painful effort, succumbing now and again to attacks of nausea. It was the old depression exaggerated; all the world had become Cordelia Street. Yet somehow he was not afraid of anything, was absolutely calm; perhaps because he had looked into the dark corner at last, and knew. It was bad enough, what he saw there; but somehow not so bad as his long fear of it had been. He saw everything clearly now. He had a feeling that he had made the best of it, that he had lived the sort of life he was meant to live, and for half an hour he sat staring at the revolver. But he told himself that was not the way, so he went downstairs and took a cab to the ferry.

When Paul arrived at Newark, he got off the train and took another cab, directing the driver to follow the Pennsylvania tracks out of the town. The snow lay heavy on the roadways and had drifted deep in the open fields. Only here and there the dead grass or dried weed stalks projected, singularly black, above it. Once well into the country, Paul dismissed the carriage and walked, floundering along the tracks, his mind a medley of irrelevant things. He seemed to hold in his brain an actual picture of everything he had seen that morning. He remembered every feature of both his drivers, the toothless old woman from whom he had bought the red flowers in his coat, the agent from whom he had got his ticket, and all of his fellow-passengers on the ferry. His mind, unable to cope with vital matters near at hand, worked feverishly and deftly at sorting and grouping these images. They made for him a part of the ugliness of the world, of the ache in his head, and the bitter burning on his tongue. He stooped and put a handful of snow into his mouth as he walked, but that, too, seemed hot. When he reached a little hillside, where the tracks ran through a cut some twenty feet below him, he stopped and sat down.

The carnations in his coat were drooping with the cold, he noticed; all their red glory over. It occurred to him that all the flowers he had seen in the show windows that first night must have gone the same way, long before this. It was only one splendid breath they had, in spite of their brave mockery at the winter outside the glass. It was a losing game in the end, it seemed, this revolt against the homilies by which the world is run. Paul took one of the blossoms carefully from his coat and scooped a little hole in the snow, where he covered it up. Then he dozed a while, from his weak condition, seeming insensible to the cold.

The sound of an approaching train woke him, and he started to his feet, remembering only his resolution, and afraid lest he should be too late. He stood watching the approaching locomotive, his teeth chattering, his lips drawn away from them in a frightened smile; once or twice he glanced nervously sidewise, as though he were being watched. When the right moment came, he jumped. As he fell, the folly of his haste occurred to him with merciless clearness, the vastness of what he had left undone. There flashed through his brain, clearer than ever before, the blue of Adriatic water, the yellow of Algerian sands.

He felt something strike his chest,—his body was being thrown swiftly through the air, on and on, immeasurably far and fast, while his limbs gently relaxed. Then, because the picture-making mechanism was crushed, the disturbing visions flashed into black, and Paul dropped back into the immense design of things.

3. The cyclothymic character is similar to the manic depressive, but in a lower key. Leskov's heroine, "The Amazon," illustrates all of the following cyclothymic character traits: the importance of hyperactivity, the denial of underlying depression, the lack of real human intimacy at the same time that hundreds of acquaintances exist. The cycle of depression after her husband's death, followed by hypomania, followed in turn by depression and asceticism as she becomes a nun, is typical.

The Amazon

Nikolai Leskov (1831–1895)

. . . I feel I must describe Domna Platonovna to my readers at greater length.

Domna Platonovna is not a tall woman; in fact, she is rather short,

From "The Amazon" by Nikolai Leskov.

but she looks big. This optical illusion is caused by the fact that Domna Platonovna is, as they say, broad in the beam, and what she lacks in height, she makes up for in breadth. Her health is not particularly good, although no one seems to remember her ever being ill, and to look at her you would never suspect that there was anything the matter with her. Her bosom alone is so immense that you cannot but be overcome at the sight of it. But she herself, Domna Platonovna, I mean, is always complaining about her poor health.

"To look at me," she'd say, "you would think I was robust, but there isn't any real strength in me as in other women of my size, and as for my sleep, it is just dreadful! Heavy is not the word for it. The minute my head touches the pillow, off I go and for all I care you can put me in the garden to scare away the birds. Until I've had my fill of sleep, I'm as good as dead. Yes, that's what I am, as good as dead!"

Domna Platonovna regarded her mighty sleep, too, as one of the ailments of her corpulent body and, as we shall see later, it had, in fact, given her a lot of trouble and caused her much unhappiness.

Domna Platonovna enjoyed nothing better than to pester people about the state of her health and ask them for medical advice. She would describe her ailments to them at great length, but she refused to take any medicines and believed only in "Haarlem" drops, which she called "Harem" drops, and a phial of which she always carried in the right-hand pocket of her capacious silk *capote*. According to her own account, she was always somewhere about forty-five years of age, but to judge by her fresh complexion and her cheerful mien, no one would give her more than forty. At the time of my first acquaintance with her, Domna Platonovna's hair was of a dark brown color, and there was not a single grey hair to be seen on her head. Her skin was quite unusually white and her red cheeks glowed with health, which, however, never satisfied her, for she used to buy some French *papier poudré* in the upper gallery of the Arcade, which greatly deepened the natural color of her cheeks, a color which steadfastly refused to be affected by any of her troubles or by the Finnish winds and fogs. Domna Platonovna's eyebrows looked as if they had been made of black satin: they were as black as jet and they shone with an unnatural glitter, for Domna Platonovna used to smear them thickly with a kind of black preparation and draw them into a thin line with her fingers. Her eyes were just like two black plums besprinkled with fresh morning dew. A mutual friend of ours, a Turkish prisoner of war by the name of Ispulat, who had been brought to St. Petersburg during the Crimean war, could never gaze calmly at Domna Platonovna's eyes. So potent was their influence on him that the poor fellow would completely lose his head and begin to give voice to his admiration in loud, ecstatic tones.

"Oh, what beautiful eyes! What lovely Greek eyes!"

Any other woman would, of course, be flattered by so sincere a compliment, but Domna Platonovna was never taken in by these Turkish blandishments and she always insisted on her pure Russian origin.

"Don't talk such rubbish, you damned infidel!" she'd reply with a merry twinkle in those "Greek" eyes of hers. "Don't you dare tell me such a thing again, you big-bellied toad! I come of a well-known and respectable family, I do, and there aren't any Greeks in the factory in our town and never have been!"

Domna Platonovna's nose was hardly what you might call a nose, so small, slender and straight was it. A nose like that you never come across on the Oka or the Zusha and, if you do, it is by mere accident. Her mouth, though, was rather big: you could tell at once that she'd been fed with a large spoon as a baby, but it was a pleasant mouth none the less and it looked so fresh, of a regular shape, with scarlet lips and teeth that might have been cut out of a young turnip. In a word, not only on an un-inhabited island, but even in so big and populous a city as St. Petersburg any man who regarded the kissing of a pretty girl as a kind of duty would not by any means consider it a hardship to kiss Domna Platonovna. But there could be no doubt that the greatest attractions of Domna Plato-novna's face were her chin, a chin that was a real peach, and the general expression of her features, which was so soft and child-like that if the thought ever crossed your mind how a woman whose face bespoke such bottomless good-nature could talk of nothing else but human treachery and malice, you could not help saying to yourself, "Oh, curse you a hundred times, Domna Platonovna, for, damn it! one look at your face is enough to conjure up such a multitude of the most dreadful problems in my head!"

Domna Platonovna was of a very sociable disposition; she was a really cheerful soul, good-hearted, not given to taking offence easily, rather simple-minded, perhaps, and a bit superstitious, too, but, on the whole, honest and straightforward, although, to be sure, as in every Rus-sian, there was a streak of cunning in her. Work and worry were Domna Platonovna's usual lot and she did not seem to be able to live without either. She was always busy, always rushing about, always worrying about something, devising some new scheme or other, or carrying it out.

"I live a lonely life," she used to say, "have no one except myself to look after in the whole world and yet to earn my bare living I have to lead a most aggravating sort of existence, running about the market like a scalded cat, and if it isn't one, then it is another who's always trying to catch me by the tail."

"But," you'd sometimes say to her, "you can't possibly do everything at once, can you?"

"Well, perhaps not everything," she'd reply, "but all the same let me tell you that it's very trying. Well, so long at present, good-bye, dear: there are people waiting for me in a dozen different places!" and she'd actually rush off in a devil of a hurry.

Domna Platonovna quite often realized herself that she did not labor for her bread alone and that her hard work and aggravating existence could be made considerably less hard and aggravating without any harm to her own personal interests; but she just could not restrain herself from bustling about.

"I can't bear the thought of losing any business," she used to say. "I'm jealous, you see, of anyone else getting it. To see something coming my way is enough to make my heart leap with joy."

But, as a matter of fact, what Domna Platonovna was jealous of was not that anybody should derive any profit from some business she might lose. No. That side often left her strangely cold. What did matter to her was that she might miss the worry and bustle involved in bringing the business to a successful issue.

"He's deceived me, the villain!" or "She's deceived me, the beast!" she'd go on complaining all day long, but next time you met her, she was again rushing about and worrying herself to death for the same villain or beast and telling herself beforehand that they would quite certainly deceive her again.

Domna Platonovna's business which gave her so much trouble was of a most diverse character. Officially, to be sure, she was just a seller of lace, that is to say, women of the artisan class and wives of poor merchants and priests used to send her from "their own parts" all kinds of lace collars, strips of lace material and cuffs which she hawked around Petersburg, or, in summer, around the different holiday resorts in the vicinity of the capital, sending back to "their own parts" the money she received after the deduction of her commission and expenses. But, besides her lace business, Domna Platonovna engaged in a most complicated business of a private character, in the carrying out of which the lace and the collars merely played the part of a pass to places where she would not otherwise have been admitted. Thus she found husbands and wives for all sorts of people, found purchasers for furniture and second-hand ladies' garments, raised loans for people with and without security, ran a kind of domestic agency of her own, finding jobs for governesses, caretakers and footmen, took confidential messages to the most famous *salons* and *boudoirs* in town of the sort that could not possibly be entrusted to the post and brought replies from the ladies in question, ladies surrounded by an atmosphere of frigid piety and devotion to good works.

But in spite of all her enthusiasm and connections, Domna Platonovna never got rich or even made a comfortable living. She had enough for her own needs, dressed, in her own words, "decently" and never begrudged herself anything; but she never had any spare money, either because she was too preoccupied with her different business worries or because her customers often deceived her, and, besides, all sorts of curious accidents always happened to her with her money.

Her chief trouble was that she was an artist: she got too much carried away by her own handiwork. Although she would invariably tell you that she had to work so hard for the sake of her daily bread, that claim of hers was scarcely just. Domna Platonovna loved her work as an artist loves his art: to contrive something, to collect something, to concoct something and then to admire her own handiwork—that was the main thing, that was what she really cared about, that was what she spent her money on and sacrificed any profit she might have obtained from the business in question which a more practical business woman would never have sacrificed.

Domna Platonovna found her vocation by sheer chance. At first she was quite satisfied with hawking her lace and it never entered her head to combine her trade with any other occupation; but the magic of our capital transformed this rather absurd Mtsensk woman into the accomplished factotum whom I knew as the inimitable Domna Platonovna, a woman who applied her native wit to any kind of business and who secured an entrée everywhere. Soon she had established herself so firmly that it was quite impossible for her not to get in wherever she wanted.

* * *

"I should like to ask you a question I've wanted to ask for a long time, Domna Platonovna," I said. "How old were you when your husband died? You were still quite a young woman, weren't you? Well, haven't you had any love affairs at all since then?"

"Love affairs?"

"Yes, I mean haven't you been in love with anyone?"

"Me in love? Good heavens, the nonsense you do sometimes talk, dear!"

"But why nonsense?"

"Because," she said, "it's only women who have nothing to do who have love-affairs. I'm much too busy rushing about day and night, leading so aggravating a life as I do, never a minute to myself . . . Why, such a thought never crosses my mind!"

"Doesn't it even cross your mind, Domna Platonovna?"

"No, dear, not as much as that even!" Domna Platonovna struck one finger-nail against another and added, "Besides, dear, let me tell you this love business is just a kind of craze: 'Oh, I can't live without him or her! Oh, I shall die!' That's all you hear from them. Now, if you ask me, dear, a man who's really in love with a woman should be always ready to help her, never let her down, that, I grant you, is real love. And as for the woman, she should never give way to temptation and should always behave decently."

"So I can take it, Domna Platonovna," I said, "that you've never been guilty of any such transgression and that in the eyes of God you're as pure as driven snow. Am I right?"

"Mind your own business, dear," she replied, "and don't you go meddling with my sins. For even if I did commit a sin, it's my sin, isn't it? Anyway, it's not yours and you're not a priest to whom I ought to confess my sins, are you?"

"I merely mentioned it, Domna Platonovna," I put in propitiatingly, "because you were so young when you lost your husband and I can see that you must have been very beautiful."

"Whether I was beautiful or not, I can't say," she replied, "but I was never considered a plain woman."

"That's it!" I said, "Anybody can see it even now."

Domna Platonovna passed a finger over an eyebrow and fell into thought.

"I've often wondered," she began slowly, "whether or not I had been guilty of a particular sin. Tell me, O Lord, was I guilty of that sin or not? That was how I'd ask for the Lord's guidance, but I never received a proper answer to that question from anyone. One nun once persuaded me to let her write down my story so that I could give it to the priest at confession. I let her write it down, but on my way to the church I dropped the paper and couldn't find it."

"What story are you referring to, Domna Platonovna?"

"I don't rightly know to this day whether it was a sin or whether I imagined it all."

"Well, even if you did imagine it all, Domna Platonovna, I should very much like to hear it."

"It all happened a very long time ago when I was still living with my husband."

"What kind of life did you have with your husband, dear Domna Platonovna?"

"Not a bad kind of life. Our house was a little too small perhaps, but it occupied a very good position, for it stood on the market place, and we had many market days in our town, mostly for household goods and provisions of one sort or another, only there was precious little of either, that was the trouble. We were not particularly well off, but we were not exactly poor, either. We sold fish, lard, liver and anything else we could. My husband, Fyodor Ilyich, was a young man, but a queer one, aye, a queer one, very haggard he was, but he had a pair of the most extraordinary lips. I never met a man with such lips in my life. He had, God forgive me, a terrible temper, very quarrelsome he was and quick to take offence, but I, too, was a real Amazon, dearly loved a fight as a girl, I did. Having married, I was at first as meek as a lamb, but that didn't please him at all, so that every morning before breakfast we used to have a grand old fight together. I was not very much in love with him, nor did we often agree, for we both were rare fighters, and, besides, you couldn't help fighting with him, for however nice you tried to be to him, he'd always look glum and glower at you. However, we carried on for eight whole years and did not separate. Now and again, of course, we'd have a row, but it was very rarely that we had a real fight. Once, it is true, he hit me over the head, but I was not altogether blameless myself, for I had been trimming his hair at the time and I cut off a bit of his ear with the scissors. We had no children, but we had friends at Nizhny to whose children I stood godmother. They weren't well off. He called himself a tailor and even had a diploma from a society, but he didn't earn his living by his needle, but by singing psalms for the dead and being a member of the Cathedral choir. As for earning a living, getting something for their home, it was his wife, Praskovya Ivanovna, who had to worry about it. She was a woman in a thousand, brought up all her children and made ends meet somehow.

"Well, once—it was in the same year that my husband died (everything was going topsy-turvy with us just then)—Praskovya Ivanovna invited us to her place to celebrate her birthday. We went and no sooner did we arrive than it began to pour and, as I had an awful headache at the time (I had had three glasses of punch and some Caucasian brandy and there's nothing worse than that Caucasian brandy for your head), I lay down for a bit on a couch in another room. 'Stay with your guests, dear,' I said to Praskovya Ivanovna, 'and I'll just go and lie down for a rest on the couch here.' But she wouldn't let me lie down on the couch, because, she said, it was too hard, so I went and lay down on their bed and dropped off to sleep immediately. Did I do anything wrong?" Domna Platonovna asked me.

"Why, no," I said, "you didn't do anything wrong."

"Very well, now listen to what happened. I felt in my sleep that somebody was embracing me and, you see, not just embracing me, either. I thought it was my husband, Fyodor Ilyich, and yet it didn't seem to be Fyodor Ilyich, for he was rather delicate, you know and shy, but I couldn't wake up, and when at last I did wake up, it was morning. I found myself in my friend's bed and beside me lay my friend's husband. I sort of scampered over him quickly, trembling all over, and there on the floor, on a feather bed, lay my friend and beside her was my husband, Fyodor Ilyich . . . I nudged her and then she, too, realized what had happened and began crossing herself. 'How did it all happen?' I asked her. 'Oh, dear,' she said, 'it's all my fault, for after everybody went away your husband and mine sat down to finish up the drinks and I didn't want to waken you in the darkness, so I lay down where I had made a bed for you and your husband, well, I just spat, so vexed was I.' 'What shall we do now?' I asked. But she said there was nothing we could do and that we'd better keep quiet about it. Yes, dear," Domna Platonovna said, "you're the first I ever told this story to after so many years, but it has been worrying me terribly all the time and whenever I think of it, I'm ready to curse that heavy sleep of mine."

"Don't distress yourself so much, Domna Platonovna," I said, "for whatever happened was against your will."

"Of course it happened against my will! I should think so! Still, it did worry me, I can tell you, and after that I was overtaken by one trouble after another. Fyodor Ilyich soon died, and not a natural death, either. Was crushed to death, he was, under a load of logs which collapsed on top of him on the bank of a river. I had no notion of the Petersburg circumstances then and I didn't know what to do to distract myself, but sometimes of an evening when I'd remember what had happened to me at that birthday party, I'd sit down at the window, all alone in the house, and sing, 'Take away my gold, take away my honors all,' and I'd burst out crying, tears gushing in a flood out of my eyes, so that it was a real wonder my heart didn't burst with sorrow. Oh, I felt so terrible when I'd remember the words of that song, 'My dear love in the dank ground lies sleeping,' that many a time I thought of putting a noose round my neck and ending it all. So I sold everything, gave up my business and left our town, for I decided that it was best to make a clean break with my past life."

"I can believe that, Domna Platonovna," I said, "for there's nothing worse than being depressed."

"Thank you, dear, for your kind words," said Domna Platonovna. "Indeed, there's nothing worse than that and may the Holy Virgin bless you and comfort you for your pity and understanding. But you can hardly be expected to know what I have been through, if I don't tell you how scurvily I was treated once and how shamelessly I was insulted. That my bag was stolen or that Lekanida Petrovna was so ungrateful to me, all that is nothing compared with what happened to me on another occasion. For there was such a day in my life, dear, when I prayed to God to send a serpent or a scorpion to suck my eyes out and devour my heart. And who do you think it was who did that wrong to me? I'll tell you: Ispulat, the Turk, that's who it was, that infidel Turk, in league with my own friends, Christians, baptized and anointed with myrrh!"

Poor Domna Platonovna burst into a flood of tears.

"A friend of mine, the wife of a government messenger," she went on, wiping her tears, "used to live in Lopatin's house on Nevsky Avenue and that Turkish war prisoner began to worry her about getting him a job. She asked me to see if I couldn't find some work for him. 'Find some situation for that devil, Domna Platonovna,' she said to me. But what sort of a job could I find for a Turk? A footman's job was all I could think of. Well, I found him such a place and I told him about it. 'Go there,' I said, 'and you can start work at once.' So they decided to give a party to celebrate the occasion and they got a lot of drinks, for that damned Turk had renounced his religion and could now drink spirits. 'I don't want anything to drink,' I told them, but I did have a glass or two. That's the kind of silly character I have, dear. I always say 'no' at first, and drink afterwards. So it was there, too. I had a couple of drinks and got quite befuddled and lay down in the same bed with that woman friend of mine."

"And?"

"And . . . well . . . that's all there is to it and that's why now I always sew myself up before going to bed."

"Sew yourself up, Domna Platonovna?"

"Yes, dear. You see, dear, if I happen to be spending the night some-where, I just get my feet into a kind of a sack and sew myself up, and, let me tell you, even when I am at home, I can no longer trust myself, see-ing the kind of heavy sleeper I am, so I just sew myself up every night."

Domna Platonovna heaved a deep sigh and let fall her mournful head over her ample bosom.

"There you are, dear," she said after a long pause, "knowing the Petersburg circumstances as well as I do and yet I let such a thing happen to me!"

She got up, bid me good-bye and went back to her flat in Znamens-kaya Street.

A few years later I had to take a poor fellow to an emergency hospital for typhus cases. Having seen him put to bed in one of the wards, I tried to find someone who could be relied on to look after him properly.

"You'd better see Sister," I was told.

"Won't you ask Sister if she will see me?" I asked.

A woman with a faded face and sagging cheeks entered the room.

"What can I do for you, sir?" she asked.

"Good heavens," I exclaimed, "Domna Platonovna!"

"Yes, sir," she said quietly, "it's me."

"How did you get here?"

"It was God's will, I suppose." . . .

4. The paranoid personality is demonstrated by Edmund Wilson's "The Man Who Shot Snapping Turtles." Asa M. Stryker is a suspicious, stubborn man. The importance of his ducks and the danger of the snapping turtles become ideas charged with feeling beyond reason. All his hostilities find outlet and focus on the evil predatory reptiles. Isolated from the rest of the world, he finds structure for his life in his monomania.

THE MAN WHO SHOT SNAPPING TURTLES

Edmund Wilson   (1895–   )

In the days when I lived in Hecate County, I had an uncomfortable neighbor, a man named Asa M. Stryker. He had at one time, he told me, taught chemistry in some sooty-sounding college in Pennsylvania, but he now lived on a little money which he had been "lucky enough to inherit." I had the feeling about him that somewhere in the background was defeat or frustration or disgrace. He was a bachelor and kept house with two servants—a cook and a man around the place. I never knew anyone to visit him, though he would occasionally go away for short periods—when, he would tell me, he was visiting his relatives.

Mr. Stryker had a small pond on his place, and from the very first time I met him, his chief topic of conversation was the wild ducks that used to come to this pond. In his insensitive-sounding way he admired them, minutely observing their markings, and he cherished and protected them like pets. Several pairs, in fact, which he fed all the year round, settled permanently on the pond. He would call my attention in his hard accent to the richness of their chestnut browns; the ruddiness of their backs or breasts; their sharp contrasts of light with dark, and their white neck-rings and purple wing-bars, like the decorative liveries and insignia of some exalted order; the cupreous greens and blues that gave them the look of being expensively dressed.

Mr. Stryker was particularly struck by the idea that there was something princely about them—something which, as he used to say, Frick or Charlie Schwab couldn't buy; and he would point out to me their majesty as they swam, cocking their heads with such dignity and nonchalantly wagging their tails. He was much troubled by the depredations of snapping turtles, which made terrible ravages on the ducklings. He would sit on his porch, he said, and see the little ducks disappear, as the turtles grabbed their feet and dragged them under, and feel sore at his helplessness to prevent it.

As he lost brood after brood in this way, the subject came, in fact, to obsess him. He had apparently hoped that his pond might be made a sort of paradise for ducks, in which they could breed without danger: he never shot them even in season and did not approve of their being shot at all. But sometimes not one survived the age when it was little enough to fall victim to the turtles.

These turtles he fought in a curious fashion. He would stand on the bank with a rifle and pot them when they stuck up their heads, sometimes hitting a duck by mistake. Only the ducks that were thus killed accidentally did he think it right to eat. One night when he had invited me to dine with him on one of them, I asked him why he did not protect the ducklings by shutting them up in a wire pen and providing them with a small pool to swim in. He told me that he had already decided to try this, and the next time I saw him he reported that the ducklings were doing finely.

Yet the pen, as it turned out later, did not permanently solve the problem, for the wild ducks, when they got old enough, flew out of it, and they were still young enough to be caught by the turtles. Mr. Stryker could not, as he said, keep them captive all their lives. The thing was rather, he finally concluded, to try to get rid of the turtles, against which he was coming, I noted, to display a slightly morbid animosity, and, after a good deal of serious thought, he fixed upon an heroic method.

He had just come into a new inheritance, which, he told me, made him pretty well off; and he decided to drain the pond. The operation took the whole of one summer: it horribly disfigured his place, and it afflicted the neighborhood with the stench of the slime that was now laid bare. One family whose place adjoined Stryker's were obliged to go away for weeks during the heaviest days of August, when the draining had become complete. Stryker, however, stayed and personally attended to the turtles, cutting off their heads himself; and he had men posted day and night at the places where they went to lay their eggs. At last someone complained to the Board of Health, and they made him fill up his pond. He was indignant with the town authorities and declared that he had not yet got all the turtles, some of which were still hiding in the mud; and he and his crew put in a mad last day combing the bottom with giant rakes.

The next spring the turtles reappeared, though at first there were only a few. Stryker came over to see me and told me a harrowing story. He described how he had been sitting on his porch watching "my finest pair of mallard, out with their new brood of young ones. They were still just little fluffy balls, but they sailed along with that air they have of knowing that they're somebody special. From the moment that they can catch a water bug for themselves, they know that they're the lords of the pond. And I was just thinking how damn glad I was that no goblins were going to git them any more. Well, the phone rang and I went in to answer it, and when I came out again I distinctly had the impression that there were fewer ducks on the pond. So I counted them, and, sure enough, there was one duckling shy!" The next day another had vanished, and he had hired a man to watch the pond. Several snapping turtles were seen, but he had not succeeded in catching them. By the middle of the summer the casualties seemed almost as bad as before.

This time Mr. Stryker decided to do a better job. He came to see me again and startled me by holding forth in a vein that recalled the pulpit.

"If God has created the mallard," he said, "a thing of beauty and grace, how can He allow these dirty filthy mud-turtles to prey upon His handiwork and destroy it?" "He created the mud-turtles first," I said. "The reptiles came before the birds. And they survive with the strength God gave them. There is no instance on record of God's intervention in the affairs of any animal species lower in the scale than man." "But if the Evil triumphs there," said Stryker, "it may triumph everywhere, and we must fight it with every weapon in our power!" "That's the Manichaean heresy," I replied. "It is an error to assume that the Devil is contending on equal terms with God and that the fate of the world is in doubt." "I'm not sure of that sometimes," said Stryker, and I noticed that his little bright eyes seemed to dim in a curious way as if he were drawing into himself to commune with some private fear. "How do we know that some of His lowest creations aren't beginning to get out of hand and clean up on the higher ones?"

He decided to poison the turtles, and he brushed up, as he told me, on his chemistry. The result, however, was all too devastating. The chemicals he put into the water wiped out not only the turtles, but also all the other animals and most of the vegetation in the pond. When his chemical analysis showed that the water was no longer tainted, he put back the ducks again, but they found so little to eat that they presently flew away and ceased to frequent the place. In the meantime, some new ones that had come there had died from the poisoned water. One day, as Asa M. Stryker was walking around his estate, he encountered a female snapping turtle unashamedly crawling in the direction of the pond. She had obviously just been laying her eggs. He had had the whole of his place closed in with a fence of thick-meshed wire which went down a foot into the ground (I had asked him why he didn't have the pond rather than the whole estate thus enclosed, and he had explained that this would have made it impossible for him to look at the ducks from the porch); but turtles must have got in through the gate when it was open or they must have been in hiding all the time. Stryker was, as the English say, livid, and people became a little afraid of him because they thought he was getting cracked. . . .

Sociopathic Personality Disturbances

II. This category, like the first, is also made up of longstanding deviations in personality, but includes only those which are primarily antisocial. Antisocial action of an encompassing nature in an individual was in the past described under the rubric "psychopathic personality." Historically, this designation had developed from the concept, *constitutional* *psychopath*, which suggested that certain individuals with a given genetic endowment were prone to antisocial action. As the wave of social reform reached psychiatry, many were dissatisfied with this concept, which had the implication that antisocial behavior was hereditary rather than a product of the environment. The modern concept of sociopathic personality was substituted, and the old term, *pyschopath*, was relinquished. But this term has been reluctant to die, and in fact there is some evidence which suggests that although environment plays a critical part in antisocial behavior, constitution may make this pattern an easier pathway.

1. Pia Baroja has captured the quality of the sociopath in his story "Gálvez the Absurd." The apparent lack of moral standards is characteristic of these patients.

GÁLVEZ THE ABSURD

Pio Baroja   (1872–1956)

Pedro Luis de Gálvez was an absurd man; I think he was a pathological type. He had been born in a village in the province of Málaga, and had been a seminarian. According to the story he told, he had written a satire in verse against one of the professors or tutors, hinting at nefarious vices, and he had been expelled for this reason.

He turned up in Madrid. At the beginning of his residence in the capital city he apparently had some resources to count on; he married and fathered several children.

He was a Bohemian by nature and could not accustom himself to any sort of regulated life. I do not believe that he was an extremist in politics, or even strongly opinionated, and yet he began to be known as a republican and syndicalist. Shortly, he was in jail in some Andalusian town. Next, when he got out, he consorted with certain republican politicians, spoke before a meeting, said some impertinent things about the king, was thereupon arrested and tried, was found guilty of the crime of lese majesty, and then, instead of availing himself of the help of the leaders of his party, who surely would have been able to save him, he let himself be taken to prison.

It seems that he served his time in Ocaña, and later he related in detail the horror of his life as a prisoner; doubtless, from some psychic perversion, he was attracted to these horrors.

"Gálvez the Absurd" by Pio Baroja. In *The Restlessness of Shanti Andia*, translated by Anthony Kerrigan for The University of Michigan Press, 1959. Copyright © The University of Michigan 1959.

Gálvez told terrible stories, especially about homosexuality in prison, where bullying became sadism and the most refined cruelties were practiced upon the weak, all accompanied by the greatest hypocrisy. He would tell about it with a certain morbid delectation.

He next passed through a Bohemian epoch, and one heard many extravagant tales about him. It was said that once, when one of his children died, he wrapped him in newspapers and took him around to the cafés, to solicit money for his burial. The same thing was told about a certain Milego, a great white-bearded character and friend of Manuel Sawa who did not, however, have anything to do with that other Milego, a Valencian who distinguished himself as an orator and was later a professor in some city in Galicia.

Gálvez, who read an anecdote about himself that I recounted in a book called *The Cavern of Humor*, reproached me not for having recounted it but for having called him Carlos Luis instead of Pedro Luis, for he felt that in setting down that particular combination of names I had obviously been thinking of Carlos Luis de Cuenca, an identification he found offensive.

Following his Bohemian period in Madrid, Gálvez disappeared from the Court city; when he returned some time later, he said he had been traveling in Germany and the Balkans, and that he had served as an army officer in one of the Slav countries. I doubt the truth of this assertion.

Gálvez told me he had met and talked with Gorki and Sudermann and that both of them had asked after me. That might have been true or it might have been the flattery of a professional sponger.

Time passed, and a writer by the name of Modesto Pérez proposed to my brother-in-law, the publisher Julio Caro, that he issue a series of biographies of the writers belonging to the so-called Generation of 1898. Don Modesto himself wrote the biography of Unamuno, and Gálvez turned up at the publisher's with an offer to do mine.

It did not take me long to realize that Gálvez had not the slightest interest in his work. He got no more than fifteen or twenty pages of the biography done, and then he could go no farther. I would say to him:

"Put some stuffing into it and you'll have the book finished in no time."

Gálvez attempted to collect his fee for the book before turning the manuscript over to the printer. He was given an advance: but he wanted the entire sum. He was undoubtedly incapable of finishing the book, even by putting in bits copied from here and there.

I warned him:

"If you like, write the biography of someone else, anyone you like, and if you finish it, I'll see that you get your money at once; on the other hand, for not writing anything, nothing doing."

He would reply: "Don't say that to me; you make me so sad I could cry."

"Well, my friend, in that case you're going to spend your life in tears," I answered. "For I don't believe you'll find a publisher anywhere who will pay you for work you don't do."

"I have a different sensibility from the others; I put my soul into literature. I see that you haven't read my verses, and that makes me very unhappy."

Everything he said was make-believe: the truth was that he did not like to work.

At this time he told me how he had gone, six or seven times, to a place at some distance out along the highway to Extremadura, in the heat of summer, to fetch some cheap boots that were being distributed at a charity center and which were probably worth some twenty or twenty-five pesetas at the time. And yet he was not capable of sitting for three hours in a row at a table, writing an article for which he would have been paid rather more than the boots were worth. Anyone would have thought it was more comfortable to do it the easy way, but not he.

From time to time, Gálvez would disappear from Madrid altogether.

During one of these periods it was said that he was in prison, and then that Pedro de Répide had helped to get him out.

Répide had gone on a tour of Ocaña prison one day along with some other journalists. He caught sight of Gálvez there, and exclaimed: "What are you doing here?"

"I've been here for three years," Gálvez answered.

"But why haven't you written? We all thought you were out of the country."

Répide used his influence with his friends, and Gálvez was soon out of prison.

Then the tales began again. It was said that he had written books that other men had signed.

The books mentioned included Larreta's *The Glory of Don Ramiro*, and one by Ricardo León.

None of it sounds very likely, for the simple reason that Gálvez was lazy.

But I don't know what was fact and what was fiction. It all seems like fantasy to me. It is possible that Gálvez may have done some work for Ricardo León, correcting galleys, for which he would have been paid. This would not surprise me, for I heard Gálvez speak badly of almost every writer in Madrid, especially of those who presumed to be stylists, but I never heard him say a word against Ricardo León. Later it occurred to me that this was a singular fact. I also heard that he often went to León's house to eat, and that he was given money there. The two men were from Málaga, and of about the same age.

It was also reported that the painter Zuloaga presented Gálvez in one of the most aristocratic houses of Madrid, and that he had impudently remarked: "Here you have the best poet in Spain."

Someone told me that during the dictatorship of Primo de Rivera, Gálvez had called at the home of a well-known writer who was then living in great state. Without a doubt he went there to ask for money.

The writer's manservant showed Gálvez into an elegant sitting room with shining mirrors and big heavy velvet curtains. Gálvez waited, and then, when he saw that the other man did not appear, ground his cigarette butt into one of the mirrors, by way of leaving a calling card, and marched off.

As he reached his fortieth year, Gálvez already presented a worn and haggard aspect. At the time when he was thinking of doing my biography for my brother-in-law's small publishing house, he brought them a photograph of himself taken in his prison cell in an Andalusian mining town—Peubloneuvo del Terrible, I think it was—which showed him writing at a table covered with bottles, and wearing the garb of a modernist poet, complete with long hair.

Of Gálvez' writing I never read anything but a few bits of verse without much personal character.

He also said that his verse was his best work; but since he knew I was not a great reader of verse, he never sent me any of his books.

He considered me a writer ruined by a methodic bourgeois life.

For his part, he led the most unhinged life conceivable. He accepted anyone into his household. If he, on the other hand, once wormed his way into another man's house, that man could consider himself lost. There would be no way to get him out again. He doubtless thought that this was the normal way of life.

One man would put up in the house of a second, the second would take away the first man's wife, a third man would keep the children, etc., etc. Any other course of conduct Gálvez considered mannered and routine.

Gálvez married an actress, as I remember, and then he lived with a French woman who owned a perfume shop.

The only activity for which he felt an affinity was the making of sonnets. He manufactured them as someone else would turn out doughnuts, and a number of them, some people said, were very good.

One anecdote concerning Gálvez and a Catalan publisher I thought pretty funny:

The Bohemian from Málaga had convinced the Barcelona publisher that he should publish his books; the publisher also agreed to furnish the poet three or four hundred pesetas every month so that he could go on living. One day, as the two were walking on the Ramblas, Gálvez said to the publisher: "Pardon me a moment."

The publisher watched Gálvez go up to an unknown man and engage him in a heated conversation. Finally, the man reached in his pocket and handed something over to the Bohemian.

When Gálvez returned to his side the publisher said:

"I'll bet you just hit that fellow for a loan."

"Yes, that's true."

"And how much did he give you?"

"He gave me forty *céntimos*."

The publisher exclaimed: "Why you're a pig, a shameless pig; I've given you enough to live on and you accept swill from others."

Gálvez answered this objection with an insinuating and endearing gesture: "No, no, you don't understand. I did it, you see, to keep from getting stale."

In short, so that he would not lose his touch, Gálvez was a dilettante at sponging. He took whatever he could get: a five-peseta note, or double that amount, or half it.

He hung around my brother-in-law's publishing office, and engaged the publisher and Don Modesto Pérez in conversation.

After a while, I lost sight of Gálvez.

During the Civil War I heard nothing of him until the end, when I learned that he had been shot by a firing squad.

With the outbreak of fighting, Gálvez had adopted a terrifying air and acted like a man capable of anything.

"This week I have personally accounted for two hundred men," he would say.

Perhaps all the talk was no more than show and bluster, that he did nothing more than talk, a terrible case.

I have no firsthand knowledge of my own, but I think that the hatred that welled up in Gálvez during the war was a sadistic consequence of all the suppressed humiliations that had fermented in his soul. This kind of reaction is the most repulsive part of any civil war. Hatreds based on frustrated vanity, on low and miserable failures, are stirred up. The fact that a person might have a safe and commodious position is often not enough to prevent this kind of odium.

The spectacle of humanity when these sentiments are aroused is not a very pleasant one. It is, rather, shameful and sad.

From what I was told, I gathered that Gálvez, toward the end, had become a spiritualist, and that when he was in the death house, he told a fellow prisoner, a young man whose father had already been shot, that he expected to see the father within a few hours and that he would give him news of the son. He said all this, according to the testimony, with the greatest serenity and conviction.

In the course of the war, Gálvez had given several bookshop owners some bad scares. He appeared once in Melchor García's bookshop in the guise of a Red officer, carrying a pistol, and told the clerk, Anacleto: "All right now, how much money is there in the till?"

The clerk told him that there were very few sales those days, and Gálvez told him to hand over what he had and that he would see to it that the Red militiamen did not bother him.

He seems to have carried out the same operation in Pueyo's bookshop, demanding the money in the till, and then all the money that could be found in the house.

It was said later that Gálvez did not behave badly toward his friends and that he had protected Emilio Carrere and Ricardo León as best he could. León was in hiding, changing his place of residence continually. It was said that Gálvez took him one day to a Red commissariat, and introduced him there as a friend from Málaga who had trapped the real Ricardo León, whom he had ordered shot.

Gálvez was as lazy as a Turk, and by now an inveterate alcoholic. He went around vaguely repeating that he had written novels that other men had signed and thereby gained their fame. I don't know how much truth there might be in this assertion: I do believe that Gálvez was incapable of any consistent or continuous labor.

Gálvez was condemned to death. In jail at Porlier he was like a madman, with his long white hair falling to his shoulders, his beard down to his chest, and wearing dark glasses. He stooped in walking and made use of a cane.

He went about talking with this one and that one and taking a drink whenever he could, and then he wrote a sonnet on his Last Hour, which he passed to one of the prisoners. A guard took the sonnet away from the other prisoner and tore it up.

2. One relatively rare but dramatic form of sociopathic behavior is the impostor. The impostor is not bound by society's sanctions, or by a sense of his own identity. He assumes the role and status of the part he wishes to play in life. Thomas Mann created one of the great impostors in literature, Felix Krull, and has provided us with some insight into the factors which established this disorder of character.

CONFESSIONS OF FELIX KRULL, CONFIDENCE MAN

Thomas Mann (1875–1955)

. . . Such was the home in which I was born one mild, rainy day in the merry month of May—a Sunday, to be exact. From now

From "Confessions of Felix Krull, Confidence Man." Reprinted from *Stories of Three Decades* by Thomas Mann, by permission of Alfred A. Knopf, Inc. Copyright © 1930, 1936 by Alfred A. Knopf, Inc.

on I mean to follow the order of events conscientiously and to stop anticipating. If reports are true, the birth was slow and difficult and required the assistance of our family doctor, whose name was Mecum. It appears that I—if I may so refer to that far-away and foreign little being —was extremely inactive and made no attempt to aid my mother's efforts, showing no eagerness whatever to enter the world which later I was to love so dearly. Nevertheless, I was a healthy, well-formed child and thrived most promisingly at the breast of my excellent wet-nurse. Frequent reflection on this subject, moreover, inclines me to the belief that this reluctance to exchange the darkness of the womb for the light of day is connected with my extraordinary gift and passion for sleep, a characteristic of mine from infancy. I am told that I was a quiet child, not given to crying or troublemaking, but inclined to sleep and doze to an extent most convenient for my nurses. And despite the fact that later on I had such a longing for the world and its people that I mingled with them under a variety of names and did all I could to win them to myself, yet I feel that in night and slumber I have always been most at home. Even without being physically fatigued I have always been able to fall asleep with the greatest ease and pleasure, to lose myself in far and dreamless forgetfulness, and to awake after ten or twelve or even fourteen hours of oblivion even more refreshed and enlivened than by the successes and accomplishments of my waking hours. There might seem to be a contradiction between this love of sleep and my great impulse toward life and love, about which I intend to speak in due course. As I have already mentioned, however, I have devoted much thought to this matter and I have clearly perceived more than once that there is no contradiction but rather a hidden connection and correspondence. In fact, it is only now, when I have turned forty and have become old and weary, when I no longer feel the old irrepressible urge toward the society of men, but live in complete retirement, it is only now that my capacity for sleep is impaired so that I am in a sense a stranger to it, my slumbers being short and light and fleeting; whereas even in prison—where there was plenty of opportunity— I slept better than in the soft beds of the Palace Hotel. But I am falling again into my old fault of anticipating.

Often enough I heard from my parents' lips that I was a Sunday child, and although I was brought up to reject every form of superstition, I have always thought there was a secret significance in that fact taken in connection with my Christian name of Felix (for so I was called, after my godfather Schimmelpreester), and my physical fineness and attractiveness. Yes, I have always believed myself favoured of fortune and of Heaven, and I may say that, on the whole, experience has borne me out. Indeed, it has been peculiarly characteristic of my career that whatever misfortunes and sufferings it may have contained have always seemed an exception to the natural order, a cloud, as it were, through which the sun

of my native luck continued to shine. After this digression into general-
ities, I shall continue to sketch in broad strokes the picture of my youth.

An imaginative child, my games of make-believe gave my family
much entertainment. I have often been told, and seem still to remember,
that when I was still in dresses I liked to pretend I was the Kaiser and
would persist in this game for hours at a time with the greatest determination. Sitting in my little go-cart, which my nurse would push around the
garden or the entrance hall of the house, I would draw down my mouth
as far as I could so that my upper lip was unnaturally lengthened and
would blink my eyes slowly until the strain and the strength of my emotions made them redden and fill with tears. Overwhelmed by a sense of my
age and dignity, I would sit silent in my little wagon, while my nurse
was instructed to inform all we met who I was, since I should have taken
any disregard of my fancy much amiss. "I am taking the Kaiser for a
drive," she would announce, bringing the flat of her hand to the side of
her head in an awkward salute, and everyone would pay me homage. In
particular, my godfather Schimmelpreester, a great joker, would encourage my pretence for all he was worth whenever we met. "Look, there he
goes, the old hero!" he would say with an exaggeratedly deep bow. Then
he would pretend to be the populace and, standing beside my path, would
shout: "Hurray, hurray!" throwing his hat, his cane, even his eyeglasses
into the air, and he would split his sides laughing when, from excess of
emotion, tears would roll down my long-drawn face.

I used to play the same sort of game when I was older and could no
longer demand the co-operation of grown-ups—which, however, I did not
miss, glorying as I did in the independent and self-sufficient exercise of
my imagination. One morning, for example, I awoke resolved to be an
eighteen-year-old prince named Karl, and I clung to this fantasy all day
long; indeed, for several days, for the inestimable advantage of this kind
of game is that it never needs to be interrupted, not even during the almost insupportable hours spent in school. Clothed in a sort of amiable
majesty, I moved about, holding lively imaginary conversations with the
governor or adjutant I had in fantasy assigned to myself; and the pride
and happiness I felt at my secret superiority are indescribable. What a
glorious gift is imagination, and what satisfactions it affords! The other
boys of the town seemed to me dull and limited indeed, since they obviously did not share my ability and were consequently ignorant of the
secret joys I could derive from it by a simple act of will, effortlessly and
without any outward preparation. They were common fellows, to be sure,
with coarse hair and red hands, and they would have had trouble persuad-
ing themselves that they were princes—and very foolish they would have
looked, too. Whereas my hair was silken soft, as it seldom is in the male
sex, and it was fair; like my blue-grey eyes, it provided a fascinating contrast to the golden brown of my skin, so that I hovered on the borderline

between blond and dark and might have been considered either. My hands, which I began to take care of early, were distinguished without being too narrow, never clammy, but dry and agreeably warm, with well-shaped nails that it was a pleasure to see. My voice, even before it changed, had an ingratiating tone and could fall so flatteringly upon the ear that I liked more than anything to listen to it myself, especially when I was alone and could blissfully engage in long, plausible, but quite meaningless conversations with my imaginary adjutant, accompanying them with extravagant gestures. Such personal advantages are mostly intangible and are recognizable only in their effect; they are, moreover, difficult to put into words, even for someone unusually talented. In any case, I could not conceal from myself that I was made of superior stuff, or, as people say, of finer clay, and I do not shrink from the charge of self-complacency in saying so. If someone accuses me of self-complacency, it is a matter of complete indifference to me, for I should have to be a fool or a hypocrite to pretend that I am of common stuff, and it is therefore in obedience to truth that I repeat that I am of the finest clay.

I grew up solitary, for my sister Olympia was several years older than I; I indulged in strange, introspective practises, of which I shall give two examples. First, I took it into my head to study the human will and to practise on myself its mysterious, sometimes supernatural effects. It is a well-known fact that the muscles controlling the pupils of our eyes react involuntarily to the intensity of the light falling upon them. I decided to bring this reaction under voluntary control. I would stand in front of my mirror, concentrating all my powers in a command to my pupils to contract or expand, banishing every other thought from my mind. My persistent efforts, let me assure you, were, in fact, crowned with success. At first as I stood bathed in sweat, my colour coming and going, my pupils would flicker erratically; but later I actually succeeded in contracting them to the merest points and then expanding them to great, round, mirror-like pools. The joy I felt at this success was almost terrifying and was accompanied by a shudder at the mystery of man.

There was another interior activity that often occupied me at that time and that even today has not lost its charm for me. I would ask myself: which is better, to see the world small or to see it big? The significance of the question was this: great men, I thought, field marshals, statesmen, empire-builders, and other leaders who rise through violence above the masses of mankind must be so constituted as to see the world small, like a chessboard, or they would never possess the ruthless coldness to deal so boldly and cavalierly with the weal and woe of the individual. Yet it was quite possible, on the other hand, that such a diminishing point of view, so to speak, might lead to one's doing nothing at all. For if you saw the world and the human beings in it as small and insignificant and were early persuaded that nothing was worth while, you could easily sink into indifference and indolence and contemptuously prefer your own peace of mind to any influence you might exert on the spirits of men. Added to that, your coldness and detachment would certainly give offence and cut you off from any possible success you might have achieved involuntarily. Is it preferable, then, I would ask myself, to regard the world and mankind as something great, glorious, and significant, justifying every effort to obtain some modicum of esteem and fame? Against this one might argue that with so magnifying and respectful a view one can easily fall a victim of self-depreciation and loss of confidence, so that the world passes you by as an uncertain, silly boy and gives itself to a more manly lover. On the other hand, such genuine credulity and artlessness has its advantages too, since men cannot but be flattered by the way you look up to them; and if you devote yourself to making this impression, it will give weight and seriousness to your life, lending it meaning in your own eyes and leading to your advancement. In this way I pondered, weighing the pros and cons. It has always been a part of my nature, however, to hold instinctively to the second position, considering the world a great and infinitely enticing phenomenon, offering priceless satisfactions and worthy in the highest degree of all my efforts and solicitude.

Visionary experiments and speculations of this kind served to isolate me inwardly from my contemporaries and schoolmates in the town, who spent their time in more conventional ways. But it is also true, as I was soon to learn, that these boys, the sons of winegrowers and government employees, had been warned by their parents to stay away from me. Indeed, when I experimentally invited one of them to our house, he told me to my face that he couldn't come because our family was not respectable. This pained me and made me covet an association that otherwise I should not have cared for. It must be admitted, however, that the town's opinion of our household had a certain justification.

I referred above to the disturbance in our family life caused by the presence of the Fräulein from Vevey. My poor father, in point of fact, was infatuated with the girl and pursued her until he gained his ends, or so it appeared, for quarrels arose between him and my mother and he left for Mainz, where he remained for several weeks enjoying a bachelor's life, as he had occasionally done before. My mother was entirely wrong in treating my poor father with such lack of respect. She was an unprepossessing woman and no less a prey to human weaknesses than he. My sister Olympia, a fat and inordinately sensual creature, who later had some success in comic opera, resembled her in this respect—the difference between them and my poor father being that theirs was a coarse-grained greed for pleasure, whereas his foibles were never without a certain grace. Mother and daughter lived on terms of unusual intimacy: I recall once seeing my mother measure Olympia's thigh with a tape measure, which gave me food for thought for several hours. Another time, when I was old enough to have some intuitive understanding of such matters though no words to express them, I was an unseen witness when my mother and sister began to flirt with a young painter who was at work in the house. He was a dark-eyed youth in a white smock, and they painted a green moustache on his face with his own paint. In the end they roused him to such a pitch that he pursued them giggling up the attic stairs.

Since my parents bored each other to distraction, they often invited guests from Mainz and Wiesbaden, and then our house was the scene of merriment and uproar. It was a gaudy crowd who attended these gatherings: actors and actresses, young businessmen, a sickly young infantry lieutenant who was later engaged to my sister; a Jewish banker with a wife who awesomely overflowed her jet-embroidered dress in every direction; a journalist in velvet waistcoat with a lock of hair over his brow, who brought a new helpmeet along every time. They would usually arrive for seven-o'clock dinner and the feasting, dancing, piano-playing, rough-housing, and shrieks of laughter went on all night. The tide of pleasure rose especially high at carnival time and at the vintage season. My father, who was very expert in such matters, would set off the most splendid fireworks in the garden; the whole company would wear masks and unearthly light would play upon the earthenware dwarfs. All restraint was abandoned. It was my misfortune at that time to have to attend the local high school and many mornings when I came down to the dining-room for breakfast, face freshly washed, at seven o'clock or half past, I would find the guests still sitting over coffee and liqueurs, sallow, rumpled, and blinking in the early light. They would give me an uproarious welcome.

When I was no more than half grown I was allowed, along with my sister Olympia, to take part in these festivities. Even when we were alone we always kept a good table, and my father drank champagne mixed with soda water. But at these parties there were endless courses prepared by a chef from Wiesbaden assisted by our own cook: the most tempting succession of sweets, savories, and ices: *Loreley extra cuvée* flowed in streams, but many good wines were served as well. There was for instance Berncasteler Doctor, whose bouquet especially appealed to me. In later life I became acquainted with still other notable brands and could, for instance, casually order *Grand Vin* Château Margaux or *Grand Cru* Château Mouton-Rothschild—two noble wines.

I love to recall the picture of my father presiding at the head of the table, with his white pointed beard, and his paunch spanned by a white silk waistcoat. His voice was weak and sometimes he would let his eyes drop in a self-conscious way, and yet enjoyment was written large on his flushed and shining face. "*C'est ça,*" he would say, "*épatant,*" "*parfaite-*

ment"—and with his fingers, which curved backwards at the tips, he would give delicate touches to the glasses, the napkins, and the silver. My mother and sister would surrender themselves to mindless gluttony interrupted only by giggling flirtations behind their fans with their tablemates.

After dinner, when cigar smoke began to eddy around the gas chandeliers, there were dancing and games of forfeit. As the evening advanced I used to be sent to bed; but since sleep was impossible in that din, I would wrap myself in my red woollen bedspread and in this becoming costume return to the feast, where I was received by all the ladies with cries of joy. Snacks and refreshments, punch, lemonade, herring salad, and wine jellies were served in relays until the morning coffee. Dancing was unconstrained and the games of forfeit became a pretext for kissing and fondling. The ladies, décolleté, bent low over the backs of chairs to give the gentlemen exciting glimpses of their bosoms, and the high point of the evening would come when some prankster turned out the gaslight amid general uproar and confusion.

It was mostly these social affairs that provoked the town gossip that called our household disreputable, but I learned early that it was the economic aspect of the situation that was principally in question. For it was rumoured (and with only too much justification) that my poor father's business was in desperate straits, and that the expensive fireworks and dinners would inevitably furnish the *coupe de grâce*. My sensitivity early made me aware of this general distrust, and it combined, as I have said, with certain peculiarities of my character to cause me first and last a good deal of pain. It was therefore all the more delightful to have the experience that I now set down with special pleasure.

The summer that I was eight years old my family and I went to spend several weeks at the famous near-by resort of Langenschwalbach. My father was taking mud baths for his gout, and my mother and sister made themselves conspicuous on the promenade by the exaggerated size of their hats. There as elsewhere our opportunities for social advancement were meagre. The natives, as usual, avoided us. Guests of the better class kept themselves very much to themselves as they usually do; and such society as we met did not have much to recommend it. Yet I liked Langenschwalbach and later on often made such resorts the scene of my activities. The tranquil, well-regulated existence and the sight of aristocratic, well-groomed people in the gardens or at sport satisfied an inner craving. But the strongest attraction of all was the daily concert given by a well-trained orchestra for the guests of the cure. Though I have never taken occasion to acquire any skill in that dreamlike art, I am a fanatical lover of music; even as a child I could not tear myself away from the pretty pavilion where a becomingly uniformed band played selections and potpourris under the direction of a leader who looked like a gypsy. For hours on end I would crouch on the steps of this little temple of art, enchanted to the marrow of my bones by the ordered succession of sweet sounds and watching with rapture every motion of the musicians as they manipulated their instruments. In particular I was thrilled by the gestures of the violinists, and when I went home I delighted my parents with an imitation performed with two sticks, one long and one short. The swinging movement of the left arm when producing a soulful tone, the soft gliding motion from one position to the next, the dexterity of the fingering in virtuoso passages and cadenzas, the fine and supple bowing of the right wrist, the cheek nestling in utter abandonment on the violin—all this I succeeded in reproducing so faithfully that the family, and especially my father, burst into enthusiastic applause. Being in high spirits because of the beneficial effects of the baths, he conceived the following little joke with the connivance of the long-haired, almost inarticulate little conductor. They bought a small, cheap violin and plentifully greased the bow with Vaseline. As a rule little attention was paid to my appearance, but now I was dressed in a pretty sailor suit complete with gold buttons and lanyard, silk stockings and shiny patent-leather shoes. And one Sunday afternoon at the hour of the promenade I took my place beside the little conductor and joined in the performance of a Hungarian dance, doing with my fiddle and Vaselined bow what I had done before with my two sticks. I make bold to say my success was complete.

The public, both distinguished and undistinguished, streamed up from all sides and crowded in front of the pavilion to look at the infant prodigy. My pale face, my complete absorption in my task, the lock of hair falling over my brow, my childish hands and wrists in the full, tapering sleeves of the becoming blue sailor suit—in short, my whole touching and astonishing little figure captivated all hearts. When I finished with the full sweep of the bow across all the fiddle strings, the garden resounded with applause and delighted cries from male and female throats. After the bandmaster had safely got my fiddle and bow out of the way, I was picked up and set down on the ground, where I was overwhelmed with praises and caresses. The most aristocratic ladies and gentlemen stroked my hair, patted my cheeks and hands, called me an angel child and an amazing little devil. An aged Russian princess, wearing enormous white side curls and dressed from head to toe in violet silk, took my head between her beringed hands and kissed my brow, beaded as it was with perspiration. Then in a burst of enthusiasm she snatched a lyre-shaped diamond brooch from her throat and pinned it on my blouse, amid a perfect torrent of ecstatic French. My family approached and my father made excuses for the defects of my playing on the score of my tender years. I was taken to the confectioner's, where at three different tables I was treated to chocolate and cream puffs. The children of the noble family of Siebenklingen, whom I had admired from a distance while they regarded me with haughty aloofness, came up and asked me to play croquet, and while our parents drank coffee together I went off with them in the seventh heaven of delight, my diamond brooch still on my blouse. That was one of the happiest days of my life, perhaps the happiest. A cry was raised that I should play again, and the management of the casino actually approached my father and asked for a repeat performance, but he refused, saying that he had only permitted me to play by way of exception and that repeated public appearances would not be consistent with my social position. Besides, our stay in Bad Langenschwalbach was drawing to a close. . . .

Disturbances of Personality Traits

III. In contrast to the other two types, this category focuses on long standing deviations in emotional control. There are three subtypes: the emotionally unstable, the passive-aggressive, and the compulsive. The emotionally unstable person is characterized by poor judgment under stress and a tendency to be excitable and highly emotional. His interpersonal relations are complicated by these intense emotional reactions. The passive-aggressive is characterized by one of three typical patterns: helpless dependent clinging, passive-aggressive obstruction and stubbornness, and aggressive-destructive reaction with morbid resentment.

Only one of the disturbances of personality traits has been illustrated. An example from Chekhov will emphasize how the compulsive character interacts with his environment in a controlling way at the same time that his defenses are, as shown in the "The Man in a Case," an insulation from life and emotion.

The Man in a Case

Anton Chekhov (*1860–1904*)

. . . There is no need to look far; two months ago a man called Byelikov, a colleague of mine, the Greek master, died in our town. You have heard of him, no doubt. He was remarkable for always wearing goloshes and a warm wadded coat, and carrying an umbrella even in the very finest weather. And his umbrella was in a case, and his watch was in a case made of grey chamois leather, and when he took out his penknife to sharpen his pencil, his penknife, too, was in a little case; and his face seemed to be in a case too, because he always hid it in his turned-up collar. He wore dark spectacles and flannel vests, stuffed up his ears with cotton-wool, and when he got into a cab always told the driver to put up the hood. In short, the man displayed a constant and insurmountable impulse to wrap himself in a covering, to make himself, so to speak, a case which would isolate him and protect him from external influences. Reality irritated him, frightened him, kept him in continual agitation, and, perhaps to justify his timidity, his aversion for the actual, he always praised the past and what had never existed; and even the classical languages which he taught were in reality for him goloshes and umbrellas in which he sheltered himself from real life.

" 'Oh, how sonorous, how beautiful is the Greek language!' he would say, with a sugary expression; and as though to prove his words he would screw up his eyes and, raising his finger, would pronounce 'Anthropos!'

"And Byelikov tried to hide his thoughts also in a case. The only things that were clear to his mind were government circulars and newspaper articles in which something was forbidden. When some proclamation prohibited the boys from going out in the streets after nine o'clock in the evening, or some article declared carnal love unlawful, it was to his mind clear and definite; it was forbidden, and that was enough. For him there was always a doubtful element, something vague and not fully expressed, in any sanction or permission. When a dramatic club or a reading-room or a tea-shop was licensed in the town, he would shake his head and say softly:

" 'It is all right, of course; it is all very nice, but I hope it won't lead to anything!'

"Every sort of breach of order, deviation or departure from rule, depressed him, though one would have thought it was no business of his. If one of his colleagues was late for church or if rumours reached him of some prank of the high-school boys, or one of the mistresses was seen late in the evening in the company of an officer, he was much disturbed, and said he hoped that nothing would come of it. At the teachers' meetings he simply oppressed us with his caution, his circumspection, and his characteristic reflection on the ill-behaviour of the young people in both male and female high-schools, the uproar in the classes. . . .

"Oh, he hoped it would not reach the ears of the authorities; oh, he hoped nothing would come of it; and he thought it would be a very good thing if Petrov were expelled from the second class and Yegorov from the fourth. And, do you know, by his sighs, his despondency, his black spectacles on his pale little face, a little face like a pole-cat's, you know,

he crushed us all, and we gave way, reduced Petrov's and Yegorov's
marks for conduct, kept them in, and in the end expelled them both. He
had a strange habit of visiting our lodgings. He would come to a teacher's,
would sit down, and remain silent, as though he were carefully inspecting
something. He would sit like this in silence for an hour or two and then
go away. This he called 'maintaining good relations with his colleagues';
and it was obvious that coming to see us and sitting there was tiresome to
him, and that he came to see us simply because he considered it his duty
as our colleague. We teachers were afraid of him. And even the head-
master was afraid of him. Would you believe it, our teachers were all
intellectual, right-minded people, brought up on Turgenev and Shtchedrin, yet this little chap, who always went about with goloshes and an
umbrella, had the whole high-school under his thumb for fifteen long
years! High-school, indeed—he had the whole town under his thumb!
Our ladies did not get up private theatricals on Saturdays for fear he
should hear of it, and the clergy dared not eat meat or play cards in his
presence. Under the influence of people like Byelikov we have got into
the way of being afraid of everything in our town for the last ten or fifteen years. They are afraid to speak aloud, afraid to send letters, afraid to
make acquaintances, afraid to read books, afraid to help the poor, to teach
people to read and write. . . ."

Ivan Ivanovitch cleared his throat, meaning to say something, but
first lighted his pipe, gazed at the moon, and then said, with pauses:

"Yes, intellectual, right minded people read Shtchedrin and Turgenev, Buckle, and all the rest of them, yet they knocked under and put
up with it . . . that's just how it is."

"Byelikov lived in the same house as I did," Burkin went on, "on the
same storey, his door facing mine; we often saw each other, and I knew
how he lived when he was at home. And at home it was the same story:
dressing-gown, nightcap, blinds, bolts, a perfect succession of prohibi-
tions and restrictions of all sorts, and—'Oh, I hope nothing will come of
it!' Lenten fare was bad for him, yet he could not eat meat, as people
might perhaps say Byelikov did not keep the fasts, and he ate freshwater
fish with butter—not a Lenten dish, yet one could not say that it was meat.
He did not keep a female servant for fear people might think evil of him,
but had as cook an old man of sixty, called Afanasy, half-witted and
given to tippling, who had once been an officer's servant and could cook
after a fashion. This Afanasy was usually standing at the door with his
arms folded; with a deep sigh, he would mutter always the same thing:

" 'There are plenty of *them* about nowadays!'

"Byelikov had a little bedroom like a box; his bed had curtains.
When he went to bed he covered his head over; it was hot and stuffy; the
wind battered on the closed doors; there was a droning noise in the stove
and a sound of sighs from the kitchen—ominous sighs. . . . And he felt

frightened under the bed-clothes. He was afraid that something might happen, that Afanasy might murder him, that thieves might break in, and so he had troubled dreams all night, and in the morning, when we went together to the high-school, he was depressed and pale, and it was evident that the high-school full of people excited dread and aversion in his whole being, and that to walk beside me was irksome to a man of his solitary temperament. . . .

CHAPTER eight

The Problem of Identity:
An Approach to the Study
of Social Adaptation

The categories of character pathology illustrated in the previous chapter have a pragmatic value as labels in everyday clinical psychiatric usage. They are, however, pathological caricatures rather than subtle portraits of the stamp life leaves on people. What is in danger of being overlooked is what is perhaps most important: the neurotic aspects of character that develop in most individuals attempting to adapt and function adequately in a society which, although necessary for approaching the highest ideals of men, is by its very nature apt to constrain and produce conflict.

No man has brought greater clarity to this problem than Erick Erickson. He has explored man's relation to society in a systematic way. Using the concept of identity, he has focused much of what was useful both in the Freudian and neo-Freudian points of view. The concept of identity partially unlocks the problem of character in both its moral and executive sense. It asks not only *what am I*, but *who am I*. In Erickson's hands the question of identity and social adaptation is examined for each stage of human development.

The following literary passages illustrate in different individuals at different age levels the importance and the problem of identity.

Childhood—The Problem
of Self Differentiation

I. The first excerpt is from *High Wind in Jamaica,*
a story of incredible nightmare-like insight into the minds
of children. The child in this brief section suddenly discovers
her separateness, her uniqueness, her intactness. This is the
crystallization of a sense of self, the birth of a body identity.

A High Wind in Jamaica
Richard Hughes (1900–   )

. . . And then an event did occur, to Emily, of considerable importance. She suddenly realised who she was.

There is little reason that one can see why it should not have happened to her five years earlier, or even five later; and none, why it should
have come that particular afternoon.

She had been playing houses in a nook right in the bows, behind the
windlass (on which she had hung a devil's-claw as a door-knocker); and
tiring of it was walking rather aimlessly aft, thinking vaguely about some
bees and a fairy queen, when it suddenly flashed into her mind that she
was *she.*

She stopped dead, and began looking over all of her person which
came within the range of her eyes. She could not see much, except a fore-
shortened view of the front of her frock, and her hands when she lifted
them for inspection; but it was enough for her to form a rough idea of
the little body she suddenly realised to be hers.

She began to laugh, rather mockingly. "Well!" she thought, in effect. "Fancy *you,* of all people, going and getting caught like this!—You
can't get out of it now, not for a very long time: you'll have to go
through with being a child, and growing up, and getting old, before you'll
be quit of this mad prank!"

Determined to avoid any interruption of this highly important occasion, she began to climb the ratlines, on her way to her favourite perch
at the masthead. Each time she moved an arm or a leg in this simple
action, however, it struck her with fresh amazement to find them obeying
her so readily. Memory told her, of course, that they had always done so
before: but before, she had never realised how surprising this was.

Once settled on her perch, she began examining the skin of her hands with the utmost care: for it was *hers*. She slipped a shoulder out of the top of her frock; and having peeped in to make sure she really was continuous under her clothes, she shrugged it up to touch her cheek. The contact of her face and the warm bare hollow of her shoulder gave her a comfortable thrill, as if it was the caress of some kind friend. But whether the feeling came to her through her cheek or her shoulder, which was the caresser and which the caressed, that no analysis could tell her.

Once fully convinced of this astonishing fact, that she was now Emily Bas-Thornton (why she inserted the "now" she did not know, for she certainly imagined no transmigrational nonsense of having been any-one else before), she began seriously to reckon its implications.

First, what agency had so ordered it that out of all the people in the world who she might have been, she was this particular one, this Emily; born in such-and-such a year out of all the years in Time, and encased in this particular rather pleasing little casket of flesh? Had she chosen her-self, or had God done it?

At this, another consideration: who was God? She had heard a ter-rible lot about Him, always: but the question of His identity had been left vague, as much taken for granted as her own. Wasn't she perhaps God, herself? Was it that she was trying to remember? However, the more she tried, the more it eluded her. (How absurd, to disremember such an important point as whether one was God or not!) So she let it slide: per-haps it would come back to her later.

Secondly, why had all this not occurred to her before? She had been alive for over ten years, now, and it had never once entered her head. She felt like a man who suddenly remembers at eleven o'clock at night, sitting in his own arm-chair, that he had accepted an invitation to go out to dinner that night. There is no reason for him to remember it now: but there seems equally little why he should not have remembered it in time to keep his engagement. How could he have sat there all the evening, without being disturbed by the slightest misgiving? How could Emily have gone on being Emily for ten years, without once noticing this ap-parently obvious fact?

It must not be supposed that she argued it all out in this ordered, but rather longwinded fashion. Each consideration came to her in a mo-mentary flash, quite innocent of words; and in between her mind lazed along, either thinking of nothing or returning to her bees and the fairy queen. If one added up the total of her periods of conscious thought, it would probably reach something between four and five seconds; nearer five, perhaps; but it was spread out over the best part of an hour.

Well then, granted she was Emily, what were the consequences, be-sides enclosure in that particular little body (which now began on its own

account to be aware of a sort of unlocated itch, most probably somewhere on the right thigh), and lodgement behind a particular pair of
eyes?

It implied a whole series of circumstances. In the first place, there
was her family, a number of brothers and sisters from whom, before, she
had never entirely dissociated herself; but now she got such a sudden
feeling of being a discrete person that they seemed as separate from her as
the ship itself. However, willy-nilly she was almost as tied to them as she
was to her body. And then there was this voyage, this ship, this mast
round which she had wound her legs. She began to examine it with almost
as vivid an illumination as she had studied the skin of her hands. And
when she came down from the mast, what would she find at the bottom?
There would be Jonsen, and Otto, and the crew: the whole fabric of a
daily life which up to now she had accepted as it came, but which now
seemed vaguely disquieting. What was going to happen? Were there
disasters running about loose, disasters which her rash marriage to the
body of Emily Thornton made her vulnerable to?

A sudden terror struck her: did anyone know? (Know, I mean, that
she was someone in particular, Emily—perhaps even God—not just any
little girl.) She could not tell why, but the idea terrified her. It would be
bad enough if they should discover she was a particular person—but if
they should discover she was God! At all costs she must hide *that* from
them.—But suppose they knew already, had simply been hiding it from
her (as guardians might from an infant king)? In that case, as in the other,
the only thing to do was to continue to behave as if she did not know,
and so outwit them.

But if she was God, why not turn all the sailors into white mice, or
strike Margaret blind, or cure somebody, or do some other Godlike act
of the kind? Why should she hide it? She never really asked herself why:
but instinct prompted her strongly of the necessity. Of course, there was
the element of doubt (suppose she had made a mistake, and the miracle
missed fire): but more largely it was the feeling that she would be able
to deal with the situation so much better when she was a little older. Once
she had declared herself there would be no turning back; it was much
better to keep her godhead up her sleeve, for the present.

Grown-ups embark on a life of deception with considerable misgiving, and generally fail. But not so children. A child can hide the most ap-
palling secret without the least effort, and is practically secure against
detection. Parents, finding that they see through their child in so many
places the child does not know of, seldom realise that, if there is some
point the child really gives his mind to hiding, their chances are nil.

So Emily had no misgivings when she determined to preserve her
secret, and needed have none. . . .

Adolescence—The Problem
of Sexual Identity

II. The development of a sense of self and a body
identity does not end in childhood. One of the major tasks of
the adolescent is to accept his sexual development and assimilate
the biological changes into an adequate masculine or feminine
role. This must be done while coping with the bisexual
elements that exist to varying degrees in all humans.
Sherwood Anderson has brilliantly dramatized a sexual identity
crisis in a young man, highlighting the terror evoked by
the emergence of his feminine impulses.

THE MAN WHO BECAME A WOMAN
Sherwood Anderson (*1876–1941*)

. . . That was one of the best and sweetest feelings I've
ever had in my whole life, being in that warm stall alone with that horse
that night. I had told the other swipes that I would go up and down the
row of stalls now and then and have an eye on the other horses, but I had
altogether forgotten my promise now. I went and stood with my back
against the side of the stall, thinking how mean and low and all balled-up
and twisted-up human beings can become, and how the best of them are
likely to get that way any time, just because they are human beings and
not simple and clear in their minds, and inside themselves, as animals are,
maybe.

Perhaps you know how a person feels at such a moment. There are
things you think of, odd little things you had thought you had forgotten.
Once, when you were a kid, you were with your father, and he was all
dressed up, as for a funeral or Fourth of July, and was walking along a
street holding your hand. And you were going past a railroad station, and
there was a woman standing. She was a stranger in your town and was
dressed as you had never seen a woman dressed before, and never thought
you would see one, looking so nice. Long afterwards you knew that was
because she had lovely taste in clothes, such as so few women have really,
but then you thought she must be a queen. You had read about queens in

fairy stories and the thoughts of them thrilled you. What lovely eyes the strange lady had and what beautiful rings she wore on her fingers.

Then your father came out, from being in the railroad station, maybe to set his watch by the station clock, and took you by the hand and he and the woman smiled at each other, in an embarrassed kind of way, and you kept looking longingly back at her, and when you were out of her hearing you asked your father if she really were a queen. And it may be that your father was one who wasn't so very hot on democracy and a free country and talked-up bunk about a free citizenry, and he said he hoped she was a queen, and maybe, for all he knew, she was.

Or maybe, when you get jammed up as I was that night, and can't get things clear about yourself or other people and why you are alive, or for that matter why anyone you can think about is alive, you think, not of people at all but of other things you have seen and felt—like walking along a road in the snow in the winter, perhaps out in Iowa, and hearing soft warm sounds in a barn close to the road, or of another time when you were on a hill and the sun was going down and the sky suddenly became a great soft-colored bowl, all glowing like a jewel-handled bowl, a great queen in some far away mighty kingdom might have put on a vast table out under the tree, once a year, when she invited all her loyal and loving subjects to come and dine with her.

I can't, of course, figure out what you try to think about when you are as desolate as I was that night. Maybe you are like me and inclined to think of women, and maybe you are like a man I met once, on the road, who told me that when he was up against it he never thought of anything but grub and a big nice clean warm bed to sleep in. "I don't care about anything else and I don't ever let myself think of anything else," he said. "If I was like you and went to thinking about women sometime I'd find myself hooked up to some skirt, and she'd have the old double cross on me, and the rest of my life maybe I'd be working in some factory for her and her kids."

As I say, there I was anyway, up there alone with that horse in that warm stall in that dark lonesome fair ground and I had that feeling about being sick at the thought of human beings and what they could be like.

Well, suddenly I got again the queer feeling I'd had about him once or twice before, I mean the feeling about our understanding each other in some way I can't explain.

So having it again I went over to where he stood and began running my hands all over his body, just because I loved the feel of him and as sometimes, to tell the plain truth, I've felt about touching with my hands the body of a woman I've seen and who I thought was lovely too. I ran my hands over his head and neck and then down over his hard firm round body and then over his flanks and down his legs. His flanks quivered a little I remember and once he turned his head and stuck his cold nose down along my neck and nipped my shoulder a little, in a soft playful way. It hurt a little but I didn't care.

So then I crawled up through a hole into the loft above thinking that night was over anyway and glad of it, but it wasn't, not by a long sight.

As my clothes were all soaking wet and as we race track swipes didn't own any such things as night-gowns or pajamas I had to go to bed naked, of course.

But we had plenty of horse blankets and so I tucked myself in between a pile of them and tried not to think any more that night. The being with Pick-it-boy and having him close right under me that way made me feel a little better.

Then I was sound asleep and dreaming and—bang like being hit with a club by someone who has sneaked up behind you—I got another wallop.

What I suppose is that, being upset the way I was, I had forgotten to bolt the door to Pick-it-boy's stall down below and two Negro men had come in there, thinking they were in their own place, and had climbed up through the hole where I was. They were half lit up but not what you might call dead drunk, and I suppose they were up against something a couple of white swipes, who had some money in their pockets, wouldn't have been up against.

What I mean is that a couple of white swipes, having liquored themselves up and being down there in the town on a bat, if they wanted a woman or a couple of women would have been able to find them. There is always a few women of that kind can be found around any town I've ever seen or heard of, and of course a bartender would have given them the tip where to go.

But a Negro, up there in that country, where there aren't any, or anyway mighty few Negro women, wouldn't know what to do when he felt that way and would be up against it.

It's so always. Burt and several other Negroes I've known pretty well have talked to me about it, lots of times. You take now a young Negro man —not a race track swipe or a tramp or any other low-down kind of a fellow —but, let us say, one who has been to college, and has behaved himself and tried to be a good man, the best he could, and be clean, as they say. He isn't any better off, is he? If he has made himself some money and wants to go sit in a swell restaurant, or go to hear some good music, or see a good play at the theatre, he gets what we used to call on the tracks, "the messy end of the dung fork," doesn't he?

And even in such a low-down place as what people call a "bad house" it's the same way. The white swipes and others can go into a place where they have Negro women fast enough, and they do it too, but you let a Negro swipe try it the other way around and see how he comes out.

You see, I can think this whole thing out fairly now, sitting here in my own house and writing, and with my wife Jessie in the kitchen making a pie or something, and I can show just how the two Negro men who came into that loft, where I was asleep, were justified in what they did, and I can preach about how the Negroes are up against it in this country, like a daisy, but I tell you what, I didn't think things out that way that night.

For, you understand, what they thought, they being half liquored-up, and when one of them had jerked the blankets off me, was that I was a woman. One of them carried a lantern but it was smoky and dirty and didn't give out much light. So they must have figured it out—my body being pretty white and slender then, like a young girl's body I suppose— that some white swipe had brought me up there. The kind of girl around a town that will come with a swipe to a race track on a rainy night aren't very fancy females but you'll find that kind in the towns all right. I've seen many a one in my day.

And so, I figure, these two big buck niggers, being piped that way, just made up their minds they would snatch me away from the white swipe who had brought me out there, and who had left me lying carelessly around.

"Jes' you lie still honey. We ain't gwine hurt you none," one of them said, with a little chuckling laugh that had something in it besides a laugh, too. It was the kind of laugh that gives you the shivers.

The devil of it was I couldn't say anything, not even a word. Why I couldn't yell out and say "What the hell," and just kid them a little and shoo them out of there I don't know, but I couldn't. I tried and tried so that my throat hurt but I didn't say a word. I just lay there staring at them.

It was a mixed-up night. I've never gone through another night like it.

Was I scared? Lord Almighty, I'll tell you what, I was scared.

Because the two big black faces were leaning right over me now, and I could feel their liquored-up breaths on my cheeks, and their eyes were shining in the dim light from that smoky lantern, and right in the centre of their eyes was that dancing flickering light I've told you about your seeing in the eyes of wild animals, when you were carrying a lantern through the woods at night.

It was a puzzler! All my life, you see—me never having had any sisters, and at that time never having had a sweetheart either—I had been dreaming and thinking about women, and I suppose I'd always been dreaming about a pure innocent one, for myself, made for me by God, maybe. Men are that way. No matter how big they talk about "let the women go hang," they've always got that notion tucked away inside themselves, somewhere. It's a kind of chesty man's notion, I suppose, but they've got it and the kind of up-and-coming women we have nowdays who are always saying, "I'm as good as a man and will do what the men do," are on the wrong trail if they have really ever want to, what you might say "hog-tie" a fellow of their own.

So I had invented a kind of princess, with black hair and a slender willowy body to dream about. And I thought of her as being shy and afraid to ever tell anything she really felt to anyone but just me. I suppose I fancied that if I ever found such a woman in the flesh I would be the strong sure one and she the timid shrinking one.

And now I was that woman, or something like her, myself.

I gave a kind of wriggle, like a fish you have just taken off the hook. What I did next wasn't a thought-out thing. I was caught and I squirmed, that's all.

The two niggers both jumped at me but somehow—the lantern having been kicked over and having gone out the first move they made—well in some way, when they both lunged at me they missed.

As good luck would have it my feet found the hole, where you put hay down to the horse in the stall below, and through which we crawled up when it was time to go to bed in our blankets up in the hay, and down I slid, not bothering to try to find the ladder with my feet but just letting myself go.

In less than a second I was out of doors in the dark and the rain and the two blacks were down the hole and out the door of the stall after me.

How long or how far they really followed me I suppose I'll never know. It was black dark and raining hard now and a roaring wind had begun to blow. Of course, my body being white; it must have made some kind of a faint streak in the darkness as I ran, and anyway I thought they could see me and I knew I couldn't see them and that made my terror ten times worse. Every minute I thought they would grab me.

You know how it is when a person is all upset and full of terror as I was. I suppose maybe the two niggers followed me for a while, running across the muddy race track and into the grove of trees that grew in the oval inside the track, but likely enough, after just a few minutes, they gave up the chase and went back, found their own place and went to sleep. They were liquored-up, as I've said, and maybe partly funning too.

But I didn't know that, if they were. As I ran I kept hearing sounds, sounds made by the rain coming down through the dead old leaves left on the trees and by the wind blowing, and it may be that the sound that scared me most of all was my own bare feet stepping on a dead branch and breaking it or something like that.

There was something strange and scary, a steady sound, like a heavy man running and breathing hard, right at my shoulder. It may have been my own breath, coming quick and fast. And I thought I heard that chuckling laugh I'd heard up in the loft, the laugh that sent the shivers right down through me. Of course every tree I came close to looked like a man standing there, ready to grab me, and I kept dodging and going—

bang—into other trees. My shoulders kept knocking against trees in that way and the skin was all knocked off, and every time it happened I thought a big black hand had come down and clutched at me and was tearing my flesh.

How long it went on I don't know, maybe an hour, maybe five minutes. But anyway the darkness didn't let up, and the terror didn't let up, and I couldn't, to save my life, scream or make any sound.

Just why I couldn't I don't know. Could it be because at the time I was a woman, while at the same time I wasn't a woman? It may be that I was too ashamed of having turned into a girl and being afraid of a man to make any sound. I don't know about that. It's over my head.

But anyway I couldn't make a sound. I tried and tried and my throat hurt from trying and no sound came.

And then, after a long time, or what seemed like a long time, I got out from among the trees inside the track and was on the track itself again. I thought the two black men were still after me, you understand, and I ran like a madman.

Of course, running along the track that way, it must have been up the back stretch, I came after a time to where the old slaughter-house stood, in that field, beside the track. I knew it by its ungodly smell, scared as I was. Then, in some way, I managed to get over the high old fairground fence and was in the field, where the slaughter-house was.

All the time I was trying to yell or scream, or be sensible and tell those two black men that I was a man and not a woman, but I couldn't make it. And then I heard a sound like a board cracking or breaking in the fence and thought they were still after me.

So I kept on running like a crazy man, in the field, and just then I stumbled and fell over something. I've told you how the old slaughter-house field was filled with bones, that had been lying there a long time and had all been washed white. There were heads of sheep and cows and all kinds of things.

And when I fell and pitched forward I fell right into the midst of something, still and cold and white.

It was probably the skeleton of a horse lying there. In small towns like that, they take an old worn-out horse, that has died, and haul him off to some field outside of town and skin him for the hide, that they can sell for a dollar or two. It doesn't make any difference what the horse has been, that's the way he usually ends up. Maybe even Pick-it-boy, or O My Man, or a lot of other good fast ones I've seen and known have ended that way by this time.

And so I think it was the bones of a horse lying there and he must have been lying on his back. The birds and wild animals had picked all his flesh away and the rain had washed his bones clean.

Anyway I fell and pitched forward and my side got cut pretty deep and my hands clutched at something. I had fallen right in between the ribs of the horse and they seemed to wrap themselves around me close. And my hands, clutching upwards, had got hold of the cheeks of that dead horse and the bones of his cheeks were cold as ice with the rain washing over them. White bones wrapped around me and white bones in my hands.

There was a new terror now that seemed to go down to the very bottom of me, to the bottom of the inside of me, I mean. It shook me like I have seen a rat in a barn shaken by a dog. It was a terror like a big wave that hits you when you are walking on a seashore, maybe. You see it coming and you try to run and get away but when you start to run inshore there is a stone cliff you can't climb. So the wave comes high as a mountain, and there it is, right in front of you and nothing in all this world can stop it. And now it had knocked you down and rolled and tumbled you over and over and washed you clean, clean, but dead maybe.

And that's the way I felt—I seemed to myself dead with blind terror. It was a feeling like the finger of God running down your back and burning you clean, I mean.

It burned all that silly nonsense about being a girl right out of me.

I screamed at last and the spell that was on me was broken. I'll bet the scream I let out of me could have been heard a mile and a half.

Right away I felt better and crawled out from among the pile of bones, and then I stood on my own feet again and I wasn't a woman, or a young girl any more but a man and my own self, and as far as I know I've been that way ever since. Even the black night seemed warm and alive now, like a mother might be to a kid in the dark.

Only I couldn't go back to the race track because I was blubbering and crying and was ashamed of myself and of what a fool I had made of myself. Someone might see me and I couldn't stand that, not at that moment.

So I went across the field, walking now, not running like a crazy man, and pretty soon I came to a fence and crawled over and got into another field, in which there was a straw stack, I just happened to find in the pitch darkness.

The straw stack had been there a long time and some sheep had nibbled away at it until they had made a pretty deep hole, like a cave, in the side of it. I found the hole and crawled in and there were some sheep in there, about a dozen of them.

When I came in, creeping on my hands and knees, they didn't make much fuss, just stirred around a little and then settled down.

So I settled down amongst them too. They were warm and gentle and kind, like Pick-it-boy, and being in there with them made me feel better than I would have felt being with any human person I knew at that time.

So I settled down and slept after a while, and when I woke up it was daylight and not very cold and the rain was over. The clouds were breaking away from the sky now and maybe there would be a fair the next week but if there was I knew I wouldn't be there to see it.

Because what I expected to happen did happen. I had to go back across the fields and the fairground to the place where my clothes were, right in the broad daylight, and me stark naked, and of course I knew someone would be up and would raise a shout, and every swipe and every driver would stick his head out and would whoop with laughter.

And there would be a thousand questions asked, and I would be too mad and too ashamed to answer, and would perhaps begin to blubber, and that would make me more ashamed than ever.

It all turned out just as I expected, except that when the noise and the shouts of laughter were going it the loudest, Burt came out of the stall where O My Man was kept, and when he saw me he didn't know what was the matter but he knew something was up that wasn't on the square and for which I wasn't to blame.

So he got so all-fired mad he couldn't speak for a minute, and then he grabbed a pitchfork and began prancing up and down before the other stalls, giving that gang of swipes and drivers such a royal old dressing-down as you never heard. You should have heard him sling language. It was grand to hear.

And while he was doing it I sneaked up into the loft, blubbering because I was so pleased and happy to hear him swear that way, and I got my wet clothes on quick and got down and gave Pick-it-boy a good-bye kiss on the cheek and lit out.

The last I saw of all that part of my life was Burt, still going it, and yelling out for the man who had put up a trick on me to come out and get what was coming to him. He had the pitchfork in his hand and was swinging it around, and every now and then he would make a kind of lunge at a tree or something, he was so mad through, and there was no one else in sight at all. And Burt didn't even see me cutting out along the fence through a gate and down the hill and out of the race-horse and the tramp life for the rest of my days.

Young Adulthood—The Problem of Vocational Identification

III a.   The young man searching for an identity must come to terms with what he will be in life. His vocational choice is an important part of this identity. Gerardo Mucchietto, the hero of Moravia's story, is not satisfied with

the niche his work is pushing him towards. He is reaching
out for something larger and more meaningful, until life
pushes him back again.

The Ruin of Humanity

Alberto Moravia   (1907–   )

About the middle of February the north wind, which
had made me feel so wretched during the winter, dropped, the sky filled
with clouds, and a moist breeze, which seemed to be coming from the
sea, started to blow. At the soft breath of this breeze I felt myself coming
to life again, although in a melancholy sort of way, as if it were whispering in my ear: "Come along, cheer up, while there's life there's hope."
But, just because I felt that winter was over and spring beginning, I knew
that I could no longer bear to go and work in my uncle's workshop. I
had gone into the workshop a year before, like a train going into a tunnel,
and I had not come out yet and I could not even see daylight at the other
end. Not that the work was unpleasant or repugnant to me personally:
there are worse jobs. The workshop consisted of a large shed, situated at
the far end of an enclosed piece of ground which served as a depôt for a
brick factory, halfway along the Via della Magliana. Inside the shed the
air was always full of white, flourlike sawdust, as in a mill; and in the
midst of this cloud of dust, and of the continuous humming of saws and
electric lathes, we workers and my uncle, looking like floury millers,
moved about, busy from morning till night making furniture and fittings.
My uncle, poor man, loved me like a son, the workmen were all good
chaps and, as I have already said, the work was not repugnant: first a tree-
trunk, of oak or maple or chestnut, long, twisted, leaning up against the
wall of the workshop, with all its bark upon it and even, still remaining
under the bark, the ants that had inhabited it when it was a tree; then,
after the saw had dealt with it, so many clean, white planks; then, out of
these planks, with the lathe or the plane or other tools, as occasion demanded, table-legs, parts of wardrobes, cornices; and finally, after the
piece of furniture had been nailed and screwed and glued together, the
painting and polishing. For anyone who takes pleasure in his work, this
gradual progress from a tree-trunk to a piece of furniture may become a
passion; it is always interesting, or, at the least, it is never boring. But
evidently I am made in a different way to other people: after a few
months, I could not bear the work any longer. It was not that I am not a

good worker, but that I like, every little while, to pause in my work and look round me—just so as to see who I am and where I am and what point I've reached. My uncle, on the other hand, was exactly the opposite: he was always working, fiercely, passionately, never stopping to take breath or reflect; and thus, from a chair to a bracket, from a bracket to a wardrobe, from a wardrobe to a night-table, from a night-table to a chair, he had turned fifty—for that was his age—and you could see that he would go on in the same way until his death, which would be rather like the death of a lathe that falls to pieces or a saw that loses its teeth, the death, in fact, of a tool and not of a man. And on Sundays, indeed, when he put on his best suit and walked very slowly along the pavements of the Via Arenula in company with his wife and children, his eyes half closed, his mouth twisted, and two deep lines between his mouth and his eyes, he really looked like a discarded, useless, broken tool; and I could not help remembering that he had acquired that appearance by stooping over his lathe and his saw and screwing up his eyes in a perpetual cloud of sawdust; and I said to myself that life was not worth living unless you paused now and then and reflected that you *were* alive.

The bus that starts from the Trastevere station goes out into the country and back. Peasants, labourers and all sorts of poor people bring mud into it on their boots, and the smell of sweat from their working clothes, and perhaps a few insects as well. And so, at the starting-point, they spray some kind of stinking disinfectant on the floor and even on the seats, which catches you in the throat and, like an onion, makes you weep. On one of those soft February mornings, while I was waiting—my eyes full of tears because of the disinfectant—for the bus to start, the wind from the sea, coming in through the windows, gave me a great longing to go off on my own account, to pause for a little and reflect about myself. And so, when I got off the bus near the workshop, instead of going to the right, towards the shed, I went to the left, towards the meadows that lie between the main road and the Tiber. I walked off over the pallid grass, in the gentle, moist wind, facing a sky full of white clouds. The Tiber itself I could not see, because at that point it runs through a dip in the ground; away beyond it I could see abandoned factories, a big building with arches looking like a great dovecot, and a church with a dome and pillars that support nothing and look like the wooden pillars in a child's building game. Behind me was the industrial district of Rome—tall chimneys with long plumes of black smoke, factory sheds full of big windows, the low, broad cylinders of two or three gasometers and the high, narrow ones of silos. When I thought of the workmen toiling in those factories, my leisure seemed to me even more agreeable. I felt full of cunning and watchfulness, as though I were going out hunting. And hunting indeed I was—not for game, however, but for myself.

When I reached the river, at a point where the bank is not so very steep, I slithered down the slope to the edge and sat down amongst the bushes. Only one step from my feet ran the Tiber, and I could see it twisting through the countryside like a snake, the dazzling light from the cloudy sky reflected in its yellow, wrinkled surface. On the other side of the river were more pale green meadows and, scattered over them, sheep nibbling at the grass, sheep with puffed-out, dirty wool, and here and there a perfectly white lamb, whose wool had not yet had time to go grey. I sat clasping my knees and stared at the yellow water, which at this point formed a little whirlpool from which a black branch projected, shaggy and untidy and looking like the hair of a drowned woman. And then, in the silence, with the branch, black as ebony, quivering from the force of the current but not moving, I felt all at once as though inspired; and, not with thought but with a feeling more profound than thought, I seemed to have understood something of great importance. Or rather, to be able to understand it, if only I did my utmost to grasp it. This thing, in fact, was poised delicately; it was like having, as they say, a word on the tip of one's tongue. And, in order to hold on to it and prevent its falling back into the darkness, I said, suddenly, aloud: "My name is Gerardo Mucchietto."

Immediately a mocking voice from above said: "Commonly called Mucchio. . . . Well, well, are you talking to yourself?"

I turned round and right above me saw, standing on the edge of the bank, the daughter of the custodian of the brick-yard, Gioconda, in a black velvet skirt and a pink sweater, stockingless, her hair fluttering in the wind. Now, of all the people I knew in the whole world, Gioconda was the one I would least have wished to see at that moment. She had taken a fancy to me and she persecuted me, although I had made it plain to her in every possible way that I did not care for her. I had an immediate impulse to say something unpleasant to her, so that she should go away and leave me alone to return to the thing I had been on the point of grasping when she arrived. Without moving, I said to her: "Take care, you're showing too much leg."

But brazenly she slid down beside me. "D'you mind if I keep you company?" she asked.

"I don't know what to do with your company," I said, still without looking at her; "and besides, how can you sit on the ground here, in all this dust?"

But she lifted up her dress and sat down, well satisfied, saying: "I haven't much on underneath, anyhow." The thing I wanted to think about was still there, luckily, perched on the edge of my mind, like a bird on a window-sill. Gioconda, in the meantime, all sweet and sugary, was clinging on to my arm and saying: "Gerardo, why are you so faithless? . . . I *am* so fond of you."

"I'm not faithless, it's just that I don't like you, that's all."

"Why don't you like me?"

I said hastily, fearing that, as I spoke, the thing I wanted to think about might vanish: "I don't like you because you've got a big red face covered with pimples. . . . You look like a cabbage rose. . . ."

What would most women have done after a remark like that? Gone away at once. She, on the contrary, pressed herself close up against me and said coyly: "Gerardo dear, why can't you be nicer to me?"

"All right, I will be," I said desperately, "provided you go away."

"Why, were you expecting some other woman, Gerardo dear?"

"No, no one; I wanted to be alone."

"Why alone? No, let's stay together. . . . It's so lovely to be together."

This time I said nothing: the thing was still there, on the edge of my mind, but I felt that any trifle would be enough to drive it back into the darkness out of which it had come. It was at this moment that Gioconda exclaimed: "Would you like me to guess what you're thinking about?"

Stung to the quick, I answered: "You won't guess if you try for a hundred years."

"But I tell you I *can* guess. . . . Now, let's see if I'm right. I say you were thinking about these socks I'm wearing rolled down to the ankle, that match my sweater. . . . Be truthful, that's what you were thinking about." As she spoke she held out her leg, which was big and red and covered with fair hairs, displaying her foot in its strawberry-coloured sock. I could not help raising my eyes and looking at her foot, and then, all of a sudden, I became aware that the thing had fallen back over the edge, down into the darkness. I no longer felt anything, I no longer understood anything, I was empty, dead, inert, like the stakes of seasoned wood that my uncle kept propped up against the workshop wall. At the thought that I had lost sight of that most beautiful and important thing through the chatter of this stupid girl, I was seized suddenly with an immense rage and I cried out, turning brusquely towards her: "Why did you come here? . . . You're my evil genius. . . . Couldn't you have left me alone?" And, since she continued to squeeze my arm, I tore myself away from her and hit her on the head. But she clung to me obstinately, although I beat her on her big blonde head: so then I jumped up, seized her by the hair and threw her down on the gravel and trampled on her with my feet, all over her body and even on her head. Rolled up into a ball with her face in her hands, she groaned and let forth a shriek or two, but made no attempt at resistance: possibly she was pleased. However, when I was tired of trampling on her, she got up and, all covered with dust, went off sobbing. I shouted loudly after her: "You women are the ruin of humanity." Still sobbing, she went off down a track along the gravelly bed of the Tiber and disappeared.

But the thing, by this time, had taken flight, and now, although I was alone, I felt just as inert and dull and empty as when Gioconda had been there. There was nothing to be done, for that day anyhow; and there was no knowing how long it would be before I could find another opportunity like this. Seething with rage and at the same time both undecided and full of eagerness, I roamed the fields the whole morning, cursing Gioconda and cursing my fate, unable to be still, either in mind or body. In the end I realized there was nothing for me to do except go back to the workshop, so back I went. Amongst the piles of bricks Gioconda, carrying a cooking-pot, was scattering food to the hens; she greeted me from afar with a smile. I did not respond and went on into the workshop. "Better late than never," cried my uncle when he saw me. I said nothing, but put on my overalls and resumed my work at the exact point where I had left it the day before.

Young Adulthood—The Problem of Social Identity

III b. The problem of sexual identity and vocational identity have already been presented. Along with these developmental tasks, the young adult must find a social group to identify with in order to achieve a sense of social solidarity and escape social isolation. Strindberg's *Miss Julie* is beset with all these problems. Her early life has left her sexual identity confused. Her parents' strange values and her isolated social position leave her lonely and confused about her life. She undergoes what Erickson has called identity diffusion. Lacking intimacy, she throws herself into a sexual experience. Lacking purpose and values, she alternates between contempt for others and contempt for herself. Lacking any identity and tormented by guilt, she turns to suicide. The scene begins after she has invited the peasants into the house and become sexually involved with a servant.

Miss Julie

August Strindberg (*1849–1912*)

Miss Julie. You don't mean what you say—and besides: everybody knows my secrets. You see, my mother was not an aristocrat by birth.

She came of quite simple stock. She was brought up in conformity with the ideas of her generation: equality of the sexes—the emancipation of women—and all that sort of thing. She looked upon marriage with downright aversion. Therefore, when my father proposed marriage to her, she replied that she would never be his wife—but—she married him just the same. I came into the world—against my mother's wishes, as I have learned; and now I was to be reared by my mother as a child of nature and in addition was to be taught all the things a boy has to learn, all in order to prove that a woman is quite as good as any man. I had to wear boy's clothes, had to learn how to handle horses, but I was never allowed in the cattle barn. I had to groom, harness and saddle my horse and had to go hunting—yes, I even had to try my hand at farming! And the farmhands were given women's chores to do, and the women did the men's work—and the upshot of it was that the estate almost went to rack and ruin, and we became the laughing-stock of the whole countryside. . . . At last my father seems to have come out of his inertia, for he rebelled; and after that all went according to his will. My mother took sick—what the sickness was I never learned—but she frequently had spasms, shut herself up in the attic, or secluded herself in the garden and sometimes she stayed out all night. Then came the great fire which you have heard about. The house, the stables, and the cattle barns burned down, and under suspicious circumstances that pointed to arson. The disaster happened, namely, the day after the quarterly insurance period had expired; and the insurance premium, that my father had forwarded by a messenger, had arrived too late because of the messenger's negligence or indifference. (*She fills up her glass, and drinks.*)

JEAN. You mustn't drink any more!

MISS JULIE. Ah, what do I care!—We were left with nothing, and we had no place to sleep, except in the carriages. My father was desperate; he didn't know where to get money to build again. Then my mother suggested to him that he borrow from an old friend of hers—someone she had known in her youth, a brick manufacturer not far from here. Father got the loan, and without having to pay any interest—and this was a surprise to him. And the estate was rebuilt! (*She drinks again.*) Do you know who set the place on fire?

JEAN. The Countess, your mother . . .

MISS JULIE. Do you know who the brick manufacturer was?

JEAN. Your mother's lover?

MISS JULIE. Do you know whose money it was?

JEAN. Wait a second!—No—I don't—

MISS JULIE. It was my mother's.

JEAN. In other words, your father's—the Count's—unless they had made a marriage settlement.

MISS JULIE. No, there was none. My mother had a little money of her own. She didn't want my father to have charge of it, so she—entrusted it to her friend!

JEAN. And he helped himself to it!

MISS JULIE. Precisely! He appropriated the money. All this my father came to know. He couldn't bring action against him, couldn't repay his wife's lover, couldn't prove that the money was his wife's!—That was the revenge my mother took on him because he had made himself the master in his own house. He was on the verge of committing suicide when all this happened; as a matter of fact, there was a rumor that he tried to and didn't succeed. . . . However, he took a new lease of life, and my mother had to pay the penalty for her behavior! You can imagine what the next five years did to me! I felt sorry for my father, yet I took my mother's part because I didn't know the true circumstances. She had taught me to mistrust and hate men, for she herself hated men, as I told you before—and she made me swear never to become the slave of any man . . .

JEAN. And then you became engaged to the county prosecutor!

MISS JULIE. Yes—in order to make him my slave.

JEAN. And he refused?

MISS JULIE. He would have liked it, don't worry; but I didn't give him the chance. I became bored with him . . .

JEAN. I saw that you did—out in the stableyard.

MISS JULIE. What did you see?

JEAN. Exactly what happened—how he broke off the engagement.

MISS JULIE. That's a lie! It was I who broke the engagement!—Did he tell you he did? The scoundrel!

JEAN. I wouldn't call him a scoundrel. . . . You just hate men, Miss Julie.

MISS JULIE. Yes, I do! Most men! But occasionally—when my weakness comes over me—oh, the shame of it!

JEAN. You hate me, too, don't you?

MISS JULIE. I hate you no end! I should like to have you slaughtered like an animal!

JEAN. As one shoots a mad dog, eh?

MISS JULIE. Precisely!

JEAN. But as there is nothing here to shoot with, and no dog—what are we to do?

MISS JULIE. Get away from here!

JEAN. And then torture each other to death?

MISS JULIE. No—live life for a few brief days, for a week—for as long as we can—and then—die . . .

JEAN. Die? What nonsense! No—I think it would be far better to go into the hotel business.

MISS JULIE (*who, absorbed with her thoughts, has not heard what he said*). . . . by Lake Como, where the sun is always shining—where the laurel tree is still greening at Christmas—and the oranges are golden red—

JEAN. Lake Como is a hole where it rains all the time, and I never saw any oranges there except in the grocery shops. But it's a good place for foreigners—and there are plenty of villas to be rented to lovers—and that is a business that pays! And do you know why? I'll tell you why—because they have to sign a six months' lease, and they never stay longer than three weeks!

MISS JULIE (*naïvely*). Why only three weeks?

JEAN. Because they quarrel, of course. But the rent has to be paid in full just the same. And then the house is rented out again; and that's the way it goes—on and on—for people will always be in love, although their love doesn't last very long . . .

MISS JULIE. Then you don't care to die with me, do you?

JEAN. I don't care to die at all! Not only because I like to live, but because I consider suicide a sin against God, who gave us life.

MISS JULIE. You believe in God—*you*?

JEAN. Of course I do! I go to church every other Sunday. But now—quite frankly—now I am getting tired of all this talk, and I am going to bed.

MISS JULIE. Oh, you are, are you? And you think that will be a satisfactory ending? Do you know what a man owes to a woman he has taken advantage of?

JEAN (*takes out his purse and throws a coin on the table*). There you are! Now I owe you nothing!

MISS JULIE (*pretends to ignore the insult*). Are you aware of the legal consequences?

JEAN. It's too bad that the law provides no punishment for the woman who seduces a man!

MISS JULIE. Can you think of any way out of this—other than going abroad, getting married, and being divorced?

JEAN. Suppose I refuse to enter into such a degrading marriage?

MISS JULIE. Degrading?

JEAN. Yes—for me! For, mind you, my lineage is cleaner and more respectable than yours—I have no pyromaniac in my family—

MISS JULIE. How can you be so sure of that?

JEAN. And how can you prove the opposite? We have no register of our ancestors—except in the police records! But I have seen your genealogical chart in the book on your drawing-room table. Do you know who your first ancestor was? A miller who let his wife sleep with the king one night during the Danish War!—I haven't any ancestors like that! I have no ancestry of any kind—but I can start a family tree of my own!

MISS JULIE. This is what I get for opening my heart to one like you, to an inferior . . . for betraying the honor of my family . . .

JEAN. You mean *dishonor*! . . . Well, I warned you—and now you see— People shouldn't drink, for then they start talking—and people should never be garrulous.

MISS JULIE. Oh, how I regret what I have done! How I regret it! Oh, if—at least—you had loved me!

JEAN. For the last time—what is it you want me to do? Do you want me to burst into tears? Do you want me to jump over your riding whip? Do you want me to kiss you?—to elope with you to Lake Como for three weeks?—and then. . . . What do you want me to do? What is it you want? This is getting to be intolerable! But that's what one gets for sticking one's nose into a female's business! Miss Julie—I know you must be suffering—but I can't understand you. . . . We have no such strange notions as you have—we don't hate as you do! To us love is nothing but playfulness—we play when our work is done. We haven't the whole day and the whole night for it like you! I think you must be sick. . . . Yes, I am sure you are!

MISS JULIE. You must treat me with kindness—you must speak to me like a human being . . .

JEAN. Yes, if you'll behave like one! You spit on me—but when I spit back, you object!

MISS JULIE. Oh, help me—help me! Tell me what to do—and where to go!

JEAN. In the name of Christ, I wish I knew myself!

MISS JULIE. I have behaved like a madwoman . . . but is there no way out of this?

JEAN. Stay here—and stop worrying! Nobody knows a thing.

MISS JULIE. I can't! They all know—and Kristin knows—

JEAN. They know nothing—and they wouldn't believe such a thing!

MISS JULIE (*after a moment's hesitation*). But—it might happen again!

JEAN. Yes—it might.

MISS JULIE. And have consequences? . . .

JEAN. Consequences? . . . What have I been thinking about? That never occurred to me!—Then there is only one thing to do. You must leave—and immediately! If I come with you, it would look suspicious—therefore you must go alone—go away—it doesn't matter where.

MISS JULIE. I—alone—but where? I couldn't do it!

JEAN. You must—and before the Count gets back! If you remain here, we both know what will happen. Having committed one mistake, it's easy to make another because the damage has already been done. . . . With time one gets more and more reckless—until, finally one is caught! That's why I urge you to leave! Later on you can write to the Count and tell him everything—except that it was I!—He would never suspect, of course,—and I don't think he would be anxious to know!

MISS JULIE. I'll go, if you'll come with me . . .

JEAN. Are you stark staring mad, woman? Miss Julie eloping with her lackey! It would be in the newspapers before another day had passed. The Count would never get over it!

MISS JULIE. I can't go—and I can't stay here! Can't you help me! I am so tired, so dreadfully tired!—Order me to go! Make me move! I am no longer able to think—I can't bring myself to do anything!

JEAN. Now you see what sort of miserable creature you are, don't you? Why is your sort always so overbearing? Why do you strut with your noses in the air as if you were the lords of Creation?—Very well, then—I shall order you about! Go upstairs and get dressed, take enough money with you for traveling and then come down!

MISS JULIE (*almost in a whisper*). Come upstairs with me—

JEAN. To your room?—Now you are mad again! (*He hesitates a moment.*) No! Go immediately! (*He takes her by the hand and escorts her to the door.*)

MISS JULIE (*walking toward the door*). Why don't you speak gently to me, Jean?

JEAN. An order always sounds harsh.—Now you are beginning to find out how it feels . . .

(JULIE *leaves*. . . .

MISS JULIE (*comes inside. She is dressed for travel and carries a small birdcage, covered with a towel. She places the cage on a chair*). I am ready now.

JEAN. Ssh! Kristin is awake!

MISS JULIE (*from this moment on, she shows signs of extreme nervousness*). Does she suspect anything?

JEAN. Not a thing! She knows nothing!—Lord in heaven—how you look!

MISS JULIE. Look? Why—what's the matter?

JEAN. Your face is livid! You look like a corpse . . . and if you'll pardon me, your face is not clean!

MISS JULIE. Then I must wash my face! (*She goes over to the sink and washes her face and hands.*) Would you give a towel?— Oh . . . I see the sun is rising . . .

JEAN. . . . and now the spell will be broken!

MISS JULIE. Yes, the trolls have been out this night!—But now, Jean,— you can come with me, do you hear, for I have all the money we need.

JEAN (*with disbelief and hesitation*). You have enough?

MISS JULIE. Enough to start with. . . . Please come with me! I can't travel alone now. . . . Imagine my sitting alone on a stuffy train, squeezed in among crowds of passengers gaping at me . . . and with long stops at the stations, when I would like to fly away on wings. . . . No—I can't do it—I just can't do it! And then I'll be thinking of the past—memories of the midsummer days of my childhood—the church, covered with wreaths and garlands, with leaves of birch and with lilac—the festive dinner table—relatives and friends—and the afternoon in the park, with music and dancing, games and flowers. . . . Oh—no matter how one tries to get away from the past, the memories are there, packed into one's baggage. . . . They pursue one, hitched onto the tail of the train . . . and then comes remorse—and the pangs of conscience—

JEAN. I'll come with you, but let's hurry—before it's too late! We haven't a second to lose!

MISS JULIE. Hurry up and dress! (*She picks up the birdcage.*)

JEAN. But no baggage! Then we would be found out immediately!

MISS JULIE. No, nothing . . . only what we can take with us in our compartment.

JEAN (*who has just reached for his hat, stares at the birdcage*). What's that you have there? What is it?

MISS JULIE. It's only my green siskin . . . I couldn't go without her!

JEAN. Well, of all the— Are we going to take a birdcage with us now? You must be completely out of your mind! (*He tries to take the cage from her.*) Let go of the cage!

MISS JULIE. It's the one thing I am taking with me from my home—the only living thing that loves me since Diana was faithless to me. . . . Don't be cruel! Please let me take her with me!

JEAN. Put that cage down, I tell you—and don't talk so loud! Kristin can hear us!

MISS JULIE. No—I won't part with her to anyone else! I'd rather you killed her . . .

JEAN. Give me the little beast then—I'll chop its head off!

MISS JULIE. Oh—but—don't hurt her, please!—No—I can't let you . . .

JEAN. But I can—and I know how. . . . Give it to me!

MISS JULIE (*takes the bird out of the cage. She kisses it*). Oh, my poor little Sérine, must your mother lose you—must you die?

JEAN. Let's have no scenes—it's now a question of life and death—of your own future. . . . Quick, now! (*He snatches the bird from her, goes over to the chopping block, and picks up the axe lying on it.* MISS JULIE *turns away her face.*) You should have learned how to kill chickens instead of how to shoot . . . (*He lets the hatchet fall on the bird's neck.*) . . . then the sight of a little blood wouldn't make you faint!

MISS JULIE (*screams*). Let me die too! Kill me! You—who can take the life of an innocent little creature without even a tremble of the hand! Oh—how I hate you—how I loathe you! Now there is blood between us! I curse the day I was born, the day I was conceived!

JEAN. Stop cursing—it does you no good! Let's be off!

MISS JULIE (*approaches the chopping block, as if drawn to it against her will*). No—I am not ready to go yet—I can't go—I must first see . . . (*She suddenly stops. She stands listening; all the while her eyes are riveted on the chopping block and the axe.*) You think I can't stand the sight of blood! You think I am such a weakling, do you?—Oh, I should like to see your blood—your brain—on the chopping block. . . . I should like to see your whole sex bathing in its own blood, like my little bird! . . . I even think I could drink out of your skull—I would revel in bathing my feet in your caved-in chest—and I could devour your heart roasted! You think I am a weakling—you think that I am in love with you because my womb felt a craving for your seed—you think that I yearn to carry your offspring under my heart, to nourish it with my blood—to bear your child and your name? Come to think of it, what is your name? I have never heard your last name—I guess you haven't any. . . . I was to be Mrs. Gatekeeper—or Mme. Refuseheap— You dog who wear my collar—you lackey with my family crest on your buttons! I was to share you with my cook—a rival of my own servant! Oh, oh, oh!—You think I am a coward and that I am anxious to flee! No—this time I am not leaving—come what may! When father returns he will find his chiffonier ransacked and the money gone! Immediately he will ring that bell—his usual two rings for you, Jean,—and he will send for the sheriff . . . and then—then I shall tell the whole story! The whole story! Oh, what a relief it will be to get it over with. . . . If only that moment were here! And father will have a stroke and die! . . . And that will be the end of our family. And then, at last, we shall be at rest—find peace—eternal peace! . . . And the family coat of arms will be broken against the coffin—the noble line will be extinct—but the lackey's line will go on in an orphanage—reaping laurels in the gutter, and ending in prison . . .

JEAN. There's your royal blood talking! Bravo, Miss Julie! And don't forget to stuff the miller's skeleton in your family closet!

(KRISTIN *enters. She is dressed for church and carries a prayer book.*)

MISS JULIE (*rushes toward her and flings herself into her arms, as if to plead for protection*). Help me, Kristin! Save me from this man!

KRISTIN (*stands cold and unmoved*). What kind of spectacle is this on the sabbath morning? (*She notices the dead bird and the blood on the chopping block.*) And what's this piggish mess you have made here?— What's the meaning of all this? And why are you screaming and making so much noise?

MISS JULIE. Kristin—you are a woman—and you are my friend! Look out for this man—he is a villain!

JEAN (*somewhat abashed and timid*). While you ladies are conversing, I am going in to shave.

(*He goes into his room, left.*)

MISS JULIE. I want you to understand me—I want you to listen to me—

KRISTIN. No—I must say I can't understand all these goings-on!

Where are you planning to go—you are dressed for traveling—and Jean had his hat on. . . . Why?—What's going on?

Miss Julie. Listen to me, Kristin! You must listen to me—and then I'll tell you everything . . .

Kristin. I don't care to— I don't want to know . . .

Miss Julie. You must—you must hear . . .

Kristin. Just what is it—what's it all about? Is it about this foolishness with Jean, is it?—Well, I don't let that bother me a bit—it's none of my business. . . . But if you are thinking of tricking him into running away with you—then I'll soon put a stop to that!

Miss Julie (*with extreme nervousness*). Try to be calm, Kristin, and please listen to me! I can't stay here—and Jean can't stay here—and that is why we must leave . . .

Kristin. H'm, h'm!

Miss Julie (*brightening*). Oh, I know—I have an idea! Suppose the three of us—if we should go abroad—we three together—to Switzerland—and start a hotel business— I have the money, you see. . . . (*She dangles the handbag before* Kristin.) . . . and Jean and I would run the business—and I thought you could take charge of the kitchen. Don't you think that would be perfect?—Say that you will? Do come with us—then everything will be settled! Will you? Say yes! (*She puts her arms round* Kristin *and gives her a pat on the back.*)

Kristin (*coldly reflective*). H'm, h'm!

Miss Julie (*presto tempo*). You have never been out in the world, Kristin,—you must travel and see things. You have no idea what fun it is to travel by train! Always new people, new countries! And in Hamburg we stop over and look at the Zoological Garden—you will like that . . . and when we arrive in Munich, we have the museums there—and there you'll see Rubens and Raphael and other great masters, you know. . . . You have heard of Munich, haven't you?—There is where King Ludwig lived—the king, you know, who lost his mind. . . . And then we'll visit his castles—his castles still are there; and they are beautiful like the castles in the fairy tales—and from there, you see, it is only a short distance to Switzerland—and the Alps! Think of it, they are covered with snow in the middle of the summer—and oranges grow there—and laurels that stay green the year round!

(Jean *appears from the left. While he is sharpening his razor on a strop that he holds between his teeth and his left hand, he is listening with evident satisfaction to their conversation. Now and then he nods approvingly.*)

Miss Julie (*tempo prestissimo*). And in Switzerland we'll buy a hotel—and I'll take care of the accounts while Jean looks after the guests—does the marketing—attends to the correspondence. . . . It'll be a hustle

and bustle, believe me. . . . You hear the whistle of the train—the omni-
bus arrives—the bells ring, from the hotel rooms and the dining-room.—I
make out the bills—and I know how to salt them, too. . . . You can't
imagine how diffident tourists are when their bills are presented to them!
—And you—you will preside in the kitchen! You won't have to stand at
the stove yourself, of course,—and you will have to be dressed neatly and
nicely so that you can show yourself among people . . . and with your
looks—yes, I am not trying to flatter you—with your looks, you might very
well get yourself a husband one fine day!—Some rich Englishman, why not?
They are so easy to . . . (*in a slackened pace*) . . . to capture . . . and
then we'll build ourselves a villa at the edge of Lake Como. . . . Of
course, it rains there a little occasionally, but . . . (*Her voice fades a
little.*) . . . the sun must be shining there some time—even though the
gloom seems to persist—and—so—well, we can always return home—and
then go back again . . . (*There is a pause.*) . . . here—or somewhere
else . . .

KRISTIN. Miss Julie, do you really believe all this yourself?

MISS JULIE (*crushed*). . . . If I believe it—myself?

KRISTIN. Just that!

MISS JULIE. I don't know . . . I don't believe in anything any more!
(*She sinks down on the bench, puts her head between her hands and drops
her head on the table.*) Not in anything! Not in anything!

KRISTIN (*turning toward the left where* JEAN *is standing*). So-o, you
were going to run away, were you?

JEAN (*crestfallen and looking foolish, he lays the razor on the table*).
Run away? Well—that's a strong word to use! Miss Julie told you about
her project, didn't she? Well—she is tired now after being up all night
. . . but her plan can very well be carried to success!

KRISTIN. Now you listen to me! Was it your intention that I was to
be cook for that one—

JEAN (*sharply*). You will be good enough to speak of your mistress
in a proper manner! You understand me, don't you?

KRISTIN. Mistress, yes!

JEAN. Yes, mistress!

KRISTIN. Ha, listen—listen to him!

JEAN. Yes, that's just what *you* should do—listen—and talk a little less!
Miss Julie *is* your mistress—and the very same thing that you now look
down upon her for, should make you feel contempt for yourself!

KRISTIN. I always had so much respect for myself that . . .

JEAN. . . . that you felt you could show disrespect for others!

KRISTIN. . . . that I could never let myself sink beneath my level!
Nobody can say that the Count's cook has had any goings-on with the
stablehand, or the fellow who looks after the pigs! No—nobody can say
that!

JEAN. Yes—you are lucky to have been able to catch a fine fellow like me, that's all I can say!

KRISTIN. A fine fellow, indeed,—selling the oats from the Count's stable . . .

JEAN. You should talk about that—you, who take a rake-off from the grocer and let the butcher bribe you!

KRISTIN. I don't know what you mean . . .

JEAN. And you—you can't have any respect for the family you are working for! You—you—you!

KRISTIN. Are you coming with me to church now? You could stand a good sermon after your great triumph!

JEAN. No, I am not going to church today. . . . You have to go alone and confess your *own* exploits!

KRISTIN. Yes—that's what I intend to do, and I'll come back with enough forgiveness for us both! The Saviour suffered and died on the Cross for all our sins; and if we come to Him with faith and repentence in our hearts, He will take all our trespasses upon Himself.

JEAN. Including petty grocery frauds?

JULIE (*who suddenly lifts her head*). Do you believe that, Kristin?

KRISTIN. That is my living faith, as sure as I stand here. It is the faith that was born in me as a child and that I have kept ever since, Miss Julie. . . . And where sin abounds, grace abounds much more . . .

MISS JULIE. Oh—if I only had your trusting faith! Oh, if I . . .

KRISTIN. Yes, but you see you can't have faith without God's special grace—and it is not given to all to receive that.

MISS JULIE. To whom is it given then?

KRISTIN. That, Miss Julie, is the great secret of the gift of grace . . . and God is no respecter of persons: in His Kingdom the last shall be first . . .

MISS JULIE. Well—but in that case He shows preference for the last, doesn't He?

KRISTIN (*continues*). . . . and it is easier for a camel to go through the eye of a needle than for a rich man to enter the Kingdom of Heaven. You see, Miss Julie, that is the way it is!—But now I am going—alone—and on my way I'll stop and tell the stableman not to let out any of the horses to anybody . . . just in case anybody'd like to get away before the Count returns!—Goodbye!   (*She goes out.*)

JEAN. What a bitch!—And all this just because of a green siskin!

MISS JULIE (*apathetically*). Never mind the siskin!—Can you see any way out of this? Any way to end it?

JEAN (*thinking hard*). No—I can't.

MISS JULIE. If you were in my place—what would you do?

JEAN. In your place? Let me think!—As a woman—of noble birth—who has fallen . . . I don't know. . . . Yes—now I think I know—

MISS JULIE (*picks up the razor and makes a telling gesture*). This, you mean?

JEAN. Yes . . . but *I* would never do it! Not I—for there is a difference between us two!

MISS JULIE. You mean—because you are a man and I a woman? What, then, is the difference?

JEAN. The same difference—as—between man and woman—

MISS JULIE (*with the razor in her hand*). I want to do it . . . but I can't—My father couldn't either—that time when he ought to have done it . . .

JEAN. No—he ought not to have done it! He had to take his revenge first!

MISS JULIE. And now my mother gets her revenge once more—through me!

JEAN. Did you ever love your father, Miss Julie? Did you?

MISS JULIE. Yes, I did—immensely—but, at the same time, I think I must have hated him. . . . I must have done so without being conscious of it! It was he who brought me up to look with contempt upon my own sex—to be part woman and part man! Who is to be blamed for the consequences? My father, my mother, or myself? Myself? Am I then really myself? There is nothing I can call my own; I haven't a thought that wasn't instilled in me by my father—not a passion that I didn't inherit from my mother . . . and that last notion of mine—the idea that all people are equal—that came from him, my fiancé . . . and that is why I call him a mischief-maker, a scoundrel! How can *I* possibly be to blame? To put the burden of blame on Jesus Christ as Kristin did just now—for that I have too much pride and too much sense, thanks to what my father taught me. . . . And as for the idea that a rich man may not enter Heaven —that's a lie; and Kristin, who has put her savings in the bank, won't get there either, for that matter! Now—who is to blame?—What does it matter who is to blame? After all, it is I who have to bear the burden of guilt and suffer the consequences. . . .

JEAN. Yes—but . . . (*Two abrupt rings interrupt him.* MISS JULIE *jumps to her feet;* JEAN *quickly changes his coat.*) The Count is back! What if Kristin . . . (*He goes over to the speaking tube and listens.*)

MISS JULIE. Could he have been to the chiffonier already?

JEAN. Yes, sir—this is Jean. (*He listens. The Count's voice is not heard by the audience.*) Yes, sir.—Yes, sir. Immediately!—At once, sir!—Yes, sir. In half an hour!

MISS JULIE (*in extreme agitation*). What did he say? For God's sake what did he say?

JEAN. He asked for his boots and his coffee in half an hour.

MISS JULIE. Half an hour, then! . . . Oh, I am so tired—I have no strength to do anything—not even to feel repentant—or to get away from here—or to stay here—to live—or to die! . . . Help me, please! Order me to do something—and I'll obey like a dog. . . . Do me this last service! Save my honor—save his good name! You know what I would like to have the will to do—yet don't like to do. . . . Use your willpower on me—and *make* me do it!

JEAN. I don't know why—but now *I* haven't any willpower either. I can't understand it. . . . It's just as if wearing this coat made it impossible for me to—to give orders to you; and now, after the Count spoke to me, I —well, I—I just can't explain it—but—well, it's the damned menial in me . . . and if the Count should come in here this very minute, and he should order me to cut my throat, I believe I'd do it without the slightest hesitation!

MISS JULIE. Can't you make believe that you are he, and that I am you! You did a good piece of acting just now when you were on your knees—then you acted the nobleman—or, perhaps, you have seen a hypnotist when you've been to the theatre? (JEAN *gives an affirmative nod.*) He tells his subject: "Pick up that broom!"—and he picks it up; he tells him to sweep—and he starts to sweep . . .

JEAN. But he must put his subject to sleep first . . .

MISS JULIE (*ecstatically*). I am already asleep—the whole room is like a cloud of dust and smoke before me—and you look like a tall stove—and the stove looks like a man in black with a top hat—your eyes glow like embers in a fireplace—and your face is merely a patch of white ash . . . (*The sun's rays are now falling across the room and shine on* JEAN.) . . . It's so pleasantly warm . . . (*She rubs her hands together as if she were warming them by the fire.*) And how bright it is—and so peaceful!

JEAN (*takes the razor and places it in her hand*). Here is the broom! Walk outside now while it's still light—out into the barn—and . . . (*He whispers in her ear.*)

MISS JULIE (*awake*). Thank you! I'm going—to find rest. . . . But before I go, tell me—that even those who are among the first, can receive the gift of grace. Please tell me that—even if you do not believe it!

JEAN. Among the first? No—that's something I cannot do. . . . But wait, Miss Julie. . . . Now I know the answer! Since you no longer are one of the first—you must be—among the last!

MISS JULIE. You are right!—I am among the—very last—I am the last! Oh!—But something holds me back again. . . . Tell me once again to go!

JEAN. No—I can't tell you again—I can't—

MISS JULIE. And the first shall be the last . . .

JEAN. Stop thinking—stop thinking! You are robbing me of all my strength—you are making me a coward. . . . What's that? I thought I heard the bell! No—but let's stuff it with paper. . . . Imagine, to be so afraid of a bell! Yes—but it isn't merely a bell—there is someone behind it—a hand that sets it in motion—and something else sets the hand in motion

—but you can stop your ears—stop your ears—and then—yes, then it keeps ringing louder than ever—keeps ringing until you answer—and then—it's too late! And then the sheriff appears on the scene—and then . . .

(*Two preremptory rings from the bell.*)

JEAN (*quails; then he straightens himself*). It's horrible! But it's the only way to end it!—Go!

(MISS JULIE, *with the razor in her hand, walks firmly out through the door.*)

Adulthood—The Problem of Hardening of Identity

IV. Anninka, the little niece of Saltykov-Schedrin's novel *The Golovlyov Family*, has come back from her work as an actress to the small estate she has inherited. This interruption in her customary life suddenly gives her the terrifying opportunity to look at herself and to ask, "Who am I; what am I; and where am I going?" In this brief section, Anninka has come to the end of young adulthood; she assesses her current identity. Despite all her admirers, she has neither intimacy nor the comforting solidarity of a meaningful group identification.

THE GOLOVLYOVS

M. Saltykov-Schedrin   (1826–1889)

. . . Anninka spent a restless night. She was still possessed by the nervous uneasiness that had come over her at Pogorelka. There are moments when a person who has so far merely *existed* suddenly begins to understand that he really *lives* and that there is some canker in his life. He does not as a rule clearly see how and why it formed and generally ascribes its presence to wrong causes: but he does not really care about the causes—it is sufficient for him that the canker is there. Such a sudden revelation is equally painful to everyone, but its subsequent effects vary according to the person's temperament. It regenerates some people, inspiring them with the resolution to begin a new life, on a new basis: in others it merely causes temporary distress, leading to no change for the better but making them more miserable for the moment than those

From *The Golovlyovs* by M. Saltykov-Schedrin, translated by Andrew R. MacAndrew. Copyright © 1961 by Andrew R. MacAndrew. Published by arrangement with The New American Library of World Literature, Inc., New York.

whose awakened conscience looks forward to a brighter future as a result
of their new resolutions.

Anninka was not one of those who are regenerated through understanding the evil of their lives; but, being an intelligent girl, she saw perfectly well that there was all the difference in the world between the
vague dreams of earning her own living that had led her to leave
Pogorelka in the first instance and her position as a provincial actress.
Instead of a quiet, hard-working life she had let herself in for a feverish
existence full of continual merry-making, cynical talk, and endless hustle
that led nowhere. Instead of hardships and privations which she had once
been ready to accept she had found a comparative comfort and even
luxury, that she now could not recall without blushing. And all this
change had somehow happened quite imperceptibly: it was as though she
had been going to some good place but by mistake had opened a wrong
door. Her dreams had certainly been very modest. How often, sitting in
her attic at Pogorelka, she pictured herself as a serious, hard-working girl,
longing to improve her mind, bravely enduring privations and poverty
for the sake of the ideal (though the word 'ideal' probably had no definite
meaning for her): but as soon as she took up the broad path of independence she found herself in surroundings which shattered her dreams at
once. Serious work does not come to one of itself: determined effort is
needed to find it, and previous training, which, even if imperfect, helps
one at any rate to look in the right direction. Anninka was not fitted for
such work either by temperament or by education. Easily excited, she was
not one to devote herself to a thing wholeheartedly, and her educational
equipment was insufficient to qualify her for any serious profession. Her
education had been of the genteel and artistic type, a mixture, so to speak
of the boarding school and the comic opera. It included, in chaotic disorder, the problem about a hundred flying geese, the *pas de chale*, the
preaching of Pierre of Picardy, the escapades of Helen of Troy, Dercha-
vin's ode to Felitsa, and the feelings of gratitude to the directors and
patrons of young ladies' schools. This bewildering hotch-potch (apart
from which she might justly describe herself as a *tabula rasa*) was not
likely to serve as a starting-point for practical life. It fostered not a love
of work but a love of gaiety, a desire to be popular in society, to listen to
gallantries, and, generally speaking, to plunge into the rushing and sparkling whirl of the so-called life.

Had she been more introspective when, at Pogorelka, she made her
first plans for earning her living, regarding it as a kind of deliverance from
Egyptian captivity, she would have detected that she dreamed not so
much of work as of being surrounded by congenial people and spending
time in continual conversation. Of course the people of her dreams were
intelligent and their talk was serious and high-minded, but anyway it was
the festive side of life that was in the foreground. The poor surroundings

were clean and tidy, the privations meant simply absence of luxury. And so when her hopes of work ended in her being offered an engagement as a comic-opera singer in a provincial theatre, she did not take long to make up her mind. She hastily polished up her school information about Helen's relations to Menelaus, looked up a few biographical details about Potyomkin and decided that this was quite enough for acting *La belle Hélène* and the *Grand-Duchess of Herolstein* in provincial towns and at fairs. To appease her conscience she recalled how a student whom she met at Moscow kept talking of 'holy art': she made these words her motto all the more readily because they lent a certain seemliness to her action and provided her with an excuse for entering a path to which she was instinctively and overwhelmingly attracted.

Her life as an actress threw her off her balance. With no friends, no training, and no conscious purpose in life, eager for excitement, glamour, and adulation, she soon found herself caught in a kind of whirl with innumerable people round her, succeeding one another at random. These people differed so widely in character and convictions, that her reasons for being friends with this one or that one could not have been the same, and yet they all formed her circle which proved that, strictly speaking, there could be no question of 'reasons' about it at all. It was clear that her life had become a kind of inn, at the gates of which anyone might knock if he felt young, gay, and well off. Obviously it was not a question of *selecting* a congenial set of people but of keeping in with any set to escape solitude. In truth her 'holy art' had landed her in a cesspool but she lived in such a giddy whirl that she failed to see it. The waiters' unwashed faces, the dirty stage, the noise, stench, and babble at the inns and hotels, and her admirers' impudence could not sober her. She failed to notice that she was always in men's company and that some impassable barrier had arisen between her and women of definite social standing.

Her visit to Golovlyovo did sober her for a moment.

Something had been gnawing at her ever since the morning, almost from the moment she arrived. Being an impressionable girl she quickly assimilated new experiences and no less quickly adapted herself to every situation. And so as soon as she arrived at Golovlyovo she felt that she was 'a young lady.' She recalled that she had something of her own: her house, her family graves; she wanted to see her old surroundings once more and to breathe again the atmosphere that she had only a short time before been so eager to leave behind. But this feeling was bound to disappear at the first contact with the Golovlyovo life. She was like a person who comes with a friendly expression on his face into the company of people he had not seen for some time and suddenly notices that they all regard his friendliness in a rather peculiar way. Iudushka's nasty sidelong glance at her bust at once reminded her that she had a past which was not easily left behind. When, after the naïve questions of Pogorelka servants, the priest's

and his wife's meaning sighs and Iudushka's admonitions, she was at last
left alone and considered at leisure the impressions of the day, she saw
quite clearly that the 'young lady' had gone for ever; that henceforth she
was nothing but an actress of a miserable provincial theatre, and that in
Russia an actress was regarded as little better than a woman of the streets.

So far she had lived as in a dream. She appeared half-naked in the
Belle Hélène, acted the drunken Perichole, sang shameless couplets in the
Grand-Duchess of Gerolstein, and was positively sorry that *l'amour* and
la chose were not shown on the stage, picturing to herself how seductively
and with what *chic* she would wriggle her hips and manoeuvre her train.
But it had never occurred to her to think what she was doing. She had
only been anxious to do everything 'prettily' and 'with *chic*,' and to please
the officers of the local regiment. She had never asked herself what it all
meant, and what kind of sensations her wrigglings produced in the
officers. They formed the most important section of the audience and she
knew that her success depended upon them. They intruded behind the
scenes, knocked without ceremony at her dressing-room door while she
was half-dressed, called her by pet-names—and she regarded it all as a
mere form, as an inevitable part of her trade, and merely asked herself
whether she behaved 'prettily' in those surroundings. She had never yet
felt that either her soul or her body was public property. But now when
for a moment she became a 'young lady' once more, she was suddenly
overwhelmed with disgust. It was as though she had been stripped in the
presence of all and felt all over her body the vile breaths smelling of drink
and of the stables, the touch of moist hands and slobbering lips: it seemed
to her that eyes clouded with animal lust wandered senselessly over the
curves of her naked figure, demanding, as it were, an answer from her:
What is *la chose?*

Where was she to turn? Where could she leave the burden of her
past? This question throbbed in her mind, not finding and indeed not
even seeking an answer. After all, it was all a kind of dream: the life she
had been leading was a dream and her awakening just now was a dream
too. She was depressed, overwrought—that was all. It would pass. One has
happy moments and bitter ones—that's how it always is. Both joy and
bitterness glide over the surface of life without in the least changing its
established routine. In order to change that, a great many efforts are
needed as well as courage, both moral and physical. It is almost the same
thing as suicide. A man may be cursing his life, he may feel certain that
death means freedom for him, and yet the instrument of death trembles in
his hand, the knife glides over his throat, the pistol aimed at the forehead
goes off lower down and disfigures him. It is the same thing here, only
still more difficult. Here too one has to destroy one's former life, but in
doing so one must remain alive. The 'non-being' achieved in ordinary
suicide by a momentary pull at the trigger, in the special case of suicide

that is called 'regeneration,' is achieved through strenuous, almost ascetic self-discipline. And the end is 'non-being' just the same, because an existence consisting of nothing but efforts at self-control, abstentions, and privations cannot be called life. Those whose will is weak, who are demoralized by easy living, feel giddy at the very prospect of such 'regeneration,' and instinctively turning away and shutting their eyes follow the beaten track once more, ashamed of their own cowardice and full of self-reproach.

Ah, a life of work is a great thing! But only people of character, or those who are doomed to labour as a kind of curse for original sin, take to it. They alone are not afraid of it: the first, because they understand the meaning of work and its possibilities, and are able to find enjoyment in it; the second, because for them work is a natural duty that becomes a habit.

It never entered Anninka's head to settle at Pogorelka or at Golovlyovo, and matters were much simplified for her by the fact that she had business obligations which she was instinctively determined to keep. She had been given a holiday and she had planned her time beforehand, fixing a day for leaving Golovlyovo. People of weak character find the external forms of life of great help in bearing its burdens. In cases of difficulty they instinctively cling to those forms, finding in them a justification for themselves. That was precisely what Anninka did: she decided to leave Golovlyovo as soon as possible, and, if her uncle pestered her too much, to say to him that she had to be back at the appointed time.

Waking up next morning she walked through all the rooms of the huge Golovlyovo house. Everything seemed alien and comfortless, everywhere there was a sense of death and desolation. The thought of settling in this house for good quite frightened her. "Not for anything!" she repeated to herself with strange emotion, "never!" . . .

Adulthood and Old Age—The Problem of Identity in Death

V. The last identity crisis of life comes in facing old age and death. At that point one again looks back and weighs one's life. The judgment can be either self-respect and integrity, or despair and disgust. These problems are compressed and heightened when a person develops a malignant physical disease. He must use all the resources of his personal identity and sense of values to cope with the pain, terror, and depression. This emotional burden tries the strongest, and although some welcome the surcease of death, others struggle bitterly against it. Frequently a consuming depression ensues, and the last days are a struggle not only with pain and suffering, but also a torturing final sense of meaninglessness. Tolstoy has written a story which ranks among the greatest in literature, "The Death of Ivan Ilych." The story tells of one man's struggle with dying, a struggle not just with pain, but with Ilych's own search for a value in his life, a value in himself; an identity and a belief in the face of death.

The Death of Ivan Ilych

Leo Tolstoy   (*1828–1910*)

. . . His wife returned late at night. She came in on tiptoe, but he heard her, opened his eyes, and made haste to close them again. She wished to send Gerasim away and to sit with him herself, but he opened his eyes and said: "No, go away."

"Are you in great pain?"

"Always the same."

"Take some opium."

He agreed and took some. She went away.

Till about three in the morning he was in a state of stupefied misery. It seemed to him that he and his pain were being thrust into a narrow, deep black sack, but though they were pushed further and further in they could not be pushed to the bottom. And this, terrible enough in itself, was accompanied by suffering. He was frightened yet wanted to fall through the sack, he struggled but yet cooperated. And suddenly he broke through, fell, and regained consciousness. Gerasim was sitting at the foot of the bed dozing quietly and patiently, while he himself lay with his emaciated stockinged legs resting on Gerasim's shoulders; the same shaded candle was there and the same unceasing pain.

"Go away, Gerasim," he whispered.

"It's all right, sir. I'll stay a while."

"No. Go away."

He removed his legs from Gerasim's shoulders, turned sideways onto his arm, and felt sorry for himself. He only waited till Gerasim had gone into the next room and then restrained himself no longer but wept like a child. He wept on account of his helplessness, his terrible loneliness, the cruelty of man, the cruelty of God, and the absence of God.

Reprinted from "The Death of Ivan Ilych" by Leo Tolstoy, by permission of Penguin Books. Translation copyright 1960 by Rosemary Edmunds.

"Why hast Thou done all this? Why hast Thou brought me here? Why, why dost Thou torment me so terribly?"

He did not expect an answer and yet wept because there was no answer and could be none. The pain again grew more acute, but he did not stir and did not call. He said to himself: "Go on! Strike me! But what is it for? What have I done to Thee? What is it for?"

Then he grew quiet and not only ceased weeping but even held his breath and became all attention. It was as though he were listening not to an audible voice but to the voice of his soul, to the current of thoughts arising within him.

"What is it you want?" was the first clear conception capable of expression in words, that he heard.

"What do you want? What do you want?" he repeated to himself. "What do I want? To live and not to suffer," he answered.

And again he listened with such concentrated attention that even his pain did not distract him.

"To live? How?" asked his inner voice.

"Why, to live as I used to—well and pleasantly."

"As you lived before, well and pleasantly?" the voice repeated.

And in imagination he began to recall the best moments of his pleasant life. But strange to say none of those best moments of his pleasant life now seemed at all what they had then seemed—none of them except the first recollections of childhood. There, in childhood, there had been something really pleasant with which it would be possible to live if it could return. But the child who had experienced that happiness existed no longer, it was like a reminiscence of somebody else.

As soon as the period began which had produced the present Ivan Ilych, all that had then seemed joys now melted before his sight and turned into something trivial and often nasty.

And the further he departed from childhood and the nearer he came to the present the more worthless and doubtful were the joys. This began with the School of Law. A little that was really good was still found there —there was light-heartedness, friendship, and hope. But in the upper classes there had already been fewer of such good moments. Then during the first years of his official career, when he was in the service of the Governor, some pleasant moments again occurred: they were the memories of love for a woman. Then all became confused and there was still less of what was good; later on again there was still less that was good, and the further he went the less there was. His marriage, a mere accident, then the disenchantment that followed it, his wife's bad breath and the sensuality and hypocrisy: then that deadly official life and those preoccupations about money, a year of it, and two, and ten, and twenty, and always the same thing. And the longer it lasted the more deadly it became. "It is as if I had been going downhill while I imagined I was going up.

And that is really what it was. I was going up in public opinion, but to the same extent life was ebbing away from me. And now it is all done and there is only death."

"Then what does it mean? Why? It can't be that life is so senseless and horrible. But if it really has been so horrible and senseless, why must I die and die in agony? There is something wrong!"

"Maybe I did not live as I ought to have done," it suddenly occurred to him. "But how could that be, when I did everything properly?" he replied, and immediately dismissed from his mind this, the sole solution of all the riddles of life and death, as something quite impossible.

"Then what do you want now? To live? Live how? Live as you lived in the law courts when the usher proclaimed 'The judge is coming!' The judge is coming, the judge!" he repeated to himself. "Here he is, the judge. But I am not guilty!" he exclaimed angrily. "What is it for?" And he ceased crying, but turning his face to the wall continued to ponder on the same question: Why, and for what purpose, is there all this horror? But however much he pondered he found no answer. And whenever the thought occurred to him, as it often did, that it all resulted from his not having lived as he ought to have done, he at once recalled the correctness of his whole life and dismissed so strange an idea.

Another fortnight passed. Ivan Ilych now no longer left his sofa. He would not lie in bed but lay on the sofa, facing the wall nearly all the time. He suffered ever the same unceasing agonies and in his loneliness pondered always on the same insoluble question: "What is this? Can it be that it is Death?" And the inner voice answered: "Yes, it is Death."

"Why these sufferings?" And the voice answered, "For no reason—they just are so." Beyond and besides this there was nothing.

From the very beginning of his illness, ever since he had first been to see the doctor, Ivan Ilych's life had been divided between two contrary and alternating moods: now it was despair and the expectation of this uncomprehended and terrible death, and now hope and an intently interested observation of the functioning of his organs. Now before his eyes there was only a kidney or an intestine that temporarily evaded its duty, and now only that incomprehensible and dreadful death from which it was impossible to escape.

These two states of mind had alternated from the very beginning of his illness, but the further it progressed the more doubtful and fantastic became the conception of the kidney, and the more real the sense of impending death.

He had but to call to mind what he had been three months before and what he was now, to call to mind with what regularity he had been going downhill, for every possibility of hope to be shattered.

Latterly during that loneliness in which he found himself as he lay facing the back of the sofa, a loneliness in the midst of a populous town and surrounded by numerous acquaintances and relations but that yet could not have been more complete anywhere—either at the bottom of the sea or under the earth—during that terrible loneliness Ivan Ilych had lived only in memories of the past. Pictures of his past rose before him one after another. They always began with what was nearest in time and then went back to what was most remote—to his childhood—and rested there. If he thought of the stewed prunes that had been offered him that day, his mind went back to the raw shrivelled French plums of his child-hood, their peculiar flavour and the flow of saliva when he sucked their stones, and along with the memory of that taste came a whole series of memories of those days: his nurse, his brother, and their toys. "No, I mustn't think of that. . . . It is too painful," Ivan Ilych said to himself, and brought himself back to the present—to the button on the back of the sofa and the creases in its morocco. "Morocco is expensive, but it does not wear well: there had been a quarrel about it. It was a different kind of quarrel and a different kind of morocco that time when we tore father's portfolio and were punished, and mamma brought us some tarts. . . ." And again his thoughts dwelt on his childhood, and again it was painful and he tried to banish them and fix his mind on something else.

Then again together with that chain of memories another series passed through his mind—of how his illness had progressed and grown worse. There also the further back he looked the more life there had been. There had been more of what was good in life and more of life itself. The two merged together. "Just as the pain went on getting worse and worse, so my life grew worse and worse," he thought. "There is one bright spot there at the back, at the beginning of life, and afterwards all becomes blacker and blacker and proceeds more and more rapidly—in inverse ratio to the square of the distance from death," thought Ivan Ilych. And the example of a stone falling downwards with increasing velocity entered his mind. Life, a series of increasing sufferings, flies further and further towards its end—the most terrible suffering. "I am flying. . . ." He shuddered, shifted himself, and tried to resist, but was already aware that resistance was impossible, and again with eyes weary of gazing but unable to cease seeing what was before them, he stared at the back of the sofa and waited—awaiting that dreadful fall and shock and destruction.

"Resistance is impossible!" he said to himself. "If I could only under-stand what it is all for! But that too is impossible. An explanation would be possible if it could be said that I have not lived as I ought to. But it is impossible to say that," and he remembered all the legality, correctitude, and propriety of his life. "That at any rate can certainly not be admitted," he thought, and his lips smiled ironically as if someone could see that smile and be taken in by it. "There is no explanation! Agony, death . . . What for?"

Another two weeks went by in this way and during that fortnight an event occurred that Ivan Ilych and his wife had desired. Petrishchev formally proposed. It happened in the evening. The next day Praskovya Fëdorovna came into her husband's room considering how best to inform him of it, but that very night there had been a fresh change for the worse in his condition. She found him still lying on the sofa but in a different position. He lay on his back, groaning and staring fixedly straight in front of him.

She began to remind him of his medicines, but he turned his eyes towards her with such a look that she did not finish what she was saying; so great an animosity, to her in particular, did that look express.

"For Christ's sake let me die in peace!" he said.

She would have gone away, but just then their daughter came in and went up to say good morning. He looked at her as he had done at his wife, and in reply to her inquiry about his health said dryly that he would soon free them all of himself. They were both silent and after sitting with him for a while went away.

"Is it our fault?" Lisa said to her mother. "It's as if we were to blame! I am sorry for papa, but why should we be tortured?"

The doctor came at his usual time. Ivan Ilych answered "Yes" and "No," never taking his angry eyes from him, and at last said: "You know you can do nothing for me, so leave me alone."

"We can ease your sufferings."

"You can't even do that. Let me be."

The doctor went into the drawing-room and told Praskovya Fëdorovna that the case was very serious and that the only resource left was opium to allay her huband's sufferings, which must be terrible.

It was true, as the doctor said, that Ivan Ilych's physical sufferings were terrible, but worse than the physical sufferings were his mental sufferings, which were his chief torture.

His mental sufferings were due to the fact that that night, as he looked at Gerasim's sleepy, good-natured face with its prominent cheekbones, the question suddenly occurred to him: "What if my whole life has really been wrong?"

It occurred to him that what had appeared perfectly impossible before, namely that he had not spent his life as he should have done, might after all be true. It occurred to him that his scarcely perceptible attempts to struggle against what was considered good by the most highly placed people, those scarcely noticeable impulses which he had immediately suppressed, might have been the real thing, and all the rest false. And his professional duties and the whole arrangement of his life and of his family, and all his social and official interests, might all have been false. He tried to defend all those things to himself and suddenly felt the weakness of what he was defending. There was nothing to defend.

"But if that is so," he said to himself, "and I am leaving this life with the consciousness that I have lost all that was given me and it is impossible to rectify it—what then?"

He lay on his back and began to pass his life in review in quite a new way. In the morning when he saw first his footman, then his wife, then his daughter, and then the doctor, their every word and movement confirmed to him the awful truth that had been revealed to him during the night. In them he saw himself—all that for which he had lived—and saw clearly that it was not real at all, but a terrible and huge deception which had hidden both life and death. This consciousness intensified his physical suffering tenfold. He groaned and tossed about, and pulled at his clothing which choked and stifled him. And he hated them on that account.

He was given a large dose of opium and became unconscious, but at noon his sufferings began again. He drove everybody away and tossed from side to side.

His wife came to him and said:

"Jean, my dear, do this for me. It can't do any harm and often helps. Healthy people often do it."

He opened his eyes wide.

"What? Take communion? Why? It's unnecessary! However . . ."

She began to cry.

"Yes, do, my dear. I'll send for our priest. He is such a nice man."

"All right. Very well," he muttered.

When the priest came and heard his confession, Ivan Ilych was softened and seemed to feel a relief from his doubts and consequently from his sufferings, and for a moment there came a ray of hope. He again began to think of the vermiform appendix and the possibility of correcting it. He received the sacrament with tears in his eyes.

When they laid him down again afterwards he felt a moment's ease, and the hope that he might live awoke in him again. He began to think of the operation that had been suggested to him. "To live! I want to live!" he said to himself.

His wife came in to congratulate him after his communion, and when uttering the usual conventional words she added:

"You feel better, don't you?"

Without looking at her he said "Yes."

Her dress, her figure, the expression of her face, the tone of her voice, all revealed the same thing. "This is wrong, it is not as it should be. All you have lived for and still live for is falsehood and deception, hiding life and death from you." And as soon as he admitted that thought, his hatred and his agonizing physical suffering again sprang up, and with that suffering a consciousness of the unavoidable, approaching end. And to this was added a new sensation of grinding shooting pain and a feeling of suffocation.

The expression of his face when he uttered that "yes" was dreadful. Having uttered it, he looked her straight in the eyes, turned on his face with a rapidity extraordinary in his weak state and shouted:

"Go away! Go away and leave me alone!"

From that moment the screaming began that continued for three days, and was so terrible that one could not hear it through two closed doors without horror. At the moment he answered his wife he realized that he was lost, that there was no return, that the end had come, the very end, and his doubts were still unsolved and remained doubts.

"Oh! Oh! Oh!" he cried in various intonations. He had begun by screaming "I won't!" and continued screaming on the letter O.

For three whole days, during which time did not exist for him, he struggled in that black sack into which he was being thrust by an invisible, resistless force. He struggled as a man condemned to death struggles in the hands of the executioner, knowing that he cannot save himself. And every moment he felt that despite all his efforts he was drawing nearer and nearer to what terrified him. He felt that his agony was due to his being thrust into that black hole and still more to his not being able to get right into it. He was hindered from getting into it by his conviction that his life had been a good one. That very justification of his life held him fast and prevented his moving forward, and it caused him most torment of all.

Suddenly some force struck him in the chest and side, making it still harder to breathe, and he fell through the hole and there at the bottom was a light. What had happened to him was like the sensation one sometimes experiences in a railway carriage when one thinks one is going backwards while one is really going forwards and suddenly becomes aware of the real direction.

"Yes, it was all not the right thing," he said to himself, "but that's no matter. It can be done. But what *is* the right thing?" he asked himself, and suddenly grew quiet.

This occurred at the end of the third day, two hours before his death. Just then his schoolboy son had crept softly in and gone up to the bedside. The dying man was still screaming desperately and waving his arms. His hand fell on the boy's head, and the boy caught it, pressed it to his lips, and began to cry.

At that very moment Ivan Ilych fell through and caught sight of the light, and it was revealed to him that though his life had not been what it should have been, this could still be rectified. He asked himself, "What *is* the right thing?" and grew still, listening. Then he felt that someone was kissing his hand. He opened his eyes, looked at his son, and felt sorry for him. His wife came up to him and he glanced at her. She was gazing at him open-mouthed, with undried tears on her nose and cheek and a despairing look on her face. He felt sorry for her too.

"Yes, I am making them wretched," he thought. "They are sorry, but it will be better for them when I die." He wished to say this but had not the strength to utter it. "Besides, why speak? I must act," he thought. With a look at his wife he indicated his son and said: "Take him away . . . sorry for him . . . sorry for you too. . . ." He tried to add, "forgive me," but said "forgo" and waved his hand, knowing that He whose understanding mattered would understand.

And suddenly it grew clear to him that what had been oppressing him and would not leave him was all dropping away at once from two sides, from ten sides, and from all sides. He was sorry for them, he must act so as not to hurt them: release them and free himself from these sufferings. "How good and how simple!" he thought. "And the pain?" he asked himself. "What has become of it? Where are you, pain?"

He turned his attention to it.

"Yes, here it is. Well, what of it? Let the pain be."

"And death . . . where is it?"

He sought his former accustomed fear of death and did not find it. "Where is it? What death?" There was no fear because there was no death.

In place of death there was light.

"So that's what it is!" he suddenly exclaimed aloud. "What joy!"

To him all this happened in a single instant, and the meaning of that instant did not change. For those present his agony continued for another two hours. Something rattled in his throat, his emaciated body twitched, then the gasping and rattle became less and less frequent.

"It is finished!" said someone near him.

He heard these words and repeated them in his soul.

"Death is finished," he said to himself. "It is no more!"

He drew in a breath, stopped in the midst of a sigh, stretched out, and died.

CHAPTER nine

Perversions: The Deviations of Sexual Thought and Behavior

The definition of what constitutes sexual deviation is in part culturally determined, and different societies evaluate similar sexual behavior differently. This section is based on the concept that within cultural limits perversions represent a significant deviation of sexual aims and objects, the norm being heterosexual genital intercourse within an enduring relationship.

Perversions, besides occurring as an isolated pathology, are present to varying degrees in all types of abnormal personality, and they frequently occur in a culturally acceptable form in normal individuals.

For many years the pervert was a psychiatric enigma, and knowledge about this subject consisted of little more than catalogues detailing the nature of each bizarre variant.

A major step toward the understanding of perversions was made by Freud. He outlined the psychosexual development of children indicating that in the course of this development there occurs polymorphous perverse sexual feelings. Briefly, Freud's theory suggested that there was a developmental sequence of sexual interests and impulses involving oral, anal, urethral, phallic, and genital stages. This polymorphous development involves not only different sexual aims, but also the nature of the desirable sexual object changes. During normal maturation these polymorphous impulses are in the main relinquished, or become part of adult genital sexuality where they may contribute to sexual foreplay. Freud suggested that in the course of deviant development the child might, for several reasons, become fixated or involved in one or the other of these pregenital perverse sexual aims or objects. These childhood fixations could contribute to or indeed be the basis of adult perversions.

Freud's discoveries led to a more careful consideration of the early life history of the perverted. Out of this subsequent research has come the understanding that perversions, like any other symptoms, are not simply fixations, but also represent an attempt to deal with anxiety or conflict.

The more important types of perversions will be presented in this section. The inclusion of the drug addict and the alcoholic in this category is based on the following criteria. The alcoholic and the addict both become attached to their source of gratification with an intensity that supersedes any human relationship. This attachment is not sexual in the ordinary sense of the word, but it has an urgency, an intensity, an emotional charge that outweighs all other forces of the personality. This dependency, this narrowing of interest, is similar to the earliest infantile stages where the bottle or the breast are more important than the mother, and all the infant seeks is surcease from discomfort in the pleasure of being warm, secure, and full. Thus addiction and alcoholism can be considered primitive deviations at the earliest stage of psychosexual development.

Homosexuality

I. Most psychiatrists and psychologists believe that every human being has some bisexual elements in his nature. When the bisexual feelings and impulses are particularly intense but not permitted open expression, the condition is described as latent homosexuality. The perversion of overt homosexuality with open acceptance of an attraction for members of the same sex is quite common, and recent evidence suggests that it is an increasing problem in contemporary society.

Most human beings struggle against their homosexual feelings, and in certain individuals elaborate defenses are developed to counteract and repress these impulses. D. H. Lawrence portrays such a struggle in his description of "The Prussian Officer." The colonel, a latent homosexual, cannot permit himself to become aware of the underlying nature

of his fascination for his orderly. Sadism develops as he copes
with the impulses and fantasies that threaten to erupt. His
sadism reassures him and strangely gratifies him as he finds a
way to assault his orderly while denying the sexual aspects.

The Prussian Officer

D. H. Lawrence   (1885–1930)

. . . The Captain was a tall man of about forty, grey at
the temples. He had a handsome, finely-knit figure, and was one of the
best horsemen in the West. His orderly, having to rub him down, admired the amazing riding-muscles of his loins.

For the rest, the orderly scarcely noticed the officer any more than
he noticed himself. It was rarely he saw his master's face: he did not look
at it. The Captain had reddish-brown, stiff hair, that he wore short upon
his skull. His moustache was also cut short and bristly over a full, brutal
mouth. His face was rather rugged, the cheeks thin. Perhaps the man was
the more handsome for the deep lines in his face, the irritable tension of
his brow, which gave him the look of a man who fights with life. His fair
eyebrows stood bushy over light-blue eyes that were always flashing with
cold fire.

He was a Prussian aristocrat, haughty and overbearing. But his
mother had been a Polish countess. Having made too many gambling
debts when he was young, he had ruined his prospects in the Army, and
remained an infantry captain. He had never married: his position did not
allow of it, and no woman had ever moved him to it. His time he spent
riding—occasionally he rode one of his own horses at the races—and at
the officers' club. Now and then he took himself a mistress. But after such
an event, he returned to duty with his brow still more tense, his eyes still
more hostile and irritable. With the men, however, he was merely impersonal, though a devil when roused; so that, on the whole, they feared
him, but had no great aversion from him. They accepted him as the inevitable.

To his orderly he was at first cold and just and indifferent: he did not
fuss over trifles. So that his servant knew practically nothing about him,
except just what orders he would give, and how he wanted them obeyed.
That was quite simple. Then the change gradually came.

The orderly was a youth of about twenty-two, of medium height,
and well built. He had strong, heavy limbs, was swarthy, with a soft,

black, young moustache. There was something altogether warm and young about him. He had firmly marked eyebrows over dark, expressionless eyes, that seemed never to have thought, only to have received life direct through his senses, and acted straight from instinct.

Gradually the officer had become aware of his servant's young vigorous, unconscious presence about him. He could not get away from the sense of the youth's person, while he was in attendance. It was like a warm flame upon the older man's tense, rigid body, that had become almost unliving, fixed. There was something so free and self-contained about him, and something in the young fellow's movement, that made the officer aware of him. And this irritated the Prussian. He did not choose to be touched into life by his servant. He might easily have changed his man, but he did not. He now very rarely looked direct at his orderly, but kept his face averted, as if to avoid seeing him. And yet as the young soldier moved unthinking about the apartment, the elder watched him, and would notice the movement of his strong young shoulders under the blue cloth, the bend of his neck. And it irritated him. To see the soldier's young, brown, shapely peasant's hand grasp the loaf or the wine-bottle sent a flash of hate or of anger through the elder man's blood. It was not that the youth was clumsy: it was rather the blind, instinctive sureness of movement of an unhampered young animal that irritated the officer to such a degree.

Once, when a bottle of wine had gone over, and the red gushed out on to the tablecloth, the officer had started up with an oath, and his eyes, bluey like fire, had held those of the confused youth for a moment. It was a shock for the young soldier. He felt something sink deeper, deeper into his soul, where nothing had ever gone before. It left him rather blank and wondering. Some of his natural completeness in himself was gone, a little uneasiness took its place. And from that time an undiscovered feeling had held between the two men.

Henceforward the orderly was afraid of really meeting his master. His subconsciousness remembered those steely blue eyes and the harsh brows, and did not intend to meet them again. So he always stared past his master, and avoided him. Also, in a little anxiety, he waited for the three months to have gone, when his time would be up. He began to feel a constraint in the Captain's presence, and the soldier even more than the officer wanted to be left alone, in his neutrality as servant.

He had served the Captain for more than a year, and knew his duty. This he performed easily, as if it were natural to him. The officer and his commands he took for granted, as he took the sun and the rain, and he served as a matter of course. It did not implicate him personally.

But now if he were going to be forced into a personal interchange with his master he would be like a wild thing caught, he felt he must get away.

But the influence of the young soldier's being had penetrated through the officer's stiffened discipline, and perturbed the man in him. He, however, was a gentleman, with long, fine hands and cultivated movements, and was not going to allow such a thing as the stirring of his innate self. He was a man of passionate temper, who had always kept himself suppressed. Occasionally there had been a duel, an outburst before the soldiers. He knew himself to be always on the point of breaking out. But he kept himself hard to the idea of the Service. Whereas the young soldier seemed to live out his warm, full nature, to give it off in his very movements, which had a certain zest, such as wild animals have in free movement. And this irritated the officer more and more.

In spite of himself, the Captain could not regain his neutrality of feeling towards his orderly. Nor could he leave the man alone. In spite of himself, he watched him, gave him sharp orders, tried to take up as much of his time as possible. Sometimes he flew into a rage with the young soldier, and bullied him. Then the orderly shut himself off, as it were out of earshot, and waited, with sullen, flushed face, for the end of the noise. The words never pierced to his intelligence, he made himself, protectively, impervious to the feelings of his master.

He had a scar on his left thumb, a deep seam going across the knuckle. The officer had long suffered from it, and wanted to do something to it. Still it was there, ugly and brutal on the young, brown hand. At last the Captain's reserve gave way. One day, as the orderly was smoothing out the tablecloth, the officer pinned down his thumb with a pencil, asking:

"How did you come by that?"

The young man winced and drew back at attention.

"A wood axe, Herr Hauptmann," he answered.

The officer waited for further explanation. None came. The orderly went about his duties. The elder man was sullenly angry. His servant avoided him. And the next day he had to use all his will-power to avoid seeing the scarred thumb. He wanted to get hold of it and—— A hot flame ran in his blood.

He knew his servant would soon be free, and would be glad. As yet, the soldier had held himself off from the elder man. The Captain grew madly irritable. He could not rest when the soldier was away, and when he was present, he glared at him with tormented eyes. He hated those fine, black brows over the unmeaning, dark eyes, he was infuriated by the free movement of the handsome limbs, which no military discipline could make stiff. And he became harsh and cruelly bullying, using contempt and satire. The young soldier only grew more mute and expressionless.

"What cattle were you bred by, that you can't keep straight eyes? Look me in the eyes when I speak to you."

And the soldier turned his dark eyes to the other's face, but there was no sight in them: he stared with the slightest possible cast, holding back his sight, perceiving the blue of his master's eyes, but receiving no look from them. And the elder man went pale, and his reddish eyebrows twitched. He gave his order, barrenly.

Once he flung a heavy military glove into the young soldier's face. Then he had the satisfaction of seeing the black eyes flare up into his own, like a blaze when straw is thrown on a fire. And he had laughed with a little tremor and a sneer.

But there were only two months more. The youth instinctively tried to keep himself intact: he tried to serve the officer as if the latter were an abstract authority and not a man. All his instinct was to avoid personal contact, even definite hate. But in spite of himself the hate grew, responsive to the officer's passion. However, he put it in the background. When he had left the Army he could dare acknowledge it. By nature he was active, and had many friends. He thought what amazing good fellows they were. But, without knowing it, he was alone. Now this solitariness was intensified. It would carry him through his term. But the officer seemed to be going irritably insane, and the youth was deeply frightened.

The soldier had a sweetheart, a girl from the mountains, independent and primitive. The two walked together, rather silently. He went with her, not to talk, but to have his arm round her, and for the physical contact. This eased him, made it easier for him to ignore the Captain; for he could rest with her held fast against his chest. And she, in some unspoken fashion, was there for him. They loved each other.

The Captain perceived it, and was mad with irritation. He kept the young man engaged all the evenings long, and took pleasure in the dark look that came on his face. Occasionally, the eyes of the two men met, those of the younger sullen and dark, doggedly unalterable, those of the elder sneering with restless contempt.

The officer tried hard not to admit the passion that had got hold of him. He would not know that his feeling for his orderly was anything but that of a man incensed by his stupid, perverse servant. So, keeping quite justified and conventional in his consciousness, he let the other thing run on. His nerves, however, were suffering. At last he slung the end of a belt in his servant's face. When he saw the youth start back, the pain-tears in his eyes and the blood on his mouth, he had felt at once a thrill of deep pleasure and of shame.

But this, he acknowledged to himself, was a thing he had never done before. The fellow was too exasperating. His own nerves must be going to pieces. He went away for some days with a woman.

It was a mockery of pleasure. He simply did not want the woman. But he stayed on for his time. At the end of it, he came back in an agony of irritation, torment, and misery. He rode all the evening, then came straight in to supper. His orderly was out. The officer sat with his long, fine hands lying on the table, perfectly still, and all his blood seemed to be corroding.

At last his servant entered. He watched the strong, easy young figure, the fine eyebrows, the thick black hair. In a week's time the youth had got back his old well-being. The hands of the officer twitched and seemed to be full of mad flame. The young man stood at attention, unmoving, shut off.

The meal went in silence. But the orderly seemed eager. He made a clatter with the dishes.

"Are you in a hurry?" asked the officer, watching the intent, warm face of his servant. The other did not reply.

"Will you answer my question?" said the Captain.

"Yes, sir," replied the orderly, standing with his pile of deep Army plates. The Captain waited, looked at him, then asked again:

"Are you in a hurry?"

"Yes, sir," came the answer, that sent a flash through the listener.

"For what?"

"I was going out, sir."

"I want you this evening."

There was a moment's hesitation. The officer had a curious stiffness of countenance.

"Yes, sir," replied the servant, in his throat.

"I want you to-morrow evening also—in fact you may consider your evenings occupied, unless I give you leave."

The mouth with the young moustache set close.

"Yes, sir," answered the orderly, loosening his lips for a moment.

He again turned to the door.

"And why have you a piece of pencil in your ear?"

The orderly hesitated, then continued on his way without answering. He set the plates in a pile outside the door, took the stump of pencil from his ear, and put it in his pocket. He had been copying a verse for his sweetheart's birthday card. He returned to finish clearing the table. The officer's eyes were dancing, he had a little, eager smile.

"Why have you a piece of pencil in your ear?" he asked.

The orderly took his hands full of dishes. His master was standing near the great green stove, a little smile on his face, his chin thrust forward. When the young soldier saw him his heart suddenly ran hot. He felt blind. Instead of answering, he turned dazedly to the door. As he was crouching to set down the dishes, he was pitched forward by a kick from behind. The pots went in a stream down the stairs, he clung to the pillar of the banisters. And as he was rising he was kicked heavily again and again, so that he clung sickly to the post for some moments. His master had gone swiftly into the room and closed the door. The maid-servant downstairs looked up the staircase and made a mocking face at the crockery disaster.

The officer's heart was plunging. He poured himself a glass of wine, part of which he spilled on the floor, and gulped the remainder, leaning against the cool, green stove. He heard his man collecting the dishes from the stairs. Pale, as if intoxicated, he waited. The servant entered again. The Captain's heart gave a pang, as of pleasure, seeing the young fellow bewildered and uncertain on his feet with pain.

"Schöner!" he said.

The soldier was a little slower in coming to attention.

"Yes, sir!"

The youth stood before him, with pathetic young moustache, and fine eyebrows very distinct on his forehead of dark marble.

"I asked you a question."

"Yes, sir."

The officer's tone bit like acid.

"Why had you a pencil in your ear?"

Again the servant's heart ran hot, and he could not breathe. With dark, strained eyes, he looked at the officer, as if fascinated. And he stood there sturdily planted, unconscious. The withering smile came into the Captain's eyes, and he lifted his foot.

"I forgot it—sir," panted the soldier, his dark eyes fixed on the other man's dancing blue ones.

"What was it doing there?"

He saw the young man's breast heaving as he made an effort for words.

"I had been writing."

"Writing what?"

Again the soldier looked him up and down. The officer could hear him panting. The smile came into the blue eyes. The soldier worked his dry throat, but could not speak. Suddenly the smile lit like a flame on the officer's face, and a kick came heavily against the orderly's thigh. The youth moved sideways. His face went dead, with two black, staring eyes.

"Well?" said the officer.

The orderly's mouth had gone dry, and his tongue rubbed in it as on dry brown-paper. He worked his throat. The officer raised his foot. The servant went stiff.

"Some poetry, sir," came the crackling, unrecognisable sound of his voice.

"Poetry, what poetry?" asked the Captain, with a sickly smile.

Again there was the working in the throat. The Captain's heart had suddenly gone down heavily, and he stood sick and tired.

"For my girl, sir," he heard the dry, inhuman sound.

"Oh!" he said, turning away. "Clear the table."

"Click!" went the soldier's throat; then again, "click!" and then the half-articulate:

"Yes, sir."

The young soldier was gone, looking old, and walking heavily.

The officer, left alone, held himself rigid, to prevent himself from thinking. His instinct warned him that he must not think. Deep inside him was the intense gratification of his passion, still working powerfully. Then there was a counteraction, a horrible breaking down of something inside him, a whole agony of reaction. He stood there for an hour motionless, a chaos of sensations, but rigid with a will to keep blank his consciousness, to prevent his mind grasping. And he held himself so until the worst of the stress had passed, when he began to drink, drank himself to an intoxication, till he slept obliterated. When he woke in the morning he was shaken to the base of his nature. But he had fought off the realisation of what he had done. He had prevented his mind from taking it in, had suppressed it along with his instincts, and the conscious man had nothing to do with it. He felt only as after a bout of intoxication, weak, but the affair itself all dim and not to be recovered. Of the drunkenness of his passion he successfully refused remembrance. And when his orderly appeared with coffee, the officer assumed the same self he had had the morning before. He refused the event of the past night—denied it had ever been—and was successful in his denial. He had not done any such thing—not he himself. Whatever there might be lay at the door of a stupid insubordinate servant. . . .

Pedophilia

II. Some homosexuals are attracted to young children; a perversion called pedophilia. Psychoanalytic study suggests that the pedophiliac is often attempting to find and love a replica of himself as a child.

a. Thomas Mann, whose incredible skill permits him to write with greatness on this difficult theme, has created the character of Gustave von Aschenbach, a man near death, caught up in such an emotional and sexual attachment to a child. Mann shows us that the homosexual choice in such cases is much more than an erotic object; it is a vastly overidealized symbol. That special process in which the homosexual idealizes is at the heart of understanding this strange perversion.

DEATH IN VENICE
Thomas Mann   (1875–1955)

As he sat there dreaming thus, deep, deep into the void, suddenly the margin line of the shore was cut by a human form. He gathered up his gaze and withdrew it from the illimitable, and lo, it was the lovely boy who crossed his vision coming from the left along the sand. He was barefoot, ready for wading, the slender legs uncovered above the knee, and moved slowly, yet with such a proud, light tread as to make it seem he had never worn shoes. He looked towards the diagonal row of cabins; and the sight of the Russian family, leading their lives there in joyous simplicity, distorted his features in a spasm of angry disgust. His brow darkened, his lips curled, one corner of the mouth was drawn down in a harsh line that marred the curve of the cheek, his frown was so heavy that the eyes seemed to sink in as they uttered beneath the black and vicious language of hate. He looked down, looked threateningly back once more; then giving it up with a violent and contemptuous shoulder-shrug, he left his enemies in the rear.

A feeling of delicacy, a qualm, almost like a sense of shame, made Aschenbach turn away as though he had not seen; he felt unwilling to take advantage of having been, by chance, privy to this passionate reaction. But he was in truth both moved and exhilarated—that is to say, he was delighted. This childish exhibition of fanaticism, directed against the good-naturedest simplicity in the world—it gave to the godlike and inexpressive the final human touch. The figure of the half-grown lad, a masterpiece from nature's own hand, had been significant enough when it gratified the eye alone; and now it evoked sympathy as well—the little episode had set it off, lent it a dignity in the onlooker's eyes that was beyond its years.

Aschenbach listened with still averted head to the boy's voice announcing his coming to his companions at the sand-heap. The voice was clear, though a little weak, but they answered, shouting his name—or his nickname—again and again. Aschenbach was not without curiosity to learn it, but could make out nothing more exact than two musical syllables, something like Adgio—or, oftener still, Adjiu, with a long-drawn-out *u* at the end. He liked the melodious sound, and found it fitting; said it over to himself a few times and turned back with satisfaction to his papers.

Holding his travelling-pad on his knees, he took his fountain-pen and began to answer various items of his correspondence. But presently he felt it too great a pity to turn his back, and the eyes of his mind, for the sake of mere commonplace correspondence, to this scene which was, after all, the most rewarding one he knew. He put aside his papers and swung round to the sea; in no long time, beguiled by the voices of the children at play, he had turned his head and sat resting it against the chair-back, while he gave himself up to contemplating the activities of the exquisite Adgio.

His eye found him out at once, the red breast-knot was unmistakable. With some nine or ten companions, boys and girls of his own age and younger, he was busy putting in place an old plank to serve as a bridge across the ditches between the sand-piles. He directed the work by shouting and motioning with his head, and they were all chattering in many tongues—French, Polish, and even some of the Balkan languages. But his was the name oftenest on their lips, he was plainly sought after, wooed, admired. One lad in particular, a Pole like himself, with a name that sounded something like Jaschiu, a sturdy lad with brilliantined black hair, in a belted linen suit, was his particular liegeman and friend. Operations at the sand-pile being ended for the time, they two walked away along the beach, with their arms round each other's waists, and once the lad Jaschiu gave Adgio a kiss.

Aschenbach felt like shaking a finger at him. "But you, Critobulus," he thought with a smile, "you I advise to take a year's leave. That long, at least, you will need for complete recovery." A vendor came by with strawberries, and Aschenbach made his second breakfast of the great luscious, dead-ripe fruit. It had grown very warm, although the sun had not availed to pierce the heavy layer of mist. His mind felt relaxed, his senses revelled in this vast and soothing communion with the silence of the sea. The grave and serious man found sufficient occupation in speculating what name it could be that sounded like Adgio. And with the help of a few Polish memories he at length fixed on Tadzio, a shortened form of Thaddeus, which sounded, when called, like Tadziu or Adziu.

Tadzio was bathing. Aschenbach had lost sight of him for a moment, then descried him far out in the water, which was shallow a very long way—saw his head, and his arm striking out like an oar. But his watchful family were already on the alert; the mother and governess called from the veranda in front of their bathing-cabin, until the lad's name, with its softened consonants and long-drawn *u*-sound, seemed to possess the beach like a rallying-cry; the cadence had something sweet and wild: "Tadziu! Tadziu!" He turned and ran back against the water, churning the waves to a foam, his head flung high. The sight of this living figure, virginally pure and austere, with dripping locks, beautiful as a tender young god, emerging from the depths of sea and sky, outrunning the element—it conjured up mythologies, it was like a primeval legend, handed down from the beginning of time, of the birth of form, of the origin of the gods. With closed lids Aschenbach listened to this poesy hymning itself silently within him, and anon he thought it was good to be here and that he would stop awhile.

Afterwards Tadzio lay on the sand and rested from his bathe, wrapped in his white sheet, which he wore drawn underneath the right shouder, so that his head was cradled on his bare right arm. And even when Aschenbach read, without looking up, he was conscious that the lad was there; that it would cost him but the slightest turn of the head to have the rewarding vision once more in his purview. Indeed, it was almost as though he sat there to guard the youth's repose; occupied, of course, with his own affairs, yet alive to the presence of that noble human creature close at hand. And his heart was stirred, it felt a father's kindness: such an emotion as the possessor of beauty can inspire in one who has offered himself up in spirit to create beauty.

At midday he left the beach, returned to the hotel, and was carried up in the lift to his room. There he lingered a little time before the glass and looked at his own grey hair, his keen and weary face. And he thought of his fame, and how people gazed respectfully at him in the streets, on account of his unerring gift of words and their power to charm. He called up all the worldly successes his genius had reaped, all he could remember, even his patent of nobility. Then went to luncheon down in the dining-room, sat at his little table and ate. Afterwards he mounted again in the lift, and a group of young folk, Tadzio among them, pressed with him into the little compartment. It was the first time Aschenbach had seen him close at hand, not merely in perspective, and could see and take account of the details of his humanity. Someone spoke to the lad, and he, answering, with indescribably lovely smile, stepped out again, as they had come to the first floor, backwards, with his eyes cast down. "Beauty makes people self-conscious," Aschenbach thought, and considered within himself imperatively why this should be. He had noted, further, that Tadzio's teeth were imperfect, rather jagged and bluish, without a healthy glaze, and of that peculiar brittle transparency which the teeth of chlorotic people often show. "He is delicate, he is sickly," Aschenbach thought. "He will most likely not live to grow old." He did not try to account for the pleasure the idea gave him. . . .

. . . Soon the observer knew every line and pose of this form that limned itself so freely against sea and sky; its every loveliness, though conned by heart, yet thrilled him each day afresh; his admiration knew no bounds, the delight of his eye was unending. Once the lad was summoned to speak to a guest who was waiting for his mother at their cabin. He ran up, ran dripping wet out of the sea, tossing his curls, and put out his hand, standing with his weight on one leg, resting the other foot on the toes; as he stood there in a posture of suspense the turn of his body was enchanting, while his features wore a look half shamefaced, half con-

he duty breeding laid upon him to please. Or he would lie at
, with his bath-robe around him, one slender young arm resting
nd, his chin in the hollow of his hand; the lad they called Jaschiu
g beside him, paying him court. There could be nothing lovelier
h than the smile and look with which the playmate thus singled out
rewarded his humble friend and vassal. Again, he might be at the water's
edge, alone, removed from his family, quite close to Aschenbach; standing erect, his hands clasped at the back of his neck, rocking slowly on the
balls of his feet, daydreaming away into blue space, while little waves
ran up and bathed his toes. The ringlets of honey-coloured hair clung to
his temples and neck, the fine down along the upper vertebræ was yellow
in the sunlight; the thin envelope of flesh covering the torso betrayed the
delicate outlines of the ribs and the symmetry of the breast-structure. His
armpits were still as smooth as a statue's, smooth the glistening hollows behind the knees, where the blue network of veins suggested that the body
was formed of some stuff more transparent than mere flesh. What discipline, what precision of thought were expressed by the tense youthful
perfection of this form! And yet the pure, strong will which had laboured
in darkness and succeeded in bringing this godlike work of art to the light
of day—was it not known and familiar to him, the artist? Was not the
same force at work in himself when he strove in cold fury to liberate from
the marble mass of language the slender forms of his art which he saw
with the eye of his mind and would body forth to men as the mirror and
image of spiritual beauty?

Mirror and image! His eyes took in the proud bearing of that figure
there at the blue water's edge; with an outburst of rapture he told himself that what he saw was beauty's very essence; form as divine thought,
the single and pure perfection which resides in the mind, of which an
image and likeness, rare and holy, was here raised up for adoration. This
was very frenzy—and without a scruple, nay, eagerly, the aging artist bade
it come. His mind was in travail, his whole mental background in a state
of flux. Memory flung up in him the primitive thoughts which are youth's
inheritance, but which with him had remained latent, never leaping up
into a blaze. Has it not been written that the sun beguiles our attention
from things of the intellect to fix it on things of the sense? The sun, they
say, dazzles; so bewitching reason and memory that the soul for very
pleasure forgets its actual state, to cling with doting on the loveliest of all
the objects she shines on. Yes, and then it is only through the medium of
some corporeal being that it can raise itself again to contemplation of
higher things. Amor, in sooth, is like the mathematician who in order to
give children a knowledge of pure form must do so in the language of
pictures; so, too, the god, in order to make visible the spirit, avails himself
of the forms and colours of human youth, gilding it with all imaginable

beauty that it may serve memory as a tool, the very sight of which then sets us afire with pain and longing.

Such were the devotee's thoughts, such the power of his emotions. And the sea, so bright with glancing sunbeams, wove in his mind a spell and summoned up a lovely picture: there was the ancient plane-tree outside the walls of Athens, a hallowed, shady spot, fragrant with willow-blossom and adorned with images and votive offerings in honour of the nymphs and Achelous. Clear ran the smooth-pebbled stream at the foot of the spreading tree. Crickets were fiddling. But on the gentle grassy slope, where one could lie yet hold the head erect, and shelter from the scorching heat, two men reclined, an elder with a younger, ugliness paired with beauty and wisdom with grace. Here Socrates held forth to youthful Phædrus upon the nature of virtue and desire, wooing him with insinuating wit and charming turns of phrase. He told him of the shuddering and unwonted heat that come upon him whose heart is open, when his eye beholds an image of eternal beauty; spoke of the impious and corrupt, who cannot conceive beauty though they see its image, and are incapable of awe; and of the fear and reverence felt by the noble soul when he beholds a godlike face or a form which is a good image of beauty: how as he gazes he worships the beautiful one and scarcely dares to look upon him, but would offer sacrifice as to an idol or a god, did he not fear to be thought stark mad. "For beauty, my Phædrus, beauty alone, is lovely and visible at once. For, mark you, it is the sole aspect of the spiritual which we can perceive through our senses, or bear so to perceive. Else what should become of us, if the divine, if reason and virtue and truth, were to speak to us through the senses? Should we not perish and be consumed by love, as Semele aforetime was by Zeus? So beauty, then, is the beauty-lover's way to the spirit—but only the way, only the means, my little Phædrus." . . . And then, sly arch-lover that he was, he said the subtlest thing of all: that the lover was nearer the divine than the beloved; for the god was in the one but not in the other—perhaps the tenderest, most mocking thought that ever was thought, and source of all the guile and secret bliss the lover knows. . . .

b. Frequently more than one perversion occurs in the same individual, particularly when there is a gross underlying personality disturbance. This was illustrated in Lawrence's "The Prussian Officer," where sadism and latent homosexuality were combined. James Joyce describes an "encounter" between some children and a pervert with polymorphous interests. The inexplicably frightening and confusing nature of the experience is skillfully described.

An Encounter

James Joyce   (1882–1941)

. . . There was nobody but ourselves in the field. When we had lain on the bank for some time without speaking I saw a man approaching from the far end of the field. I watched him lazily as I chewed one of those green stems on which girls tell fortunes. He came along by the bank slowly. He walked with one hand upon his hip and in the other hand he held a stick with which he tapped the turf lightly. He was shabbily dressed in a suit of greenish-black and wore what we used to call a jerry hat with a high crown. He seemed to be fairly old for his moustache was ashen-grey. When he passed at our feet he glanced up at us quickly and then continued his way. We followed him with our eyes and saw that when he had gone on for perhaps fifty paces he turned about and began to retrace his steps. He walked towards us very slowly, always tapping the ground with his stick, so slowly that I thought he was looking for something in the grass.

He stopped when he came level with us and bade us good-day. We answered him and he sat down beside us on the slope slowly and with great care. He began to talk of the weather, saying that it would be a very hot summer and adding that the seasons had changed greatly since he was a boy—a long time ago. He said that the happiest time of one's life was undoubtedly one's school-boy days and that he would give anything to be young again. While he expressed these sentiments which bored us a little we kept silent. Then he began to talk of school and of books. He asked us whether we had read the poetry of Thomas Moore or the works of Sir Walter Scott and Lord Lytton. I pretended that I had read every book he mentioned so that in the end he said:

"Ah, I can see you are a bookworm like myself. Now," he added, pointing to Mahony who was regarding us with open eyes, "he is different; he goes in for games."

He said he had all Sir Walter Scott's works and all Lord Lytton's works at home and never tired of reading them. "Of course," he said, "there were some of Lord Lytton's works which boys couldn't read." Mahony asked why couldn't boys read them—a question which agitated and pained me because I was afraid the man would think I was as stupid as Mahony. The man, however, only smiled. I saw that he had great gaps in his mouth between his yellow teeth. Then he asked us which of us had the most sweethearts. Mahony mentioned lightly that he had three totties.

The man asked me how many I had. I answered that I had none. He did not believe me and said he was sure I must have one. I was silent.

"Tell us," said Mahony pertly to the man, "how many have you yourself?"

The man smiled as before and said that when he was our age he had lots of sweethearts.

"Every boy," he said, "has a little sweetheart."

His attitude on this point struck me as strangely liberal in a man of his age. In my heart I thought that what he said about boys and sweethearts was reasonable. But I disliked the words in his mouth and I wondered why he shivered once or twice as if he feared something or felt a sudden chill. As he proceeded I noticed that his accent was good. He began to speak to us about girls, saying what nice soft hair they had and how soft their hands were and how all girls were not so good as they seemed to be if one only knew. There was nothing he liked, he said, so much as looking at a nice young girl, at her nice white hands and her beautiful soft hair. He gave me the impression that he was repeating something which he had learned by heart or that, magnetised by some words of his own speech, his mind was slowly circling round and round in the same orbit. At times he spoke as if he were simply alluding to some fact that everybody knew, and at times he lowered his voice and spoke mysteriously as if he were telling us something secret which he did not wish others to overhear. He repeated his phrases over and over again, varying them and surrounding them with his monotonous voice. I continued to gaze towards the foot of the slope, listening to him.

After a long while his monologue paused. He stood up slowly, saying that he had to leave us for a minute or so, a few minutes, and, without changing the direction of my gaze, I saw him walking slowly away from us towards the near end of the field. We remained silent when he had gone. After a silence of a few minutes I heard Mahony exclaim:

"I say! Look what he's doing!"

As I neither answered nor raised my eyes Mahony exclaimed again:

"I say . . . He's a queer old josser!"

"In case he asks us for our names," I said, "let you be Murphy and I'll be Smith."

We said nothing further to each other. I was still considering whether I would go away or not when the man came back and sat down beside us again. Hardly had he sat down when Mahony, catching sight of the cat which had escaped him, sprang up and pursued her across the field. The man and I watched the chase. The cat escaped once more and Mahony began to throw stones at the wall she had escaladed. Desisting from this he began to wander about the far end of the field, aimlessly.

After an interval the man spoke to me. He said that my friend was a very rough boy and asked did he get whipped often at school. I was going to reply indignantly that we were not National School boys to be whipped, as he called it; but I remained silent. He began to speak on the subject of chastising boys. His mind, as if magnetised again by his speech, seemed to circle slowly round and round its new centre. He said that when boys were that kind they ought to be whipped and well whipped. When a boy was rough and unruly there was nothing would do him any good but a good sound whipping. A slap on the hand or a box on the ear was no good: what he wanted was to get a nice warm whipping. I was surprised at this sentiment and involuntarily glanced up at his face. As I did so I met the gaze of a pair of bottle-green eyes peering at me from under a twitching forehead. I turned my eyes away again.

The man continued his monologue. He seemed to have forgotten his recent liberalism. He said that if ever he found a boy talking to girls or having a girl for a sweetheart he would whip him and whip him; and that would teach him not to be talking to girls. And if a boy had a girl for a sweetheart and told lies about it then he would give him such a whipping as no boy ever got in this world. He said that there was nothing in this world he would like so well as that. He described to me how he would whip such a boy as if he were unfolding some elaborate mystery. He would love that, he said, better than anything in this world; and his voice, as he led me monotonously through the mystery, grew almost affectionate and seemed to plead with me that I should understand him.

I waited till his monologue paused again. Then I stood up abruptly. Lest I should betray my agitation I delayed a few moments pretending to fix my shoe properly and then, saying that I was obliged to go, I bade him good-day. I went up the slope calmly but my heart was beating quickly with fear that he would seize me by the ankles. When I reached the top of the slope I turned round and, without looking at him, called loudly across the field:

"Murphy!"

My voice had an accent of forced bravery in it and I was ashamed of my paltry stratagem. I had to call the name again before Mahony saw me and hallooed in answer. How my heart beat as he came running across the field to me! He ran as if to bring me aid. And I was penitent; for in my heart I had always despised him a little.

Transvestism

III. One not uncommon perversion is the tendency to dress in clothes of the opposite sex. This perversion is more striking in men, where dressing in feminine attire may be accompanied by intense sexual excitement. Often the transvestite is an overt homosexual as well, but some remain latent, and use feminine attire solely to excite themselves to masturbate. Scobie, in Lawrence Durell's Alexandrian quartet, illustrates a typical form of this perversion.

BALTHAZAR

Lawrence Durrell   (1912–   )

. . . He was sitting down on the bed now and staring at his shabby shoes. "Are you going to the party Nessim's giving for Mountolive tonight?"—"I suppose so," I said. He sniffed loudly. "I'm not invited. At the Yacht Club, isn't it?"

"Yes."

"He is Sir David now, isn't he? I saw it in the paper last week. Young to be a lord, isn't he? I was in charge of the Police Guard of Honour when he arrived. They all played out of tune but he didn't notice anything, thank God!"

"Not so young."

"And to be Minister?"

"I suppose he's in his late forties?"

Abruptly, without apparent premeditation (though he closed his eyes fast as if to shut the subject away out of sight forever) Scobie lay back on the bed, hands behind his head, and said:

"Before you go, there's a small confession I'd like to make to you, old man. Right?"

I sat down on the uncomfortable chair and nodded. "Right," he said emphatically and drew a breath. "Well then: sometimes at the full moon, *I'm Took. I come under An Influence.*"

This was on the face of it a somewhat puzzling departure from accepted form, for the old man looked quite disturbed by his own revelation. He gobbled for a moment and then went on in a small humbled voice devoid of his customary swagger. "I don't know what comes over me." I did not quite understand all this. "Do you mean you walk in your sleep or what?" He shook his head and gulped again. "Do you turn into a werewolf, Scobie?" Once more he shook his head like a child upon the point of tears. "I slip on female duds and my Dolly Varden," he said, and opened his eyes fully to stare pathetically at me.

"You *what?*" I said.

To my intense surprise he rose now and walked stiffly to a cupboard which he unlocked. Inside, hanging up, moth-eaten and unbrushed, was a suit of female clothes of ancient cut, and on a nail beside it a greasy old cloche hat which I took to be the so-called "Dolly Varden." A pair of antediluvian court shoes with very high heels and long pointed toes completed this staggering outfit. He did not know how quite to respond to the laugh which I was now compelled to utter. He gave a weak giggle. "It's silly, isn't it?" he said, still hovering somewhere on the edge of tears despite his smiling face, and still by his tone inviting sympathy in misfortune. "I don't know what comes over me. And yet, you know, it's always the old thrill. . . ."

A sudden and characteristic change of mood came over him at the words: his disharmony, his discomfiture gave place to a new jauntiness. His look became arch now, not wistful, and crossing to the mirror before my astonished eyes, he placed the hat upon his bald head. In a second he replaced his own image with that of a little old tart, button-eyed and razor-nosed—a tart of the Waterloo Bridge epoch, a veritable Tuppenny Upright. Laughter and astonishment packed themselves into a huge parcel inside me, neither finding expression. "For God's sake!" I said at last. "You don't go around like that, do you, Scobie?"

"Only," said Scobie, sitting helplessly down on the bed again and relapsing into a gloom which gave his funny little face an even more comical expression (he still wore the Dolly Varden), "only when the Influence comes over me. When I'm not fully Answerable, old man."

He sat there looking crushed. I gave a low whistle of surprise which the parrot immediately copied. This was indeed serious. I understood now why the deliberations which had consumed him all morning had been so full of heart-searching. Obviously if one went around in a rig like that in the Arab quarter. . . . He must have been following my train of thought, for he said, "It's only sometimes when the Fleet's in." Then he went on with a touch of self-righteousness: "Of course, if there was ever any trouble, I'd say I was in disguise. I am a policeman when you come to think of it. After all, even Lawrence of Arabia wore a nightshirt, didn't he?" I nodded. "But not a Dolly Varden," I said. "You must admit, Scobie, it's most original . . ." and here the laughter overtook me.

Scobie watched me laugh, still sitting on the bed in that fantastic headpiece. "Take it off!" I implored. He looked serious and preoccupied now, but made no motion. "Now you know all," he said. "The best and the worst in the old skipper. Now what I was going to—"

At this moment there came a knock at the landing door. With surprising presence of mind Scobie leaped spryly into the cupboard, locking himself noisily in. I went to the door. On the landing stood a servant with a pitcher full of some liquid which he said was for the Effendi Skob. I took it from him and got rid of him, before returning to the room and shouting to the old man who emerged once more—now completely himself, bareheaded and blazered.

"That was a near shave," he breathed. "What was it?" I indicated the pitcher. "Oh, that—it's for the Mock Whisky. Every three hours."

"Well," I said at last, still struggling with these new and indigestible revelations of temperament, "I must be going." I was still hovering explosively between amazement and laughter at the thought of Scobie's second life at full moon—how had he managed to avoid a scandal all these years?—when he said: "Just a minute old man. I only told you all this because I want you to do me a favour." His false eye rolled around earnestly now under the pressure of thought. He sagged again. "A thing like that could do me Untold Harm," he said, "Untold Harm, old man."

"I should think it could."

"Old man," said Scobie, "I want you to confiscate my duds. It's the only way of controlling the Influence."

"Confiscate them?"

"Take them away. Lock them up. It'll save me, old man. I know it will. The whim is too strong for me otherwise, when it comes."

"All right," I said.

"God bless you, son."

Together we wrapped his full-moon regalia in some newspapers and tied the bundle up with string. His relief was tempered with doubt. "You won't lose them?" he said anxiously.

"Give them to me," I said firmly and he handed me the parcel meekly. As I went down the stairs he called after me to express relief and gratitude, adding the words: "I'll say a little prayer for you, son." I walked back slowly through the dock-area with the parcel under my arm, wondering whether I would ever dare to confide this wonderful story to someone worth sharing it with. . . .

"I told you of Scobie's death" (so wrote Balthazar) "but I did not tell you in detail the manner of it. I myself did not know him very well but I knew of your affection for him. It was not a very pleasant business and I was concerned in it entirely by accident—indeed, only because Nimrod, who runs the Secretariat, and was Scobie's chief at three removes happened to be dining with me on that particular evening. . . .

". . . Well, as I say, here we all were when the great man [Nimrod] was called away to the telephone.

"He came back after a while, looking somewhat grave, and said: 'It was from the Police Station by the docks. Apparently an old man has been kicked to death by the ratings of H.M.S. *Milton*. I have reason to believe that it might be one of the eccentrics of Q branch—there is an old Bimbashi employed there. . . .' He stood irresolutely on one leg. 'At any rate,' he went on, 'I must go down and make sure. You never know. Apparently,' he lowered his voice and drew me to one side in confidence, 'he was dressed in woman's clothes. There may be a scandal. . . .'"

Sadism and Masochism

IV. Sadism implies pleasure in inflicting pain and masochism implies pleasure in receiving pain. When sadism and masochism become directly and overtly related to sexual gratification, they are considered perversions. These terms are used in many other ways, however. For example, masochism is used in three different ways: First, moral masochism, implying a person who subjects himself to repeated suffering in his life; second, feminine masochism, in which the woman enjoys the feminine, passive, but actively receptive position in her dealings with men; and finally, sexual masochism, the perversion in which pain produces sexual pleasure and even orgasm. Freud believed that all human beings pass through a stage when they are particularly interested in sadism and masochism. Successful development involves passing through this phase with minor residues that can be traced out in the moral character or in aspects of sex foreplay, such as the love bite. Sadism and masochism are frequently linked as problems, and when one is present, the other, though unconscious, is usually important.

Minor neurotic features involving sadism and masochism are quite common. For example, some neurotic women repeatedly fantasy a child being beaten on the buttocks. This fantasy, which sometimes has a sadistic and sometimes a masochistic component, is sexually exciting and is accompanied by masturbation. Intense sadism with overt sadistic acts is apt to be present in more disturbed persons who are psychotic or near psychotic. (Cf. Asa Stryker, the paranoid character, in Edmund Wilson's story.) Dostoevsky, one of the greatest literary psychologists, gives us an insight into masochism and sadism.

THE HOUSE OF THE DEAD

Fyodor Dostoevsky   (1821–1881)

I don't know how it is today, but in the not-too-distant past, there were distinguished people to whom beating some victim afforded feelings similar to those of the Marquis de Sade and the Marquise de Brinvilliers. I think that there is something in these sensations that, in these people, make the heart stop in agonizing delight. There are people like tigers who long for a taste of blood. Anyone who has once experienced this power, this unlimited control over the body, blood, and spirit of a man like himself, a fellow creature, his brother in Christ—anyone who has experienced the power to inflict supreme humiliation upon another being, created like himself in the image of God, is bound to be ruled by his emotions. Tyranny is a habit; it grows upon us and, in the long run, turns into a disease. I say that the most decent man in the world can, through habit, become as brutish and coarse as a wild beast. Blood and power intoxicate, callousness and vice develop; the most abnormal things become first acceptable, then sweet to the mind and heart. The human being, the member of society, is drowned forever in the tyrant, and it is practically impossible for him to regain human dignity, repentance, and regeneration. One such instance—the realization that such arbitrary power can be exercised—can infect all society; such power is seductive. A society which can watch this happen with equanimity must itself be basically infected.

Thus, the power given to one man to inflict corporal punishment upon another is a social sore; it is perhaps the surest way of nipping the civic spirit in the bud. It will inevitably lead to the disintegration of society.

Society abhors a flogger. But gentlemen-whippers are far from being abhorred. The latter opinion has been disputed, but only in books, and abstractly at that. And not all those who have disputed it have managed to suppress their own need to tyrannize. Every manufacturer, every business man, must feel a sort of peevish pleasure in the realization that the worker and all his family are sometimes entirely dependent upon him. That is certainly so, for one generation does not so easily tear itself away from what it has inherited; a man does not deny so quickly what is in his blood, what he has drunk in, one might say, with his mother's milk. Such sudden reversals do not occur. To recognize one's guilt and the sins of one's fathers is a small part of it, a very small part; one must rid oneself of the habit altogether. And that cannot be done so quickly.

I have mentioned floggers. There are traces of the whipper in almost every man. But then, the bestial side does not develop equally in all men. If the beast in a man overpowers all his other sides, he becomes horrible, monstrous.

There are two kinds of floggers: the volunteers, and those who are forced into it. Of course, the volunteers are worse, from every point of view, than the others; yet people abhor the latter, displaying terror, revulsion, and an unaccountable, almost superstitious fear of them. Why this horror for the one and such indifference, bordering on approval, of the other?

I have known the most incredible instances where people—even good, honest, respected people—could not bear it if the victim undergoing punishment did not cry out under the birch, cringe, and beg for mercy. Men being punished are supposed to cry out and beg for mercy. It is considered the decent thing to do and quite essential. Once when the victim refused to cry out, the flogger, a man whom I knew and who, in other respects, could even be considered kindly, took it as a personal offense. At first he had intended to make the punishment a light one. But when the usual cries for mercy were not forthcoming, he grew furious and ordered fifty extra lashes, seeking both cries and begging—and he had his way.

"What could I do—the man was so insolent," he said quite seriously in answer to my questions.

The ordinary flogger, the man who has been ordered to do his job, is just another prisoner. Instead of being deported to Siberia, he is retained in a central penitentiary to serve as flogger. First he has to learn his trade from an experienced colleague. Then, when he has learned, he is kept permanently in one prison, where he keeps to himself, has his own room, and even does his own housekeeping, although he is almost always under guard. Of course, a man is not a machine; although he beats another man because he has to, he sometimes becomes emotionally involved. Nevertheless, he hardly ever feels personal hatred for his victim, even though he may derive a certain pleasure from his work. His self-esteem is heightened by his agility in administering his blows, by his mastery of his trade, by his desire to show off before his audience. He does his best for art's sake. Besides, he knows very well that he is a total outcast, that everywhere he goes he will be met by superstitious fear—and it is impossible to assert that this has no influence upon him, that it doesn't push him toward further violence and exacerbate his bestial inclinations. Even the children know that "he has disowned father and mother." Strangely enough, every flogger I have ever known was intelligent, clever, and sensible, with an extraordinary amount of self-respect and even pride. Did they develop this pride to counteract the general scorn? Was it strengthened by their awareness of the fear they inspire in their victims and their feeling of mastery over them? I can't say. Perhaps the ceremoniousness and theatricality of their appearance before the public contribute to the development of a certain haughtiness in them.

I used to know a flogger, and was able to observe him closely. He was a fellow of about forty, of medium height, lean and muscular, with a pleasant, intelligent face and curly hair. He was always very dignified and composed and, outwardly at least, conducted himself like a gentleman. When I spoke to him he always answered briefly, to the point, even amiably, but with a sort of haughty amiability, as if he felt somewhat superior. I detected a certain respect for him in the way the officers on duty talked to him in my presence. He sensed this, and in talking to an officer, deliberately doubled his politeness, his terseness, his air of self-esteem. The more amiable the officer's tone, the more unbending he became and, although he in no way departed from the most refined politeness, I'm sure that he considered himself immeasurably above the officer. It was written all over his face.

Sometimes, on very hot summer days, he was sent, under guard and armed with a long, thin pole, to round up the town's stray dogs. There were an incredible number of dogs in that town that belonged to no one and multiplied with extraordinary rapidity. In hot weather, they were a menace, and by order of the authorities, the executioner was sent to exterminate them. But even this degrading job did not seem to degrade him. He walked through the streets of the town, accompanied by his weary guard, with such dignity, it had to be seen to be believed. The mere sight of him frightened the women and children, and he calmly, even patronizingly, met the gaze of everyone he encountered.

However, floggers have an easy life. They have money, they eat very well, they get vodka. They get the money from bribes. The civilian prisoner sentenced to corporal punishment always gives the flogger something, even if it is his last kopek. And of an affluent prisoner, the flogger himself demands money, fixing the sum according to the man's reputed means. It can be as high as thirty rubles and more. There may be quite a bit of bargaining with the very well-off.

Of course, the flogger cannot make the punishment too obviously mild—he'd answer for it with his own back. Nevertheless, for a certain sum, he promises the victim not to beat him very painfully. Almost everyone agrees to his price, for if they don't, he can make the punishment really savage. He will sometimes demand a considerable sum from a poor prisoner. The man's relatives go to him and bargain with him most respectfully, and God pity the victim if they don't satisfy him. On these occasions, the superstitious fear he inspires is a great asset.

All sorts of legends circulate about floggers. Prisoners themselves have assured me that they can kill a man with a single blow. Yet, when has this contention ever been tested? But, after all, it could be so. The prisoners were certainly convinced of it, and a flogger himself assured me that he could do it. I have also been told that he can strike a prisoner on the back with a full swing in such a way that not even a tiny welt will be raised by the blow, and the prisoner will not feel the slightest pain. But there are already far too many stories about these tricks and subleties.

Be that as it may, even when an executioner takes a bribe to beat a man lightly, he still delivers the first blow with his full strength. This is a tradition. The subsequent blows he softens, especially if he has been paid beforehand. But whether he has been paid or not, the first blow is his own. I'm sure I don't know why there is such a custom. Is it so that the victim will be prepared for the subsequent blows, on the theory that after such a heavy blow the light ones won't seem so terrible? Or is it simply a desire to show the victim who is master, to instill fear in him, to stun him from the start, to make him see who he has to deal with, to show the flogger's actual power? In any case, prior to the beating, the flogger is in a state of excitement; he has a sense of his own power, feels himself the lord and master. At that moment he is an actor; he fills the public with wonder and terror, and it is with a feeling of pleasure that he shouts to his victim before the first blow: "Look out now! I'll scorch you!"—the sinister words usually used.

It's hard to imagine to what an extent a man's nature can be corrupted.

Voyeurism

V. Voyeurism is a perversion in which sexual pleasure is achieved in looking. Like certain others of the perversions, it is a special attachment or fixation to one of the normal aspects of adult sexual foreplay. Children pass through a phase where they are intensely curious about sexual differences. They take great pleasure in looking and exploring. This aspect of sexuality occasionally intensifies and becomes a primary goal.

Voyeurism is an aspect of sexuality which has many accepted cultural outlets. Nonetheless, the "peeping Tom" is a common social problem. There is some evidence to suggest that this occurs because the voyeurist is particularly attracted to looking at the forbidden. Malamud describes the frantic efforts of a young man to gratify his wish to see.

The Assistant

Bernard Malamud   (1914–   )

. . . Helen was with her mother as Ida counted the cash.
Frank stood behind the counter, cleaning his fingernails with his jack-knife blade, waiting for them to leave so he could close up.

"I think I'll take a hot shower before I go to bed," Helen said to her mother. "I've felt chilled all night."

"Good night," Ida said to Frank. "I left five dollars change for the morning."

"Good night," said Frank.

They left by the rear door and he heard them go up the stairs. Frank closed the store and went into the back. He thumbed through tomorrow's *News*, then got restless.

After a while he went into the store and listened at the side door; he unlatched the lock, snapped on the cellar light, closed the cellar door behind him so no light would leak out into the hall, then quietly descended the stairs.

He found the air shaft where an old unused dumb-waiter stood, pushed the dusty box back and gazed up the vertical shaft. It was pitch-dark. Neither the Bobers' bathroom window nor the Fusos' showed any light.

Frank struggled against himself but not for long. Shoving the dumb-waiter back as far as it would go, he squeezed into the shaft and then boosted himself up on top of the box. His heart shook him with its beating.

When his eyes got used to the dark he saw that her bathroom window was only a couple of feet above his head. He felt along the wall as high as he could reach and touched a narrow ledge around the air shaft. He thought he could anchor himself on it and see into the bathroom.

But if you do it, he told himself, you will suffer.

Though his throat hurt and his clothes were drenched in sweat, the excitement of what he might see forced him to go up.

Crossing himself, Frank grabbed both of the dumb-waiter ropes and slowly pulled himself up, praying the pulley at the skylight wouldn't squeak too much.

A light went on over his head.

Holding his breath, he crouched motionless, clinging to the swaying ropes. Then the bathroom window was shut with a bang. For a while he couldn't move, the strength gone out of him. He thought he might lose his grip and fall, and he thought of her opening the bathroom window and seeing him lying at the bottom of the shaft in a broken, filthy heap.

It was a mistake to do it, he thought.

But she might be in the shower before he could get a look at her, so, trembling, he began again to pull himself up. In a few minutes he was straddling the ledge, holding onto the ropes to steady himself yet keep his full weight off the wood.

Leaning forward, though not too far, he could see through the un-curtained crossed sash window into the old-fashioned bathroom. Helen was there looking with sad eyes at herself in the mirror. He thought she would stand there forever, but at last she unzipped her housecoat, stepping out of it.

He felt a throb of pain at her nakedness, an overwhelming desire to love her, at the same time an awareness of loss, of never having had what he wanted most, and other such memories he didn't care to recall.

Her body was young, soft, lovely, the breasts like small birds in flight, her ass like a flower. Yet it was a lonely body in spite of its lovely form, lonelier. Bodies are lonely, he thought, but in bed she wouldn't be. She seemed realer to him now than she had been, revealed without clothes, personal, possible. He felt greedy as he gazed, all eyes at a banquet, hungry so long as he must look. But in looking he was forcing her out of reach, making her into a thing only of his seeing, her eyes reflecting his sins, rotten past, spoiled ideals, his passion poisoned by his shame.

Frank's eyes grew moist and he wiped them with one hand. When he gazed up again she seemed, to his horror, to be staring at him through the window, a mocking smile on her lips, her eyes filled with scorn, pitiless. He thought wildly of jumping, bolting, broken-boned, out of the house; but she turned on the shower and stepped into the tub, drawing the flowered plastic curtain around her.

The window was quickly covered with steam. For this he was relieved, grateful. He let himself down silently. In the cellar, instead of the grinding remorse he had expected to suffer, he felt a moving joy.

Exhibitionism

VI. Exhibitionism is a perversion in which there is gratification in displaying one's body. Many neurotics have conflicts about exhibitionism, but direct sexual exposure of the genitalia is primarily a male perversion, and is often an attempt to cope with feelings of sexual inadequacy. Exhibitionism is linked to voyeurism, and they are often found in the same person in a fashion similar to sadism and masochism. Jean-Jacques Rousseau had the courage to describe this impulse in himself.

The Confessions of Jean-Jacques Rousseau

Jean-Jacques Rousseau   *(1712–1778)*

. . . Having left Madame de Vercellis's house in almost the same state as I had entered it, I went back to my old landlady, with

From *The Confessions of Jean-Jacques Rousseau.*

whom I remained for five or six weeks, during which health, youth, and idleness again rendered my temperament troublesome. I was restless, absent-minded, a dreamer. I wept, I sighed, I longed for a happiness of which I had no idea, and of which I nevertheless felt the want. This state cannot be described; only few men can even imagine it, because most of them have forestalled this fulness of life, at once so tormenting and so delicious, which, in the intoxication of desire, gives a foretaste of enjoyment. My heated blood incessantly filled my brain with girls and women; but, ignorant of the relations of sex, I made use of them in my imagination in accordance with my distorted notions, without knowing what else to do with them; and these notions kept my feelings in a state of most uncomfortable activity, from which, fortunately, they did not teach me how to deliver myself. I would have given my life to have found another Mademoiselle Goton for a quarter of an hour. But it was no longer the time when childish amusements took this direction as if naturally. Shame, the companion of a bad conscience, had made its appearance with advancing years; it had increased my natural shyness to such an extent that it made it unconquerable; and never, neither then nor later, have I been able to bring myself to make an indecent proposal, unless she, to whom I made it, in some measure forced me to it by her advances, even though I knew that she was by no means scrupulous, and felt almost certain of being taken at my word.

My agitation became so strong that, being unable to satisfy my desires, I excited them by the most extravagant behaviour. I haunted dark alleys and hidden retreats, where I might be able to expose myself to women in the condition in which I should have liked to have been in their company. What they saw was not an obscene object, I never even thought of such a thing; it was a ridiculous object. The foolish pleasure I took in displaying it before their eyes cannot be described. There was only one step further necessary for me to take, in order to gain actual experience of the treatment I desired, and I have no doubt that some woman would have been bold enough to afford me the amusement, while passing by, if I had had the courage to wait. This folly of mine led to a disaster almost as comical, but less agreeable for myself.

One day, I took up my position at the bottom of a court where there was a well, from which the girls of the house were in the habit of fetching water. At this spot there was a slight descent which led to some cellars by several entrances. In the dark I examined these underground passages, and finding them long and dark, I concluded that there was no outlet, and that, if I happened to be seen and surprised, I should find a safe hiding-place in them. Thus emboldened, I exhibited to the girls who came to the well a sight more laughable than seductive. The more modest pretended to see nothing; others began to laugh; others felt insulted and cried out. I ran into my retreat; someone followed me. I heard a man's voice, which I had not expected, and which alarmed me. I plunged underground at the risk of losing myself; the noise, the voices, the man's voice, still followed me. I had always reckoned upon the darkness; I saw a light. I shuddered, and plunged further into the darkness. A wall stopped me, and, being unable to go any further, I was obliged to await my fate. In a moment I was seized by a tall man with a big moustache, a big hat, and a big sword, who was escorted by four or five old women, each armed with a broom-handle, amongst whom I perceived the little wretch who had discovered me, and who, no doubt, wanted to see me face to face.

The man with the sword, seizing me by the arm, asked me roughly what I was doing there. It may be imagined that I had no answer ready. However, I recovered myself; and, in desperation, at this critical moment I invented a romantic excuse which proved successful. I begged him in a suppliant voice to have pity upon my age and condition; I said that I was a young stranger of good birth, whose brain was affected; that I had run away from home, because they wanted to shut me up; that I was lost if he betrayed me; but that, if he would let me go, I might some day be able to reward him for his kindness. Contrary to all expectation, my words and demeanour took effect; the terrible man was touched by them, and, after administering a short reproof, he let me go quietly without questioning me further. From the demeanour of the girl and the old women, when they saw me go, I judged that the man whom I feared so much had been of great service to me, and that I should not have got off so easily with them alone. I heard them murmur something or other to which I hardly paid attention; for, provided that the man and his sword did not interfere, I felt confident, active and vigorous as I was, of escaping from them and their cudgels.

A few days afterwards, while walking down a street with a young Abbé, my neighbour, I nearly ran into the man with the sword. He recognised me, and, imitating me mockingly, said: "I am a prince, I am a prince, and I am a coward; but don't let his highness come back again!" He said no more, and I sneaked away, not venturing to look up, and thanking him in my heart for his discretion. I judged that the confounded old women had made him ashamed of his credulity. Anyhow, Piedmontese as he was, he was a good man, and I never think of him without a feeling of gratitude; for the story was so funny that, merely from the desire of creating a laugh, anyone else in his place would have shamed me. This adventure, without having the consequences which I dreaded, nevertheless made me careful for a long time. . . .

Chronic Alcoholism

VII. Millions of human beings all over the world are addicted to alcohol. The choice of addiction is in part culturally determined. Some societies either forbid alcohol, or use it in such a ritualized way that addiction is rare. Other societies make alcohol the center of sociability and comradeship; in such societies alcoholism is a rampant problem.

The cultural factors are, however, superimposed, and interact with individual needs and impulses that lead one person rather than another to depend increasingly on alcohol. Alcohol, like many other chemicals, has an effect on the brain. In the case of alcohol, the effect is to impede the function of certain areas of the brain. Apparently in some individuals alcohol very quickly alleviates conscience and alters the capacity for moral judgment, as illustrated by Ogden Nash's advice to would-be Don Juans, "Candy is dandy, but liquor is quicker."

In addition to loosening the ties of conscience, alcohol for certain individuals relieves social anxieties and eases depression. Protracted dependence on alcohol as a means of dealing with painful feelings constitutes a serious undermining of personality and character. Ordinarily when a person becomes anxious or depressed, he must develop some resource within his personality either to cope or to endure. Over the years in this way the healthy ego builds defenses and works out adaptations which increase the capacity to tolerate painful feelings. The alcoholic, however, gradually erodes his ego strength as he turns to a source outside himself to alter his feeling state chemically.

Many alcoholics are depressed people who ward off their depression in an endless round of drinking. Dorothy Parker has described such a person in "Big Blonde," a woman who becomes emptier and emptier as her alcoholic intake becomes greater and greater.

BIG BLONDE

Dorothy Parker   (1893–   )

. . . More and more, her days lost their individuality. She never knew dates, nor was sure of the day of the week.

"My God, was that a year ago!" she would exclaim, when an event was recalled in conversation.

She was tired so much of the time. Tired and blue. Almost everything could give her the blues. Those old horses she saw on Sixth Avenue —struggling and slipping along the car-tracks, or standing at the curb, their heads dropped level with their worn knees. The tightly stored tears would squeeze from her eyes as she teetered past on her aching feet in the stubby, champagne-colored slippers.

The thought of death came and stayed with her and lent her a sort of drowsy cheer. It would be nice, nice and restful, to be dead.

There was no settled, shocked moment when she first thought of killing herself; it seemed to her as if the idea had always been with her. She pounced upon all the accounts of suicides in the newspapers. There was an epidemic of self-killings—or maybe it was just that she searched for the stories of them so eagerly that she found many. To read of them roused reassurance in her; she felt a cozy solidarity with the big company of the voluntary dead.

She slept, aided by whisky, till deep into the afternoons, then lay abed, a bottle and glass at her hand, until it was time to dress to go out for dinner. She was beginning to feel towards alcohol a little puzzled distrust, as toward an old friend who has refused a simple favor. Whisky could still soothe her for most of the time, but there were sudden, inexplicable moments when the cloud fell treacherously away from her, and she was sawed by the sorrow and bewilderment and nuisance of all living. She played voluptuously with the thought of cool, sleepy retreat. She had never been troubled by religious belief and no vision of an after-life intimidated her. She dreamed by day of never again putting on tight shoes, of never having to laugh and listen and admire, of never more being a good sport. Never.

But how would you do it? It made her sick to think of jumping from heights. She could not stand a gun. At the theater, if one of the actors drew a revolver, she crammed her fingers into her ears and could not even look at the stage until after the shot had been fired. There was no gas in her flat. She looked long at the bright blue veins in her slim wrists—a cut with a razor blade, and there you'd be. But it would hurt, hurt like hell, and there would be blood to see. Poison—something tasteless and quick and painless—was the thing. But they wouldn't sell it to you in drugstores, because of the law.

She had few other thoughts.

There was a new man now—Art. He was short and fat and exacting and hard on her patience when he was drunk. But there had been only occasionals for some time before him, and she was glad of a little stability. Too, Art must be away for weeks at a stretch, selling silks, and that was restful. She was convincingly gay with him, though the effort shook her.

"The best sport in the world," he would murmur, deep in her neck. "The best sport in the world."

One night, when he had taken her to Jimmy's, she went into the dressing-room with Mrs. Florence Miller. There, while designing curly mouths on their faces with lip-rouge, they compared experiences of insomnia.

"Honestly," Mrs. Morse said, "I wouldn't close an eye if I didn't go to bed full of Scotch. I lie there and toss and turn and toss and turn. Blue! Does a person get blue lying awake that way!"

"Say, listen, Hazel," Mrs. Miller said, impressively, "I'm telling you I'd be awake for a year if I didn't take veronal. That stuff makes you sleep like a fool."

"Isn't it poison, or something?" Mrs. Morse asked.

"Oh, you take too much and you're out for the count," said Mrs. Miller. "I just take five grains—they come in tablets. I'd be scared to fool around with it. But five grains, and you cork off pretty."

"Can you get it anywhere?" Mrs. Morse felt superbly Machiavellian.

"Get all you want in Jersey," said Mrs. Miller. "They won't give it to you here without you have a doctor's prescription. Finished? We'd better go back and see what the boys are doing."

That night, Art left Mrs. Morse at the door of her apartment; his mother was in town. Mrs. Morse was still sober, and it happened that there was no whisky left in her cupboard. She lay in bed, looking up at the black ceiling.

She rose early, for her, and went to New Jersey. She had never taken the tube, and did not understand it. So she went to the Pennsylvania Station and bought a railroad ticket to Newark. She thought of nothing in particular on the trip out. She looked at the uninspired hats of the women about her and gazed through the smeared window at the flat, gritty scene.

In Newark, in the first drug-store she came to, she asked for a tin of talcum powder, a nailbrush, and a box of veronal tablets. The powder and the brush were to make the hypnotic seem also a casual need. The clerk was entirely unconcerned. "We only keep them in bottles," he said, and wrapped up for her a little glass vial containing ten white tablets, stacked one on another.

She went to another drug-store and bought a facecloth, an orange-wood stick, and a bottle of veronal tablets. The clerk was also uninterested.

"Well, I guess I got enough to kill an ox," she thought, and went back to the station.

At home, she put the little vials in the drawer of her dressing-table and stood looking at them with a dreamy tenderness.

"There they are, God bless them," she said, and she kissed her fingertip and touched each bottle.

The colored maid was busy in the living-room.

"Hey, Nettie," Mrs. Morse called. "Be an angel, will you? Run around to Jimmy's and get me a quart of Scotch."

She hummed while she awaited the girl's return.

During the next few days, whisky ministered to her as tenderly as it had done when she first turned to its aid. Alone, she was soothed and vague, at Jimmy's she was the gayest of the groups. Art was delighted with her.

Then, one night, she had an appointment to meet Art at Jimmy's for an early dinner. He was to leave afterward on a business excursion, to be away for a week. Mrs. Morse had been drinking all the afternoon; while she dressed to go out, she felt herself rising pleasurably from drowsiness to high spirits. But as she came out into the street the effects of the whisky deserted her completely, and she was filled with a slow, grinding wretchedness so horrible that she stood swaying on the pavement, unable for a moment to move forward. It was a gray night with spurts of mean, thin snow, and the streets shone with dark ice. As she slowly crossed Sixth Avenue, consciously dragging one foot past the other, a big, scarred horse pulling a rickety express-wagon crashed to his knees before her. The driver swore and screamed and lashed the beast insanely, bringing the whip back over his shoulder for every blow, while the horse struggled to get a footing on the slippery asphalt. A group gathered and watched with interest.

Art was waiting, when Mrs. Morse reached Jimmy's.

"What's the matter with you, for God's sake?" was his greeting to her.

"I saw a horse," she said. "Gee, I—a person feels sorry for horses. I— it isn't just horses. Everything's kind of terrible, isn't it? I can't help getting sunk."

"Ah, sunk, me eye," he said. "What's the idea of all the bellyaching? What have you got to be sunk about?"

"I can't help it," she said.

"Ah, help it, me eye," he said. "Pull yourself together, will you? Come on and sit down, and take that face off you."

She drank industriously and she tried hard, but she could not overcome her melancholy. Others joined them and commented on her gloom, and she could do no more for them than smile weakly. She made little dabs at her eyes with her handkerchief, trying to time her movements so they would be unnoticed, but several times Art caught her and scowled and shifted impatiently in his chair.

When it was time for him to go to his train, she said she would leave, too, and go home.

"And not a bad idea, either," he said. "See if you can't sleep yourself out of it. I'll see you Thursday. For God's sake, try and cheer up by then, will you?"

"Yeah," she said. "I will."

In her bedroom, she undressed with a tense speed wholly unlike her usual slow uncertainty. She put on her nightgown, took off her hair-net and passed the comb quickly through her dry, vari-colored hair. Then she took the two little vials from the drawer and carried them into the bathroom. The splintering misery had gone from her, and she felt the quick excitement of one who is about to receive an anticipated gift.

She uncorked the vials, filled a glass with water and stood before the mirror, a tablet between her fingers. Suddenly she bowed graciously to her reflection, and raised the glass to it.

"Well, here's mud in your eye," she said.

The tablets were unpleasant to take, dry and powdery and sticking obstinately half-way down her throat. It took her a long time to swallow all twenty of them. She stood watching her reflection with deep, impersonal interest, studying the movements of the gulping throat. Once more she spoke aloud.

"For God's sake, try and cheer up by Thursday, will you?" she said. "Well, you know what he can do. He and the whole lot of them."

She had no idea how quickly to expect effect from the veronal. When she had taken the last tablet, she stood uncertainly, wondering, still with a courteous, vicarious interest, if death would strike her down then and there. She felt in no way strange, save for a slight stirring of sickness from the effort of swallowing the tablets, nor did her reflected face look at all different. It would not be immediate, then; it might even take an hour or so.

She stretched her arms high and gave a vast yawn.

"Guess I'll go to bed," she said. "Gee, I'm nearly dead."

That struck her as comic, and she turned out the bathroom light and went in and laid herself down in her bed, chuckling softly all the time.

"Gee, I'm nearly dead," she quoted. "That's a hot one!"

Nettie, the colored maid, came in late the next afternoon to clean the apartment, and found Mrs. Morse in her bed. But then, that was not unusual. Usually, though, the sounds of cleaning waked her, and she did not like to wake up. Nettie, an agreeable girl, had learned to move softly about her work.

But when she had done the living-room and stolen in to tidy the little square bedroom, she could not avoid a tiny clatter as she arranged the objects on the dressing-table. Instinctively, she glanced over her shoulder at the sleeper, and without warning a sickly uneasiness crept over her. She came to the bed and stared down at the woman lying there.

Mrs. Morse lay on her back, one flabby, white arm flung up, the wrist against her forehead. Her stiff hair hung untenderly along her face. The bed covers were pushed down, exposing a deep square of soft neck and a pink nightgown, its fabric worn uneven by many launderings; her great breasts, freed from their tight confiner, sagged beneath her arm-pits.

Now and then she made knotted, snoring sounds, and from the corner of her opened mouth to the blurred turn of her jaw ran a lane of crusted spittle.

"Mis' Morse," Nettie called. "Oh, Mis' Morse! It's terrible late."

Mrs. Morse made no move.

"Mis' Morse," said Nettie. "Look, Mis' Morse. How'm I goin' get this bed made?"

Panic sprang upon the girl. She shook the woman's hot shoulder. "Ah, wake up, will yuh?" she whined. "Ah, please wake up."

Suddenly the girl turned and ran out in the hall to the elevator door, keeping her thumb firm on the black, shiny button until the elderly car and its Negro attendant stood before her. She poured a jumble of words over the boy, and led him back to the apartment. He tiptoed creakingly in to the bedside; first gingerly, then so lustily that he left marks in the soft flesh, he prodded the unconscious woman.

"Hey, there!" he cried, and listened intently, as for an echo.

"Jeez. Out like a light," he commented.

At his interest in the spectacle, Nettie's panic left her. Importance was big in both of them. They talked in quick, unfinished whispers, and it was the boy's suggestion that he fetch the young doctor who lived on the ground floor. Nettie hurried along with him. They looked forward to the limelit moment of breaking their news of something untoward, something pleasurably unpleasant. Mrs. Morse had become the medium of drama. With no ill wish to her, they hoped that her state was serious, that she would not let them down by being awake and normal on their return. A little fear of this determined them to make the most, to the doctor, of her present condition. "Matter of life and death," returned to Nettie from her thin store of reading. She considered startling the doctor with the phrase.

The doctor was in and none too pleased at interruption. He wore a yellow and blue striped dressing-gown, and he was lying on his sofa, laughing with a dark girl, her face scaly with inexpensive powder, who perched on the arm. Half-emptied highball glasses stood beside them, and her coat and hat were neatly hung up with the comfortable implication of a long stay.

Always something, the doctor grumbled. Couldn't let anybody alone after a hard day. But he put some bottles and instruments into a case, changed his dressing-gown for his coat and started out with the Negroes.

"Snap it up there, big boy," the girl called after him. "Don't be all night."

The doctor strode loudly into Mrs. Morse's flat and on to the bedroom, Nettie and the boy right behind him. Mrs. Morse had not moved; her sleep was as deep, but soundless, now. The doctor looked sharply at her, then plunged his thumbs into the lidded pits above her eyeballs and threw his weight upon them. A high, sickened cry broke from Nettie.

"Look like he tryin' to push her right on th'ough the bed," said the boy. He chuckled.

Mrs. Morse gave no sign under the pressure. Abruptly the doctor abandoned it, and with one quick movement swept the covers down to the foot of the bed. With another he flung her nightgown back and lifted the thick, white legs, cross-hatched with blocks of tiny, iris-colored veins. He pinched them repeatedly, with long cruel nips, back of the knees. She did not awaken.

"What's she been drinking?" he asked Nettie, over his shoulder.

With the certain celerity of one who knows just where to lay hands on a thing, Nettie went into the bathroom, bound for the cupboard where Mrs. Morse kept her whisky. But she stopped at the sight of the two vials, with their red and white labels, lying before the mirror. She brought them to the doctor.

"Oh, for the Lord Almighty's sweet sake!" he said. He dropped Mrs. Morse's legs, and pushed them impatiently across the bed. "What did she want to go taking that tripe for? Rotten yellow trick, that's what a thing like that is. Now we'll have to pump her out, and all that stuff. Nuisance, a thing like that is; that's what it amounts to. Here, George, take me down in the elevator. You wait here, maid. She won't do anything."

"She won't die on me, will she?" cried Nettie.

"No," said the doctor. "God, no. You couldn't kill her with an ax."

After two days, Mrs. Morse came back to consciousness, dazed at first, then with a comprehension that brought with it the slow, saturating wretchedness.

"Oh, Lord, oh, Lord," she moaned, and tears for herself and for life striped her cheeks.

Nettie came in at the sound. For two days she had done the ugly, incessant tasks in the nursing of the unconscious, for two nights she had caught broken bits of sleep on the living-room couch. She looked coldly at the big, blown woman in the bed.

"What you been tryin' to do, Mis' Morse?" she said. "What kine o' work is that, takin' all that stuff?"

"Oh, Lord," moaned Mrs. Morse, again, and she tried to cover her eyes with her arms. But the joints felt stiff and brittle, and she cried out at their ache.

"Tha's no way to ack, takin' them pills," said Nettie. "You can thank you' stars you heah at all. How you feel now?"

"Oh, I feel great," said Mrs. Morse. "Swell, I feel."

Her hot, painful tears fell as if they would never stop.

"Tha's no way to take on, cryin' like that," Nettie said. "After what you done. The doctor, he says he could have you arrested, doin' a thing like that. He was fit to be tied, here."

"Why couldn't he let me alone?" wailed Mrs. Morse. "Why the hell couldn't he have?"

"Tha's terr'ble, Mis' Morse, swearin' an' talkin' like that," said Nettie, "after what people done for you. Here I ain' had no sleep at all for two nights, an' had to give up goin' out to my other ladies!"

"Oh, I'm sorry, Nettie," she said. "You're a peach. I'm sorry I've given you so much trouble. I couldn't help it. I just got sunk. Didn't you ever feel like doing it? When everything looks just lousy to you?"

"I wouldn' think o' no such thing," declared Nettie. "You got to cheer up. Tha's what you got to do. Everybody's got their troubles."

"Yeah," said Mrs. Morse. "I know."

"Come a pretty picture card for you," Nettie said. "Maybe that will cheer you up."

She handed Mrs. Morse a post-card. Mrs. Morse had to cover one eye with her hand, in order to read the message; her eyes were not yet focusing correctly.

It was from Art. On the back of a view of the Detroit Athletic Club he had written: "Greeting and salutations. Hope you have lost that gloom. Cheer up and don't take any rubber nickles. See you on Thursday."

She dropped the card to the floor. Misery crushed her as if she were between great smooth stones. There passed before her a slow, slow pageant of days spent lying in her flat, of evenings at Jimmy's being a good sport, making herself laugh and coo at Art and other Arts; she saw a long parade of weary horses and shivering beggars and all beaten, driven, stumbling things. Her feet throbbed as if she had crammed them into the stubby champagne-colored slippers. Her heart seemed to swell and harden.

"Nettie," she cried, "for heaven's sake pour me a drink, will you?"

The maid looked doubtful.

"Now you know, Mis' Morse," she said, "you been near daid. I don't know if the doctor he let you drink nothin' yet."

"Oh, never mind him," she said. "You get me one, and bring in the bottle. Take one yourself."

"Well," said Nettie.

She poured them each a drink, deferentially leaving hers in the bathroom to be taken in solitude, and brought Mrs. Morse's glass in to her.

Mrs. Morse looked into the liquor and shuddered back from its odor. Maybe it would help. Maybe, when you had been knocked cold for a few days, your very first drink would give you a lift. Maybe whisky would be her friend again. She prayed without addressing a God, without knowing a God. Oh, please, please, let her be able to get drunk, please keep her always drunk.

She lifted the glass.

"Thanks, Nettie," she said. "Here's mud in your eye."

The maid giggled. "Tha's the way, Mis' Morse," she said. "You cheer up, now."

"Yeah," said Mrs. Morse. "Sure."

Addiction

VIII. The addict, like the alcoholic, has come to look for a solution outside himself. Rather than struggle with his impulses, his conflicts, his anxiety; rather than cope with the complex world of reality, he narrows life's interests down to one single issue: will he or will he not get his next dose. Human relationships, moral values, lose their meaning; the chronic addict eventually has one goal—to secure enough drug to guarantee the special feeling that nothing can trouble him.

a. Two samples are given; the first, by Malraux, illustrates how addiction can be organized into a cultural setting. The addiction here is under control, and periodic surcease rather than perpetual oblivion is the goal.

MAN'S FATE

Andre Malraux   (1901–   )

. . . He got up, opened the drawer of the low table where he kept his opium tray, above a collection of small cactuses. Under the tray, a photograph: Kyo. He pulled it out, looked at it without any precise thoughts, sank bitterly into the certainty that, at the point he had reached, no one knew anyone—and that even the presence of Kyo, which he had so longed for just now, would have changed nothing, would only have rendered their separation more desperate, like that of friends whom one embraces in a dream and who have been dead for years. He kept the photograph between his fingers: it was as warm as a hand. He let it drop back into the drawer, took out the tray, turned out the electric light and lit the lamp.

Two pipes. Formerly, as soon as his craving began to be quenched, he would contemplate men with benevolence, and the world as an infinite of possibilities. Now, in his innermost being, the possibilities found no place: he was sixty, and his memories were full of tombs. His exquisitely pure sense of Chinese art, of those bluish paintings on which his lamp cast only a dim light, of the whole civilization of suggestion which China spread around him, which, thirty years earlier, he had been able to put to such delicate uses—his sense of happiness—was now nothing more than a thin cover beneath which anguish and the obsession of death were awakening, like restless dogs stirring at the end of their sleep.

Yet his mind hovered over the world, over mankind with a burning passion that age had not extinguished. It had long been his conviction that there is a paranoiac in every man, in himself first of all. He had thought once—ages ago—that he imagined himself a hero. No. This force, this furious subterranean imagination which was in him (were I to go mad, he had thought, this part of me alone would remain . . .) was ready to assume every form, like light. Like Kyo, and almost for the same reasons, he thought of the records of which the latter had spoken to him; and almost in the same fashion, for Kyo's modes of thought were born of his own. Just as Kyo had not recognized his own voice because he had heard it with his throat, so he—Gisors—probably could not reduce his consciousness of himself to that which he could have of another person, because it was not acquired by the same means. It owed nothing to the senses. He felt himself penetrating into a domain which belonged to him more than any other. With his intruding consciousness he was anxiously treading a forbidden solitude where no one would ever join him. For a second he had the sensation that it was *that* which must escape death. . . . His hands, which were preparing a new pellet, were slightly trembling. Even his love for Kyo did not free him from this total solitude. But if he could not escape from himself into another being, he knew how to find relief: there was opium.

Five pellets. For years he had limited himself to that, not without difficulty, not without pain sometimes. He scratched the bowl of his pipe; the shadow of his hand slipped from the wall to the ceiling. He pushed back the lamp a fraction of an inch; the contours of the shadow became lost. The objects also were vanishing: without changing their form they ceased to be distinct from himself, joined him in the depth of a familiar world where a benign indifference mingled all things—a world more true than the other because more constant, more like himself; sure as a friendship, always indulgent and always accessible: forms, memories, ideas, all plunged slowly towards a liberated universe. He remembered a September afternoon when the solid gray of the sky made a lake's surface appear milky, in the meshes of vast fields of water-lilies; from the moldy gables of an abandoned pavilion to the magnificent and desolate horizon he saw only a world suffused with a solemn melancholy. Near his idle bell, a Buddhist priest leaned on the balustrade of the pavilion, abandoning his sanctuary to the dust, to the fragrance of burning aromatic woods; peasants gathering water-lily seeds passed by in a boat without the slightest sound; at the edge of the farthest flowers two long waves grew from the rudder, melted listlessly in the gray water. They were vanishing now in himself, gathering in their fan all the oppressiveness of the world, but an oppressiveness without bitterness, brought by opium to an ultimate purity. His eyes shut, carried by great motionless wings, Gisors contemplated his solitude: a desolation that joined the divine, while at the same time the wave of serenity that gently covered the depths of death widened to infinity. . . .

b. The second example, by Nelson Algren, illustrates the problem of addiction as it occurs in contemporary United States. Algren describes the interaction between the pusher and the addict, thus enabling one to see the intense sadism and sense of power of the pusher, and the helpless masochistic surrender of the addict. The consuming passion of the addict for his drug is portrayed here with frightening candor.

The Man with the Golden Arm
Nelson Algren (1909–   )

. . . By the time Frankie got inside the room he was so weak Louie had to help him onto the army cot beside the oil stove. He lay on his back with one arm flung across his eyes as if in shame; and his lips were blue with cold. The pain had hit him with an icy fist in the groin's very pit, momentarily tapering off to a single probing finger touching the genitals to get the maximum of pain. He tried twisting to get away from the finger: the finger was worse than the fist. His throat was so dry that, though he spoke, the lips moved and made no sound. But Fomorowski read such lips well.

"Fix me. Make it stop. Fix me."

"I'll fix you, Dealer," Louie assured him softly.

Louie had his own bedside manner. He perched on the red leather and chrome bar stool borrowed from the Safari, with the amber toes of his two-tone shoes catching the light and the polo ponies galloping down his shirt. This was Nifty Louie's Hour. The time when he did the dealing and the dealer had to take what Louie chose to toss him in Louie's own good time.

He lit a match with his fingertip and held it away from the bottom of the tiny glass tube containing the fuzzy white cap of morphine, holding it just far enough away to keep the cap from being melted by the flame. There was time and time and lots of time for that. Let the dealer do a bit of melting first; the longer it took the higher the price. "You can pay me off when Zero pays you," he assured Frankie. There was no hurry. "You're good with me any time, Dealer."

Frankie moaned like an animal that cannot understand its own pain. His shirt had soaked through and the pain had frozen so deep in his bones nothing could make him warm again.

"Hit me, Fixer. Hit me."

A sievelike smile drained through Louie's teeth. This was his hour and this hour didn't come every day. He snuffed out the match's flame as it touched his fingers and snapped the head of another match into flame with his nail, letting its glow flicker one moment over that sievelike smile; then brought the tube down cautiously and watched it dissolve at the flame's fierce touch. When the stuff had melted he held both needle and tube in one hand, took the dealer's loose-hanging arm firmly with the other and pumped it in a long, loose arc. Frankie let him swing it as if it were attached to someone else. The cold was coming *up* from within now: a colorless cold spreading through stomach and liver and breathing across the heart like an odorless gas. To make the very brain tighten and congeal under its icy touch.

"Warm. Make me warm."

And still there was no rush, no hurry at all. Louie pressed the hypo down to the cotton; the stuff came too high these days to lose the fraction of a drop. "Don't vomit, student," he taunted Frankie to remind him of the first fix he'd had after his discharge—but it was too cold to answer. He was falling between glacial walls, he didn't know how anyone could fall so far away from everyone else in the world. So far to fall, so cold all the way, so steep and dark between those morphine-colored walls of Private McGantic's terrible pit.

He couldn't feel Louie probing into the dark red knot above his elbow at all. Nor see the way the first blood sprayed faintly up into the delicate hypo to tinge the melted morphine with blood as warm as the needle's heated point.

When Louie sensed the vein he pressed it down with the certainty of a good doctor's touch, let it linger a moment in the vein to give the heart what it needed and withdrew gently, daubed the blood with a piece of cotton, tenderly, and waited.

Louie waited. Waited to see it hit.

Louie liked to see the stuff hit. It meant a lot to Louie, seeing it hit.

"Sure I like to watch," he was ready to acknowledge any time. "Man, their *eyes* when that big drive hits 'n goes tingling' down to the toes.

They retch, they sweat, they itch—then the big drive hits 'n here they come out of it cryin' like a baby 'r laughin' like a loon. *Sure* I like to watch. *Sure* I like to see it hit. Heroin got the drive awright—but there's not a tingle to a ton—you got to get M to get that tingle-tingle."

It hit all right. It hit the heart like a runaway locomotive, it hit like a falling wall. Frankie's whole body lifted with that smashing surge, the very heart seemed to lift up-up-up then rolled over and he slipped into a long warm bath with one long orgasmic sigh of relief. Frankie opened his eyes.

He was in a room. Somebody's dust-colored wavy-walled room and he wasn't quite dead after all. He had died, had felt himself fall away and die but now he wasn't dead any more. Just sick. But not too sick. He wasn't going to be really sick, he wasn't a student any more. Maybe he wasn't going to be sick at all, he was beginning to feel just right.

Then it went over him like a dream where everything is love and he wasn't even sweating. All he had to do the rest of his life was to lie right here feeling better and better with every beat of his heart till he'd never felt so good in all his life.

"Wow," he grinned gratefully at Louie, "that was one good *whan*."

"I seen it," Louie boasted smugly. "I seen it was one good *whan*"— and lapsed into the sort of impromptu jargon which pleases junkies for no reason they can say—"vraza-s'vraza-s'vraza—it was one good *whan-whan-whan*." He dabbed a silk handkerchief at a blob of blood oozing where the needle had entered Frankie's arm.

"There's a silver buck and a buck 'n a half in change in my jacket pocket," Frankie told him lazily. "I'm feelin' too good to get up 'n get it myself."

Louie reached in the pocket with the handkerchief bound about his palm and plucked the silver out. Two-fifty for a quarter grain wasn't too high. He gave Frankie the grin that drained through the teeth for a receipt. The dealer was coming along nicely these days, thank you.

The dealer didn't know that yet, of course. That first fix had only cost him a dollar, it had quieted the everlasting dull ache in his stomach and sent him coasting one whole week end. So what was the use of spending forty dollars in the bars when you could do better at home on one? That was how Frankie had it figured *that* week end. To Louie, listening close, he'd already talked like a twenty-dollar-a-day man.

Given a bit of time.

And wondered idly now where in the world the dealer would get that kind of money when the day came that he'd need half a C just to taper off. He'd get it all right. They always got it. He'd seen them coming in the rain, the unkjays with their peculiarly rigid, panicky walk, wearing some policeman's castoff rubbers, no socks at all, a pair of Salvation Army pants a size too small or a size too large and a pajama top for a shirt—but with twenty dollars clutched in the sweating palm for that big twenty-dollar fix.

"Nothing can take the place of junk—just junk"—the dealer would learn. As Louie himself had learned long ago.

Louie was the best fixer of them all because he knew what it was to need to get well. Louie had had a big habit—he was one man who could tell you you lied if you said no junkie could kick the habit once he was hooked. For Louie was the one junkie in ten thousand who'd kicked it and kicked it for keeps.

He'd taken the sweat cure in a little Milwaukee Avenue hotel room cutting himself down, as he put it, "from monkey to zero." From three full grains a day to one, then a half of that and a half of that straight down to zero, though he'd been half out of his mind with the pain two nights running and was so weak, for days after, that he could hardly tie his own shoelaces.

Back on the street at last, he'd gotten the chuck horrors: for two full days he'd eaten candy bars, sweet rolls and strawberry malteds. It had seemed that there would be no end to his hunger for sweets.

Louie never had the sweet-roll horrors any more. Yet sometimes himself sensed that something had twisted in his brain in those nights when he'd gotten the monkey off his back on Milwaukee Avenue.

"*Habit? Man*," he liked to remember, "I had a great *big* habit. One time I knocked out one of my own teet' to get the gold for a fix. You call that bein' hooked or not? *Hooked?* Man, I wasn't hooked, I was *crucified*. The monkey got so big he was carrying *me*. 'Cause the way it starts is like this, students: you let the habit feed you first 'n one morning you wake up 'n you're feedin' the habit.

"But don't tell *me* you can't kick it if you *want* to. When I hear a junkie tell me he wants to kick the habit but he just can't I know he lies even if *he* don't know he does. He *wants* to carry the monkey, he's punishin' hisself for somethin' 'n don't even know it. It's what I was doin' for six years, punishin' myself for things I'd done 'n thought I'd for-got. So I told myself how I wasn't to blame for what I done in the first place, I was only tryin' to live like everyone else 'n doin' them things was the only way I had of livin'. Then I got forty grains 'n went up to the room 'n went from monkey to nothin' in twenny-eight days 'n that's nine-ten years ago 'n the monkey's dead."

"The monkey's never dead, Fixer," Frankie told him knowingly.

Louie glanced at Frankie slyly. "You know that awready, Dealer? You know how he don't die? It's what they say awright, the monkey never dies. When you kick him off he just hops onto somebody else's back." Behind the film of glaze that always veiled Louie's eyes Frankie saw the twisted look. "*You* got my monkey, Dealer? You take my nice old monkey away from me? Is that my monkey ridin' your back these days, Dealer?"

The color had returned to Frankie's cheeks, he felt he could make it almost any minute now. "No more for me, Fixer," he assured Louie confidently. "Somebody else got to take your monkey. I had the Holy Jumped-up-Jesus Horrors for real this time—'n I'm one guy knows when he got enough. I learned my lesson but *good*. Fixer—you just give the boy with the golden arm his very lastest fix."

CHAPTER ten

The Psychotherapeutic Process

The history of treatment methods for psychological abnormality is an admixture of bizarre, humane, and scientific elements. During the 17th and 18th centuries, still dominated by the ideas of supernatural possession, therapy was aimed at exorcizing the devils. The earliest "medical" treatments were often equally inappropriate, and patients were held under water and whirled in huge centrifuges. But the major trend in the 19th century was towards the so-called "moral treatment" of the insane. Pinel in France, Tuke in England, Rush in America were leaders in this movement. Their efforts were directed towards treating the mentally ill with forbearance and consideration so as to maintain and rebuild social skills. This was an important advance which at the least prevented some of the further deterioration to which the mentally ill of previous centuries had been subject.

During the subsequent decades of the 19th and 20th centuries many efforts towards more potent treatment methods were attempted. These came in the form of both organic and psychological treatment methods. The most common form of psychological treatment today is psychotherapy. Psychotherapy is difficult to define, but in its barest essentials consists of a patient talking about his problems to an expert. There are several important aspects of this process which are thought to account for its effectiveness.

Catharsis

I. Conceptualized by Aristotle in the 4th century B.C., this phenomenon has been rediscovered periodically over the subsequent centuries. Some of the other terms applied to this

concept are "abreaction," "ventilation," "discharge of affect."
Basically the concept of catharsis suggests that human beings
achieve a positive and therapeutic effect by simply expressing
in words their unspoken, unformulated concerns and feelings.
The importance of emotional catharsis and the need for it are
beautifully portrayed in Chekhov's story, "Grief." Chekhov has
captured the intensity of the human need to share emotion
and feeling. The taxi driver caught up in his grief reaches
out desperately for any sympathetic ear.

The need for catharsis is one of the important forces that
motivate patients to enter psychotherapy. However, most
patients are more discriminating than Chekhov's taxi driver,
and they can only confide in someone they trust. Therapy,
therefore, in its cathartic aspects ordinarily proceeds apace
with the patient's capacity to develop trust, and the
therapist's capacity to earn this trust.

GRIEF

Anton Chekhov (1860–1904)

It is twilight. A thick wet snow is slowly twirling around
the newly lighted street-lamps, and lying in soft thin layers on the roofs,
the horses' backs, people's shoulders and hats. The cab-driver, Iona Pota-
pov, is quite white, and looks like a phantom; he is bent double as far as
a human body can bend double; he is seated on his box, and never makes
a move. If a whole snowdrift fell on him, it seems as if he would not find
it necessary to shake it off. His little horse is also quite white, and remains
motionless; its immobility, its angularity, and its straight wooden-looking
legs, even close by give it the appearance of a ginger-bread horse worth a
kopeck. It is, no doubt, plunged in deep thought. If you were snatched
from the plough, from your usual grey surroundings, and were thrown
into this slough full of monstrous lights, unceasing noise and hurrying
people, you too would find it difficult not to think.

Iona and his little horse have not moved from their place for a long
while. They left their yard before dinner, and, up to now, not a "fare."
The evening mist is descending over the town, the white lights of the
lamps are replacing brighter rays, and the hubbub of the street is getting
louder. "Cabby, for Viborg way!" suddenly hears Iona. "Cabby!"

Iona jumps, and through his snow-covered eyelashes, sees an officer
in a greatcoat, with his hood over his head.

"Grief" by Anton Chekhov.

"Viborg way!" the officer repeats. "Are you asleep, eh? Viborg way!"

With a nod of assent Iona picks up the reins, in consequence of which layers of snow slip off the horse's back and neck. The officer seats himself in the sleigh, the cab-driver smacks his lips to encourage his horse, stretches out his neck like a swan, sits up, and, more from habit than necessity, brandishes his whip. The little horse also stretches his neck, bends his wooden-looking legs, and makes a move undecidedly.

"What are you doing, were-wolf!" is the exclamation Iona hears, from the dark mass moving to and fro as soon as they started.

"Where the devil are you going? To the r-r-right!"

"You do not know how to drive. Keep to the right!" calls the officer angrily.

A coachman from a private carriage swears at him; a passer-by, who has run across the road and rubbed his shoulder against the horse's nose, looks at him furiously as he sweeps the snow from his sleeve. Iona shifts about on his seat as if he were on needles, moves his elbows as if he were trying to keep his equilibrium, and gapes about like someone suffocating, and who does not understand why and wherefore he is there.

"What scoundrels they all are!" jokes the officer; "one would think they had all entered into an agreement to jostle you or fall under your horse."

Iona looks round at the officer, and moves his lips. He evidently wants to say something, but the only sound that issues is a snuffle.

"What?" asks the officer.

Iona twists his mouth into a smile, and with an effort says hoarsely:

"My son, barin, died this week."

"Hm! What did he die of?"

Iona turns with his whole body towards his fare, and says:

"And who knows! They say high fever. He was three days in hospital, and then died. . . . God's will be done."

"Turn round! The devil!" sounded from the darkness. "Have you popped off, old doggie, eh? Use your eyes!"

"Go on, go on," said the officer, "otherwise we shall not get there by to-morrow. Hurry a bit!"

The cab-driver again stretches his neck, sits up, and, with a bad grace, brandishes his whip. Several times again he turns to look at his fare, but the latter had closed his eyes, and apparently is not disposed to listen. Having deposited the officer in the Viborg, he stops by the tavern, doubles himself up on his seat, and again remains motionless, while the snow once more begins to cover him and his horse. An hour, and another . . . . Then, along the footpath, with a squeak of goloshes, and quarrelling, came three young men, two of them tall and lanky, the third one short and hump-backed.

"Cabby, to the Police Bridge!" in a cracked voice calls the hump-back. "The three of us for two griveniks!" (20 kopecks).

Iona picks up his reins, and smacks his lips. Two griveniks is not a fair price, but he does not mind if it is a rouble or five kopecks—to him it is all the same now, so long as they are wayfarers. The young men, jostling each other and using bad language, approach the sleigh, and all three at once try to get on to the seat; then begins a discussion which two shall sit and who shall be the one to stand. After wrangling, abusing each other, and much petulance, it was at last decided that the hump-back should stand, as he was the smallest.

"Now then, hurry up!" says the hump-back in a twanging voice, as he takes his place, and breathes in Iona's neck. "Old furry. Here, mate, what a cap you have got, there is not a worse one to be found in all Petersburg! . . ."

"Hi—hi,—hi—hi," giggles Iona. "Such a . . ."

"Now you, 'such a,' hurry up, are you going the whole way at this pace? Are you? . . . Do you want it in the neck?"

"My head feels like bursting," says one of the lanky ones. "Last night at the Donkmasovs, Vaska and I drank the whole of four bottles of cognac."

"I don't understand what you lie for," said the other lanky one angrily; "you lie like a brute."

"God strike me, it's the truth!"

"It's as much a truth as that a louse coughs!"

"Hi, hi," grins Iona, "what gay young gentlemen!"

"Pshaw, go to the devil!" indignantly says the hump-back.

"Are you going to get on or not, you old pest? Is that the way to drive? Use the whip a bit! Go on, devil, go on, give it him well!"

Iona feels at his back the little man wriggling, and the tremble in his voice. He listens to the insults hurled at him, sees the people, and little by little the feeling of loneliness leaves him. The hump-back goes on swearing until he gets mixed up in some elaborate six-foot oath, or chokes with coughing. The lankies begin to talk about a certain Nadejda Petrovna. Iona looks round at them several times; he waits for a temporary silence, then, turning round again, he murmurs:

"My son—died this week."

"We must all die," sighed the hump-back, wiping his lips after an attack of coughing. "Now, hurry up, hurry up! Gentlemen, I really cannot go any farther like this! When will he get us there?"

"Well, just you stimulate him a little in the neck!"

"You old pest, do you hear, I'll bone your neck for you! If one treated the like of you with ceremony one would have to go on foot! Do you hear, old sepent Gorinytch! Or do you not care a spit?"

Iona hears rather than feels the blows they deal him.

"Hi, hi," he laughs. "They are gay young gentlemen, God bless 'em!"

"Cabby, are you married?" asks a lanky one.

"I? Hi, hi, gay young gentlemen! Now I have only a wife: the moist ground. . . . Hi, ho, ho . . . that is to say, the grave! My son has died, and I am alive. . . . A wonderful thing, death mistook the door . . . instead of coming to me, it went to my son. . . ."

Iona turns round to tell them how his son died, but at this moment the hump-back, giving a little sigh, announces, "Thank God, they have at last reached their destination," and Iona watches them disappear through the dark entrance. Once more he is alone, and again surrounded by silence. . . . His grief, which had abated for a short while, returns and rends his heart with greater force. With an anxious and a hurried look, he searches among the crowds passing on either side of the street to find if there is just one person who will listen to him. But the crowds hurry by without noticing him or his trouble. Yet it is such an immense, illimitable grief. Should his heart break and the grief pour out, it would flow over the whole earth it seems, and yet, no one sees it. It has managed to conceal itself in such an insignificant shell that no one can see it even by day and with a light.

Iona sees a hall-porter with some sacking, and decides to talk to him.

"Friend, what sort of time is it?" he asks.

"Past nine. What are you standing here for? Move on."

Iona moves on a few steps, doubles himself up, and abandons himself to his grief. He sees it is useless to turn to people for help. In less than five minutes he straightens himself, holds up his head as if he felt some sharp pain, and gives a tug at the reins: he can bear it no longer, "The stables," he thinks, and the little horse, as if he understood, starts off at a trot.

About an hour and a half later Iona is seated by a large dirty stove. Around the stove, on the floor, on the benches, people are snoring; the air is thick and suffocatingly hot. Iona looks at the sleepers, scratches himself, and regrets having returned so early.

"I have not even earned my fodder," he thinks. "That's what's my trouble. A man who knows his job, who has had enough to eat, and his horse too, can always sleep peacefully."

A young cab-driver in one of the corners half gets up, grunts sleepily, and stretches towards a bucket of water.

"Do you want a drink?" Iona asks him.

"Don't I want a drink!"

"That's so? Your good health! But listen, mate—you know, my son is dead. . . . Did you hear? This week, in hospital. . . . It's a long story."

Iona looks to see what effect his words have, but sees none—the young man has hidden his face, and is fast asleep again. The old man sighs, and scratches his head. Just as much as the young one wanted to drink, the old man wanted to talk. It will soon be a week since his son died, and he has not been able to speak about it properly to anyone. One must tell it slowly and carefully; how his son fell ill, how he suffered, what he said before he died, how he died. One must describe every detail of the funeral, and the journey to the hospital to fetch the defunct's clothes. His daughter Anissia remained in the village—one must talk about her too. Was it nothing he had to tell? Surely the listener would gasp and sigh, and sympathise with him? It is better, too, to talk to women; although they are stupid, two words are enough to make them sob.

"I'll go and look at my horse," thinks Iona; "there's always time to sleep. No fear of that!"

He puts on his coat, and goes to the stables to his horse; he thinks of the corn, the hay, the weather. When he is alone, he dare not think of his son; he could speak about him to anyone, but to think of him, and picture him to himself, is unbearably painful.

"Are you tucking in?" Iona asks his horse, looking at his bright eyes; "go on, tuck in, though we've not earned our corn, we can eat hay. Yes! I am too old to drive—my son could have, not I. He was a first-rate cab-driver. If only he had lived!"

Iona is silent for a moment, then continues:

"That's how it is, my old horse. There's no more Kuzma Ionitch. He has left us to live, and he went off pop. Now let's say, you had a foal, you were that foal's mother, and suddenly, let's say, that foal went and left you to live after him. It would be sad, wouldn't it?"

The little horse munches, listens, and breathes over his master's hand. . . .

Iona's feelings are too much for him, and he tells the little horse the whole story.

Insight

II. A second aspect of psychotherapy is insight. In its broadest sense psychological insight is a new recognition that an important relationship exists—for example, between the past and the present, or between unconscious needs and conscious thoughts and action. In psychotherapy an important insight often will permit change to occur: a pattern is recognized that can then be altered. Unfortunately, insight does not always bring such positive change, and the example below is such an instance. Oblomov is gradually slipping into an oblivion of passive withdrawal from life. One day in his musing he suddenly

has a flash of insight: he realizes the pattern of his behavior.
But the insight is too much for him, and his pathology is
unrelenting; he slips back from the harsh light of his insight
into the dark peaceful retreat of sleep.

OBLOMOV

Ivan Goncharov   (1812–1891)

A slight, pleasant numbness spread over his limbs and his
senses were clouded with sleep, just as the surface of water is clouded by
the slight early frosts; another minute and his mind would have slipped
Heaven knows where, when suddenly Ilya Ilyitch came to himself and
opened his eyes.

"Why, I haven't washed! How is that? And I haven't done anything," he whispered. "I wanted to put down my plan on paper and I
haven't done it; I haven't written to the police captain or the Governor; I
began and didn't finish the letter to the landlord; I haven't checked the
accounts or given Zahar the money—the morning has been wasted!" He
pondered. "What does it mean? And *other people* would have done it all,"
flashed through his mind. "Other people . . . what are they?"

He began comparing himself to "others." He thought and thought,
and ideas, very different from those he had expounded to Zahar, came
into his mind. He had to admit that "others" would have found time to
write all the letters and write them so that "which" and "that" never
jostled each other; "others" would have moved to a new flat, carried out
the plan, gone to the country. . . .

"I, too, could do all this, one would have thought," he reflected. "I
can write well enough and have written in my time less simple things than
letters! What has become of it all? And what is there so dreadful about
moving? One has only to make up one's mind! Other people never wear
a dressing-gown . . ." he added, by way of characterizing "others" . . .
then he yawned; "they hardly sleep at all . . . they enjoy life, go everywhere, see all there is to see, take an interest in everything. . . . And I?
I . . . am different," he said, sadly this time, and sank into thought. He
actually put his head out from under the blanket.

This was one of the lucid, conscious moments in Oblomov's life.
Horror possessed him when there arose before him a clear and vivid idea
of what human destiny was meant to be as compared with his own existence, when the problems of life wakened within him and whirled through
his mind like frightened birds roused suddenly by a ray of sunlight in a

From *Oblomov* by Ivan Goncharov. Translated by Natalie Duddington. Every-
man's Library. Reprinted by permission of E. P. Dutton & Co., Inc.

slumbering ruin. It grieved and hurt him to think that he was undeveloped, that his spiritual forces had stopped growing, that some dead weight hampered him; he bitterly envied those whose lives were rich and full, while he felt as though a heavy stone had been thrown on to the narrow and pitiful path of his existence. It hurt his timid mind to grasp that many sides of his nature had never been awakened, others barely so, and none had developed fully. And yet he was painfully conscious that something fine and good lay buried in him and was, perhaps, already dead or hidden like gold in the depths of a mountain, although it was high time for the gold to be current coin. But the treasure was deeply buried under a heavy load of rubbish and dirt. It was as though the treasures bestowed on him by the world and life had been stolen from him and hidden in the depths of his own soul. Something hindered him from flinging himself into the arena of life and using his will and intellect to go full speed forward. It was as though some secret enemy had laid a heavy hand upon him at the beginning of his journey and thrown him far back from the right road . . . . And it did not seem that he could ever find his way to the straight path from the thick jungle. The forest around him and in his mind grew thicker and darker; the path was more and more overgrown; clear consciousness wakened more and more seldom, and his slumbering forces were roused but for a moment. His mind and will had been paralysed, hopelessly, it seemed. The events in his life had dwindled down to microscopic proportions, but even so they were more than he could cope with; he did not pass from one to another, but was tossed to and fro by them as by waves; he had not the strength of will to oppose one course or to follow another rationally. He felt bitter at having to confess all this to himself. Fruitless regrets for the past, burning reproaches of conscience went through him like stings; he struggled hard to throw off the burden of these reproaches, to find someone else to blame and turn the sting against. But against whom?

"It's all . . . Zahar's fault!" he whispered. He recalled the details of the scene with Zahar and his face burned with shame. "What if someone had overheard it?" he thought, turning cold at the idea. "Thank Heaven Zahar won't be able to repeat it to anyone; and, indeed, no one would believe him, thank Heaven!"

He sighed, cursed himself, turned from side to side, sought for someone to blame and could find no one. His groans and sighs reached Zahar's ears.

"The way he carries on after that *kvass!*" Zahar muttered angrily.

"Why am I like this?" Oblomov asked himself almost with tears, and hid his head under the blanket again. "Why?" After seeking in vain for the hostile power that prevented him from living like "other people" he sighed, closed his eyes, and in a few minutes drowsiness began once more to benumb his senses. "I, too . . . wished," he said, blinking with diffi-

culty, "for something fine . . . has nature dealt unfairly with me? . . .
No, thank Heaven, I can't complain that it has. . . ." Then came the
sound of a sigh of resignation. He was passing from agitation to his
normal state of calm and apathy. "It must be my fate. . . . What can I
do?" he was hardly able to whisper, overcome by sleep. "Some two thousand less than last year," he suddenly said aloud, dreaming. "Directly,
directly, wait . . ." and he half awoke. "And yet . . . I wish I knew why
. . . I am . . . like this!" he said in a whisper again. His eyelids closed
altogether. "Yes, why? . . . It must be . . . because . . ." he tried to
say the word and could not.

He never arrived at the cause after all; his tongue and lips stopped in
the middle of a word and remained half open. Instead of a word another
sigh was heard, and then the even snoring of a man peacefully asleep.

Sleep stopped the slow and lazy flow of his thoughts and instantly
transferred him to other times, other people, to another place, where the
reader and I will follow him in the next chapter.

Emotional Support

III. A third important aspect of most psychotherapy
is the emotional support that the disturbed person gains from
the therapist. This comes about in many ways: the accepting,
neutral, and uncritical nature of the therapist; the helpful and
understanding comments; the individual attention; the evidence
of emotional response and interest. Emotional support can come
not only from the therapist as a person, but from the
therapeutic process as well. This occurs when the patient
learns that he can effectively rely on the therapeutic setting to
examine and understand his problems. The emotional
commitment between a therapist and a patient is often
particularly important for the more disturbed patients.
Although "love is not enough," many of the qualities of love are
apt to be represented in a therapeutic relationship, in a
relationship that permits a change for the better.

a. Chekhov describes in the following story a remarkable
cure, the rescue of a derelict. Was it the confrontation, the
harangues and exhortations, or the gratifying emotional and
tangible support that brought about this cure? Was it all of
these? The reader must form his own opinion, for scientific

studies have been unable to isolate the curative factors
in psychotherapy.

THE BEGGAR

Anton Chekhov *(1860–1904)*

"Kind sir, be so good as to notice a poor, hungry man. I
have not tasted food for three days. . . . I have not a five-kopeck piece
for a night's lodging. . . . I swear by God! For five years I was a village
schoolmaster and lost my post through the intrigues of the Zemstvo. I
was the victim of false witness. I have been out of a place for a year now."

Skvortsov, a Petersburg lawyer, looked at the speaker's tattered dark
blue overcoat, at his muddy, drunken eyes, at the red patches on his
cheeks, and it seemed to him that he had seen the man before.

"And now I am offered a post in the Kaluga province," the beggar
continued, "but I have not the means for the journey there. Graciously
help me! I am ashamed to ask, but . . . I am compelled by circumstances."

Skvortsov looked at his goloshes, of which one was shallow like a
shoe, while the other came high up the leg like a boot, and suddenly remembered.

"Listen, the day before yeterday I met you in Sadovoy Street," he
said, "and then you told me, not that you were a village schoolmaster,
but that you were a student who had been expelled. Do you remember?"

"N-o. No, that cannot be so!" the beggar muttered in confusion. "I
am a village schoolmaster, and if you wish it I can show you documents to
prove it."

"That's enough lies! You called yourself a student, and even told me
what you were expelled for. Do you remember?"

Skvortsov flushed, and with a look of disgust on his face turned away
from the ragged figure.

"It's contemptible, sir!" he cried angrily. "It's a swindle! I'll hand
you over to the police, damn you! You are poor and hungry, but that
does not give you the right to lie so shamelessly!"

The ragged figure took hold of the door-handle and, like a bird in a
snare, looked round the hall desperately.

"I . . . I am not lying," he muttered. "I can show documents."

"Who can believe you?" Skvortsov went on, still indignant. "To exploit the sympathy of the public for village schoolmasters and students —it's so low, so mean, so dirty! It's revolting!"

Skvortsov flew into a rage and gave the beggar a merciless scolding. The ragged fellow's insolent lying aroused his disgust and aversion, was an offence against what he, Skvortsov, loved and prized in himself: kindliness, a feeling heart, sympathy for the unhappy. By his lying, by his treacherous assault upcn compassion, the individual had, as it were, defiled the charity which he liked to give to the poor with no misgivings in his heart. The beggar at first defended himself, protested with oaths, then he sank into silence and hung his head, overcome with shame.

"Sir!" he said, laying his hand on his heart, "I really was . . . lying! I am not a student and not a village schoolmaster. All that's mere invention! I used to be in the Russian choir, and I was turned out of it for drunkenness. But what can I do? Believe me, in God's name, I can't get on without lying—when I tell the truth no one will give me anything. With the truth one may die of hunger and freeze without a night's lodging! What you say is true, I understand that, but . . . what am I to do?"

"What are you to do? You ask what are you to do?" cried Skvortsov, going close up to him. "Work—that's what you must do! You must work!"

"Work. . . . I know that myself, but where can I get work?"

"Nonsense. You are young, strong, and healthy, and could always find work if you wanted to. But you know you are lazy, pampered, drunken! You reek of vodka like a pothouse! You have become false and corrupt to the marrow of your bones and fit for nothing but begging and lying! If you do graciously condescend to take work, you must have a job in an office, in the Russian choir, or as a billiard-marker, where you will have a salary and have nothing to do! But how would you like to undertake manual labour? I'll be bound, you wouldn't be a house porter or a factory hand! You are too genteel for that!"

"What things you say, really . . ." said the beggar, and he gave a bitter smile. "How can I get manual work? It's rather late for me to be a shopman, for in trade one has to begin from a boy; no one would take me as a house porter, because I am not of that class. . . . And I could not get work in a factory; one must know a trade, and I know nothing."

"Nonsense! You always find some justification! Wouldn't you like to chop wood?"

"I would not refuse to, but the regular woodchoppers are out of work now."

"Oh, all idlers argue like that! As soon as you are offered anything you refuse it. Would you care to chop wood for me?"

"Certainly I will. . . ."

"Very good, we shall see. . . . Excellent. . . . We'll see!" Skvortsov, in nervous haste, and not without malignant pleasure, rubbing his hands, summoned his cook from the kitchen.

"Here, Olga," he said to her, "take this gentleman to the shed and let him chop some wood."

The beggar shrugged his shoulders as though puzzled, and irresolutely followed the cook. It was evident from his demeanour that he had consented to go and chop wood, not because he was hungry and wanted to earn money, but simply from shame and *amour propre*, because he had been taken at his word. It was clear, too, that he was suffering from the effects of vodka, that he was unwell, and felt not the faintest inclination to work.

Skvortsov hurried into the dining room. There from the window which looked out into the yard he could see the woodshed and everything that happened in the yard. Standing at the window, Skvortsov saw the cook and the beggar come by the back way into the yard and go through the muddy snow to the woodshed. Olga scrutinized her companion angrily, and jerking her elbow unlocked the woodshed and angrily banged the door open.

"Most likely we interrupted the woman drinking her coffee," thought Skvortsov. "What a cross creature she is!"

Then he saw the pseudo-schoolmaster and pseudo-student seat himself on a block of wood, and, leaning his red cheeks upon his fists, sink into thought. The cook flung an axe at his feet, spat angrily on the ground, and, judging by the expression of her lips, began abusing him. The beggar drew a log of wood towards him irresolutely, set it up between his feet, and diffidently drew the axe across it. The log toppled and fell over. The beggar drew it towards him, breathed on his frozen hands, and again drew the axe along it as cautiously as though he were afraid of its hitting his golosh or chopping off his fingers. The log fell over again.

Skvortsov's wrath had passed off by now, he felt sore and ashamed at the thought that he had forced a pampered, drunken, and perhaps sick man to do hard, rough work in the cold.

"Never mind, let him go on . . ." he thought, going from the dining room into his study. "I am doing it for his good!"

An hour later Olga appeared and announced that the wood had been chopped up.

"Here, give him half a ruble," said Skvortsov. "If he likes, let him come and chop wood on the first of every month. . . . There will always be work for him."

On the first of the month the beggar turned up and again earned half a ruble, though he could hardly stand. From that time forward he took to turning up frequently, and work was always found for him: sometimes he would sweep the snow into heaps, or clear up the shed, at another he used to beat the rugs and the mattresses. He always received thirty to forty kopecks for his work, and on one occasion an old pair of trousers was sent out to him.

When he moved, Skvortsov engaged him to assist in packing and moving the furniture. On this occasion the beggar was sober, gloomy, and silent; he scarcely touched the furniture, walked with hanging head behind the furniture vans, and did not even try to appear busy; he merely shivered with the cold, and was overcome with confusion when the men with the vans laughed at his idleness, feebleness, and ragged coat that had once been a gentleman's. After the removal Skvortsov sent for him.

"Well, I see my words have had an effect upon you," he said, giving him a ruble. "This is for your work. I see that you are sober and not disinclined to work. What is your name?"

"Lushkov."

"I can offer you better work, not so rough, Lushkov. Can you write?"

"Yes, sir."

"Then go with this note tomorrow to my colleague and he will give you some copying to do. Work, don't drink, and don't forget what I said to you. Good-bye."

Skvortsov, pleased that he had put a man in the path of rectitude, patted Lushkov genially on the shoulder, and even shook hands with him at parting. Lushkov took the letter, departed, and from that time forward did not come to the backyard for work.

Two years passed. One day as Skvortsov was standing at the ticket-office of a theatre, paying for his ticket, he saw beside him a little man with a lambskin collar and a shabby cat's-skin cap. The man timidly asked the clerk for a gallery ticket and paid for it with kopecks.

"Lushkov, is it you?" asked Skvortsov, recognizing in the little man his former woodchopper. "Well, what are you doing? Are you getting on all right?"

"Pretty well. . . . I am in a notary's office now. I earn thirty-five rubles."

"Well, thank God, that's capital. I rejoice for you. I am very, very glad, Lushkov. You know, in a way, you are my godson. It was I who shoved you into the right way. Do you remember what a scolding I gave you, eh? You almost sank through the floor that time. Well, thank you, my dear fellow, for remembering my words."

"Thank you too," said Lushkov. "If I had not come to you that day, maybe I should be calling myself a schoolmaster or a student still. Yes, in your house I was saved, and climbed out of the pit."

"I am very, very glad."

"Thank you for your kind words and deeds. What you said that day was excellent. I am grateful to you and to your cook, God bless that kind, noble-hearted woman. What you said that day was excellent; I am indebted to you as long as I live, of course, but it was your cook, Olga, who really saved me."

"How was that?"

"Why, it was like this. I used to come to you to chop wood and she would begin: 'Ah, you drunkard! You God-forsaken man! And yet death does not take you!' and then she would sit opposite me, lamenting, looking into my face and wailing: 'You unlucky fellow! You have no gladness in this world, and in the next you will burn in hell, poor drunkard! You poor sorrowful creature!' and she always went on in that style, you know. How often she upset herself, and how many tears she shed over me I can't tell you. But what affected me most—she chopped the wood for me! Do you know, sir, I never chopped a single log for you—she did it all! How it was she saved me, how it was I changed, looking at her, and gave up drinking, I can't explain. I only know that what she said and the noble way she behaved brought about a change in my soul, and I shall never forget it. It's time to go up, though, they are just going to ring the bell."

Lushkov bowed and went off to the gallery.

b. Psychotherapy has undergone many striking modifications as imaginative therapists have attempted to cope with the difficulties presented by special groups of patients; e.g., delinquents, psychotics, alcoholics. One of the most important of these modifications was the development of psychotherapeutic techniques for children.

Unlike the adult, the child comes to treatment not on his own volition or motivation. Furthermore, his verbal capacity to discuss problems and his ability to comprehend the meaning and purpose of treatment is limited. Hence, he is unprepared to enter into an agreement to be treated—the so-called therapeutic contract.

Child therapy usually involves an initial phase devoted to the establishment of trust and to educating the child to the purpose and value of working on his problems. Because of the inherent verbal difficulty, the young child is often encouraged to present and explore his emotional problems through techniques which utilize the child's natural capacity for play. The child's play frequently will reflect his central problems and his efforts to cope with them. T. C. Worsley has written a brilliant description of a therapeutic success in play therapy. The young boy of the story has developed marked inhibitions related to his repressed anger towards his dominating and

controlling mother. His tutor first earns his trust, then through
play gets a glimpse of the enormous hatred being contained by
lethargy and inhibitions. Finally, the rage is expressed and acted
out, and the child's symptoms disappear. Worsley provides us
with a further important insight, for the child and his family
in the end turn on the tutor, making him a scapegoat. There has
not been a complete insight and acceptance of the anger by
the family; rather, it has in part been displaced. The child's
early intense attachment to the tutor is illustrative of what has
been called a positive transference, and his later disdain
exemplifies the negative transference. The reasons for the child's
final attitude towards the tutor are left unexplored, but they
are probably due in part to his fear and anger at being made
aware of his rage, a step which was necessary to permit the
lifting of symptoms. Furthermore, having been enabled to
move on in his emotional development, he has less need for
the relationship.

The child of this story has a typical neurotic symptom:
inhibition and loss of interest. It is one symptom of neurotic
depression; as such it is generally responsive to treatment,
here artfully demonstrated by Worsley.

The Sacred Table

T. C. Worsley   (1907–   )

Mrs. Moroney was the sort of woman who went straight
to the point, even when the point was an unpleasant one. At the very beginning of her first interview with the prospective tutor, she held her
finger on the pulse of the problem.

"It's not," she said, "that I particularly want the boy to be interested
in my sort of thing" (and it was perfectly clear that this was just what
she did want) "if only he was interested in *something.*"

She kept returning to this, to her young son's listlessness, all the time
that she was walking round her special room displaying to him her
"things." She moved about, touching a jug, edging forward a chair, adding the animation of her pleasure in them to the lights that glowed in the
woods and flickered across the coloured porcelain. Spread across the
sacred table, her special treasure, were some William Morris stuffs and a

portfolio of drawings, which she came back to handle lovingly, caressingly, her restlessness stilled and centred round them.

"Philip seems to care about nothing any longer," she deplored. "Nothing. If only he liked rugger, it would be something." But not, the prospective tutor felt, very much.

"Why on earth," she went on, picking up and fingering the stuff, "why on earth should he keep running away from school to us, only to be bored to extinction when he gets here? It isn't that he appreciates his home any more," and she picked up the stuff and the drawings which her Philip no longer cared about and put them tenderly away.

It was on the strength of his unprompted admiration for that table when he first came into the room that the tutor—so he later felt—had been finally engaged. His academic qualifications were not striking, his "experience" non-existent. His application in answer to an advertisement in *The Times* had been the result of a sudden whim, prompted in part by a temporary financial embarrassment. Six guineas a week for three months, all found, had been tempting; and having no very clear notion of what a tutorship entailed except that he wouldn't allow it to be exacting, he had looked forward to a spell of heavy reading. He took himself seriously, if not his duties.

But the household caught his interest from the outset. When he first approached the Edwardian villa on the outskirts of the little country town, his heart had sunk as his imagination ran too easily forward to a vision of stuffy domesticity, of insipid suety meals, of long evenings during which he might be made the victim of B.B.C. variety or the reminiscences of a retired planter. Mrs. Moroney herself had been a first hint of the unusual. Vague and restless, in her faded Pre-Raphaelite shades, she had all the same struck him as decided. She knew what she wanted even if it was not plainly formulated. She was the one that counted, too. Mr. Moroney was not to be consulted. He was never to come much into the picture, was always to remain a background figure who nursed some powerful disease in the privacy of his workshop emerging only to preside in silence over meals and long summer evenings. A large heavy man with a blunt wedgelike face, he had made some surrender to her, of golf probably, and his bridge and his clubs, and, in an outside shed, he manufactured endless small boxes inlaid with mother o' pearl, which he turned on a number of small lathes; they piled up, these boxes, endlessly under his indefatigable industry—to become Christmas presents for friends and relations or to decorate numberless stalls in numberless bazaars for numberless more or less good causes. They were anyhow a success; the demand always seemed to exceed his supply and gave him no rest from his chipping and turning and his endless treadle.

Mr. Moroney was soon dismissed to his "work," being given time only for a hand-shake after which the prospective tutor was conducted

for the interview to Mrs. Moroney's special room. This came as a second
surprise after the Edwardian exterior, and the shapeless colourless parlour-
maid who had answered the old-fashioned bell. The sacred table made its
immediate impression of light dignity and elegant poise. It was featured:
the room was arranged towards it: everything else was there to heighten
its effect. It was also a kind of Test. The Tutor saw, so soon as he had remarked on it approvingly to Mrs. Moroney, that he had "passed." He was
as good as engaged.

But the interest soon shifted from Mrs. Moroney's "things," which
were not so remarkable except in the lively pleasure she had from them.
The Moroneys were only mediumly well-to-do and she couldn't—apart
from the table—go in for rarities. No, the interest was in the sad queer
little story of her only son, Philip, and in what she wanted from him in
relation to this boy; and whether he would be able to help her get it—
whether, even, it was desirable that he should if he could.

What it was that she wanted soon became clear:

"You see, Philip wasn't always like this, by any manner of means,"
she told him. "Before he went to school he bubbled with life and vitality
and energy. . . . And he was so unusual. He had the liveliest interest in
all my things, and, besides, one special interest of his own. It was by an
accident that I discovered his passion for dancing. I used to play to him
every evening and one day quite on his own, quite spontaneously, he began to dance. He was only six, but I can't tell you how beautifully he felt
the music. And I was always careful about choosing it. From the very
first I'd always made sure that he only came in contact with the best—
music, books, stuff, everything. So I insisted from the first when he started
dancing that it should be in keeping with the best. Not that there was
much need to insist. He had a natural taste from the beginning . . . in
everything he touched. He'd seize up a scarf and a shawl and combine
them always in just the right balance of tone. But it was dancing that became almost our life. I've never liked potted music, but I did buy a
gramophone and chose the records carefully, so that he should dance to
every sort of thing—and always he gave this beautiful interpretation of
the quality. Later he used to act for me—scenes from Shakespeare and, oh,
one thing and another. He knew acres and acres of The Plays by heart
. . . I wasn't going to let him go to school too early. They go away from
home much too soon nowadays, don't you agree? Of course when you
see some of their homes——! But if a boy has a home where——well,
hadn't he much better benefit by it as long as possible instead of being
plunged into the barbarity of a boys' school? Wasn't I right?"

The tutor could only assent.

"His father wanted him packed off to some beastly seminary at eight
and a half. He thought I was molly-coddling him. But of course I wasn't.
There's nothing molly-coddling about Shakespeare and dancing, is there?

His father couldn't be expected to understand. But I kept to my plan. I was going to be quite sure; sure that the foundation was solid before I risked it being broken up. By the time he was ten I thought it was all right. By then he really 'knew.' I felt it as safe to let him choose as to choose myself. That was the moment. He could go to school and learn what he had to."

Mrs. Moroney took another restless turn round the room before she went on with her story. He had gone to school, and he had positively enjoyed it. That was what was so extraordinary. He'd got on surprisingly well. He'd learnt quickly and come out top in his classes. He'd shown a great aptitude for—of all things!—cricket. She was almost as pleased as her husband who was thoroughly delighted with these signs of ordinariness. She felt completely justified. She had never believed there need be any division between art and life. Of course his taste and his art didn't interfere with the ordinary pursuits. They helped. She hadn't been surprised that he was outstripping his companions. It was what she had expected.

Then, for no reason, without any warning, with no preparatory tears, fuss, or outward signs, he ran away. He walked out of the school one night and found himself a train and turned up at the house at midnight. He could give no explanation. He was not "upset." He didn't know in the least why he had done it. The school could provide no clue. After a week —a week in which he mooched aimlessly about the house and countryside, he volunteered to go back. And after six weeks he ran away again. It was the same pattern. No explanation, no tears, no fuss. But—and this was the trouble—no animation. All the enthusiasm, all the spontaneity, all the precious responsiveness, had abruptly vanished. The boy didn't want to do anything. He was stuck, like a clock that had gone wrong, and no manner of shaking could set him off again.

He went back to school once more, only to run away once more. Doctors were consulted and proved expensively unhelpful. The school refused to take any further responsibility. They recommended her to find a tutor.

"You must bring him alive again," was Mrs. Moroney's final instruction to the newly engaged tutor. "I don't mind how you do it. I don't care what form it takes. I shouldn't even object—" and this was evidently the proof of her despair—"if he starts to like rugger. But bring him alive. Get him interested in *something*, I don't mind what."

But when she went on to give a hint about *interesting* ruins and a church with an antiquarian interest within bicycle reach, the tutor saw which way her mind was moving. Without quite knowing why, dimly foreseeing a possible need for desperate remedies without so much as having yet seen the child, "I should have to have a quite free hand," he suddenly found it necessary to insist.

"Naturally," she answered quickly; too quickly. The tutor felt that she hadn't really listened.

"I might have to do—well, anything."

"Do what you like." But he still felt that she didn't really mean it. Yet he began to enjoy the situation. He felt he had, at twenty-three, some sort of power which he could use. But he had to ensure himself absolutely in advance.

"You'll have to surrender the final responsibility to me."

She gave him one careful look. "Of course," she said. "I won't interfere. You must completely take him on."

(2)

He didn't meet the boy that day. He was left to wonder what he was like during the three days they gave him to collect his belongings from London. As he talked the thing over with his friends, the smattering of psychological phrases and technical terms which everyone has at their tongue's end nowadays were invoked to help him. It was generally decided that the parents were the culprits and that it would be them rather than the boy he would have to straighten out. The tutor was too interested in himself and his own future to be very objective about it; but he was intrigued by the situation, and he felt, without anything much to justify the feeling, that just because he was himself, a young man full of vigour and life and interests, he must therefore be able to help. He contrasted himself—all youth and hope and expectation—with something that he thought of, in recollection, as "anti-life" in Mrs. Moroney. Vitality she had, yet somehow it was muffled; interests she had, yet somehow they were blunted; passion she had, yet somehow it was withheld. Passion, interest, vitality—they were more his than hers. Both of them claimed them, but her claim was not valid; his own, just because he was twenty-three, was. Above all—and it was why he had intuitively felt it essential to press the point—she had never really intended to give him a free hand. There was something quite definite she reserved.

What, on the other hand, it was that he so wanted a free hand over, he didn't in the least know; and his first meeting with the boy, when he came back from London, didn't in the least clear it up. If he had hoped that anything in the boy's manner would be suggestive, he was soon disappointed.

Philip Moroney was twelve, a slight, well-made boy, who stood regarding the tutor amiably but without friendliness. The hazel which lay like an undercoat beneath a warm complexion paled off, the tutor observed, into whiteness above the cheek-bones. He didn't look very well. Mrs. Moroney effected an introduction between pupil and master and left them together, facing each other across the sacred table. It was a moment for which the tutor had almost consciously not prepared himself. Faced with it now, he really didn't know how to begin. What did one, what on earth did one, say to even a normal boy of twelve? Two openings alone insisted on obtruding themselves, and either was hopelessly tactless. The questions that came uppermost were: "Why *did* you run away?" and then much more insistently, "What do you think of your mother?" He asked the first in sheer despair to avoid asking the second. The boy shrugged his shoulders as much as to say, how should *he* know, and then surprised the tutor, after a pause, by offering a suggestion.

"To get equal with them?"

The tutor didn't make much of that. Equal with whom and for what? But he wasn't going to lose a chance.

"It was the best thing you could do."

The child looked puzzled. "But it doesn't work."

The tutor felt a renewal of power: "We'll try and make it."

"No, it won't work," the boy repeated.

"We'll find something," the tutor said, and from that moment was determined that he would. "What about a walk?" and, the boy assenting, they went off for a stroll in the flat Essex country before dinner. But conversation was desultory. No opening through which to approach the main question presented itself. Nor did any for the next three weeks.

But the time passed amicably at least. Lessons were arranged for the morning, more to keep the child occupied than in any hope of getting anything learnt. For the enthusiasm which his mother had described him so vividly as possessing was now quite dormant, so much so that the tutor began to wonder if it hadn't only existed in her imagination. The boy listlessly did what he was told, learned his lessons with a dull obedience, unprotestingly walked or cycled in the afternoon; he took his lead obediently from the tutor, grateful, it appeared, to have someone to make up his mind for him, since he had none of his own to make up. Mrs. Moroney watched and waited. Mr. Moroney chipped and twiddled in his outside shed. The tutor discovered no clue.

He looked for it first, as his friends had suggested, in the mother. He observed her carefully, and, in the evenings, when the boy was asleep— he slept mercifully early and late—tried to draw her out by artful questions. She was quite shrewd enough to parry him with equally artful evasions. He learnt a good deal about Chinese painting and the origins and development of brown lustre. But about herself he learned nothing. She was a discreet reticent woman who liked nothing so much as sharing her enthusiasms, and nothing so little as displaying her feelings. Her son she treated with a brusque affection, being very punctilious about his manners and appearance. He would be sent away from table for the faintest indication of dirty finger-nails and reprimanded for the slightest indication of childish greed. He took such reproofs with a sort of weary docility, just as he accepted her morning and evening kiss with an air of resigned patience.

But if, in the three weeks, the tutor felt himself no nearer a solution, he counted it as something that he was gaining the boy's confidence. He rather wished sometimes that he belonged to the earlier generation of his own schoolmasters who had still been sure enough of their ground to pick out a goal—house matches, prefectship, something of that sort—and had driven their charges roughshod towards it. He himself was acutely conscious of knowing only enough to know that the human machine was excessively delicate and that a false suggestion or a clumsy question might be enough to delay recovery. He bided his time, deciding, as his only point of policy, to try to give an impression that whatever in the world the lad was up to would have his unreserved approval.

Not that the boy seemed to be up to anything in particular. The first sign he gave of any feeling was so small and so negative that the tutor made little of it. It happened during the fourth week when one day he interrupted their mechanical translating of Sophocles to digress a little on the life of the Greeks. He felt it was up to him—that Mrs. Moroney would especially consider it up to him—to waken the boy's interest in Greek art. He approached it circuitously, picturing in modern terms the life of a Greek boy. Philip listened obediently to the first part of his description, but the moment he reached art in the shape of describing a chorus by Pindar in praise of a victorious athlete, the tutor noticed an obstinate expression shut down the boy's face. It was, anyhow, a sign of *something;* it was better than the docile attention which was all the boy gave him as a rule. The tutor continued as if he noticed nothing:

"And in the evening there would be a dinner, with the victor garlanded as guest of honour, and some of the other boys would dance to the song which Pindar had composed. The boy himself might have danced too—"

Philip broke his pencil with a quiet snap. He had hung his head and his body was tensed to resist taking in what the tutor was saying; the tutor pushed on:

"Boys in those days danced as naturally as today they play cricket. They were all trained in it from childhood. Quite early on they—"

In the rudest voice the boy interrupted:

"This is very dull. Let's go on translating."

The tutor was disconcerted. He'd quite expected an outburst but somehow, against all reason, was a little nettled to hear his efforts described as dull.

"If you find it dull, by all means. I was trying to make it interesting."

His pique evidently affected Philip. "I didn't mean you were dull," he said, and it was plainly an apology.

"What *did* you mean, I wonder?"

But that was too big a question. "Let's go on translating."

It was the first time anyhow that the boy had wanted to translate. But the tutor pressed the point:

"You mean dancing's dull?"

The child looked miserable and cornered. He turned away his head. "Let's go on translating," he finally repeated, bringing the repetition out from some depth of misery.

They went on translating.

His pique, the tutor noted, had made its effect. That gave him at least some kind of weapon, although it was one that he instinctively felt he must be extremely sparing in the use of. But it was from this incident that things began to happen. The boy took to following him around. Previously he had been quite content to be left on his own, and had only given the tutor his company at the prescribed times, or at the tutor's express suggestion. Now he began to attach himself whenever he could. It was part of the arrangement with Mrs. Moroney that the tutor was to have to himself the interval between tea and dinner, and it was his usual practice to go to his own room to read. One day the boy sought him out there; he opened the door shyly and said, "Do you mind if I come in? I'll be quite quiet," and he settled himself noiselessly at the window and stared out of it, his handsome little face cupped in his hands, his elbows propped up on the sill. He didn't apparently want anything from the tutor except his presence, and when the tutor began speaking, the boy rebuked him:

"You go on with what you're doing. I don't want to disturb you." It was solemn and grown up and touching. The tutor had the feeling that the child, in his demonstrated silence, was offering some kind of sacrifice that it would be offending to refuse. All the same he felt an awkwardness in going on reading his law books with that grave, speechless, staring boy sitting in the window waiting.

With half an hour to spare before dinner, he announced that he would take a bath; and the boy not responding or stirring he undressed; just as he was getting into his dressing-gown the boy turned and spoke.

"How old are you?"

"Twenty-three. Why?"

"You're terrifically strong, aren't you?"

The tutor felt so curiously complimented that he had to deprecate. "Oh, I don't know about that."

"Yes, you are," the boy said, "terrifically."

The tutor turned and looked at Philip. "Well, you know, so are you for your age."

"Not as strong as you," Philip said, turning back to the window.

"You soon will be," the tutor said.

For one moment the boy's face lighted up. "Do you think I will?" It was the long-awaited moment of returned excitement and it died the very moment that it flared. "No, I won't. I can't be."

"Of course you can be and you will." But the boy had presented his back again and cupped his chin in his hands and was staring out on to the small neat lawn.

All the same Mrs. Moroney noticed a change in the boy that evening and the next day. It was slight but discernible.

"Something's stirring," she said to the tutor. "I don't know how you've managed it, but something's moving, don't you notice it?"

"Don't expect too much," the tutor was prompted to answer, "and above all don't watch all the time."

For Mrs. Moroney, although she took no overt interest in the child's progress, never so much as asking what they were doing or how they were getting on, was all the time, the tutor had been feeling, present with her eyes; all the time she was out shopping or paying visits or going up to London, all the time she was dusting, rearranging, quietly reading, her eyes, he felt, were following them expectantly, in their lessons, on their walks, so that he had even contemplated suggesting that he and the boy should go away on their own. He had just before this hinted at the possibility and found Mrs. Moroney obstinately hostile. But he kept the idea up his sleeve in case it might be wanted.

The next evening, after Mrs. Moroney had, at luncheon, announced her intention of being out to tea, the boy turned up again at the tutor's room and installed himself in the same position at the window. The tutor after the merest welcome went on reading, but watched Philip covertly from behind his book. The boy had picked up a pencil and notebook from the window-sill and had begun scribbing. Presently his face tightened into concentration and the small tongue stuck out between the lips in the effort of doing something precise and difficult. He was drawing, his face and hand screwed tight; then there was a relaxation: the pencil travelled freely and wildly in circles round the paper, gathering momentum, speed and strength, as the circles decreased in diameter towards a centre, and on that centre it was struck down in a sudden burst of violence, slashing across and across, till it tore the centre out.

The boy turned round with a sudden friendly grin:

"You wouldn't like to come out and play cricket? I've got a ball and some things in the shed."

Surprised and delighted, the tutor agreed. Stumps were found and pitched on the narrow lawn between the house and the poplar trees. The tutor's suggestion that a soft ball would be best—he had put it on the ground of the windows—had been rejected, and a new fresh jumping enthusiasm easily over-rode his objections. He had persuaded the boy to bat presuming his refusal to be prompted by politeness. But he found him

to be a bad bat, alternately absurdly over-cautious, when he would step
back and cover his wicket, allowing anything a fraction wide to go past
and bang against the shed door—or wildly rash, when he would shut his
eyes and swipe, missing completely each time—mercifully, for the tutor
felt that Mrs. Moroney would turn out to be very unindulgent in respect
to her windows, especially the long fragile French window which guarded
so inadequately her special room. The boy soon got tired of his ineffectual efforts and called out "Now let me bowl!"

Then the tutor saw why. Without being an expert he could tell that
the boy had a fine natural left-hand action, graceful, easy and by no
means slow. He bowled, for his age, fast, too fast for the tutor who, without pads, found that his shins were in constant danger from balls that
swung in nastily and late. He had, if he wasn't to retire hurt, to give all
his attention to the bowling for the first over or two. Only then could he
take notice of the fact that the boy was a changed person, that he had a
confident smile, held himself erect and was thoroughly enjoying showing
off to his tutor his graceful run, his lithe and smooth swing. He began, as
small boys commonly do, to bowl faster and faster; but unlike most small
boys did not allow himself to become correspondingly wild. He bowled
with a deliberate precision at the tutor's body and hardly for a single ball
was it out of danger. All the same, in an interval the tutor, out of the
inveterate habit of instructors, advised the boy to control his speed.
"Length, not pace," was a maxim that returned to him from his own
schooldays. Philip, he noticed, did not respond favourably, and when
they resumed, he started off at his fastest and seemed intent on proving
that he could bowl faster yet.

After only five or six balls, the tutor's wicket was spread flat; and
then from behind the bowler came an unexpected clap. The tutor looked
up: the boy turned round: there was Mrs. Moroney who had returned
from her tea, standing, head on one side, in her flowing clothes, decorously
applauding. The animation faded from the boy's face, and when the tutor
set up the wicket again and threw the ball back to him, he let it drop, put
his hands in his pockets and announced:

"I'm tired."

"Do go on, do go on," his mother called out. "I want to see you hit
for a sixer." The tutor saw Philip wince at the word, and when he
obediently picked up the ball and started bowling it was with a desultory
indolence which was nothing like his real style. The tutor pulled up the
stumps and called out to her:

"We're too tired. We've been going a long time," and the game was
abandoned.

Up till then he had been thinking Mrs. Moroney remarkably sensible:
having reconciled herself to there being no intimacy between herself and
her son, she had never tried to invent it. But the cricket evidently per-

suaded her that a basis for it had now returned. Instead of talking at
dinner, as she usually did, on indifferent topics to him or to her husband,
she tried now to draw the boy in. She introduced cricket as a subject and
didn't seem to see that the child squirmed. When she asked him a question about school—a subject that hadn't in four weeks been mentioned—he
didn't answer. She repeated her question:

"What was the name of that nice master you used to talk about, the
one who admired your bowling?"

Philip went on eating. Mrs. Moroney looked at the tutor, as if for
support, but he too pretended to be intent on his food.

Mr. Moroney made a sudden descent into action:

"Answer your mother when she speaks to you, can't you? You've a
tongue in your head."

But the boy didn't speak.

"Answer your mother or clear off to bed." And the boy put down
knife and fork, stood up, pushed in his chair and walked, with a dignity
the tutor couldn't help admiring, out of the door. He didn't even slam it
behind him.

When the tutor returned that night to his room, he picked up the
notebook in which the boy had been scribbling and turned to the page. It
was difficult to make anything out among the scrawl and scribble. It
looked as if, beneath the circles, the leaf pattern of a William Morris
paper had been copied. But whatever had been drawn in the centre of the
page had been utterly obliterated by the last fierce onslaught.

(3)

There was no more cricket for the next three or four days, not till
Mrs. Moroney announced one day at breakfast that she and her husband
were going up to Town for the day, and would not be back until late in
the evening. But during those days the tutor noticed a distinct advance in
his pupil; he was becoming more ordinary. Instead of walking warily,
circumspectly, almost daintily, he kicked about with his shoes: he would
run on ahead: he thought nothing of arguing, disputing, scuffling even
with his tutor; Mrs. Moroney had to reprove him several times for kicking, idly, the wainscoting or the door. He was taking an interest in his
lessons, especially as the tutor now conducted them, talking with him
about things more than teaching. There was a big illustrated book of
Athenian pottery which Mrs. Moroney had said the boy used to enjoy
and which the tutor had at the beginning, with no sort of result, tried to
interest him in. Now Philip demanded it as the foundation of his lessons,
delighting in the athletes, the warriors, the great gods, the battle pieces,
the trussed-up sacrificial victims. He wanted them all explained and expanded, and it was noticeable to the tutor that he seemed to identify himself always with the most muscle-bound figure in any frieze. There was

one plate that particularly fascinated, of a youth dancing, a heavily built young man who seemed to be stamping in a grinning triumph, wearing a helmet and greaves and shaking a spear. The boy didn't seem able to believe that he was dancing. "But he looks so fierce," he kept saying. "But he looks so fierce—" and then he added—"and happy."

"Is there any reason why dancing shouldn't be fierce—and happy?" the tutor asked, watching the boy's head bent in concentrated delight over the terra-cotta plate, as if he were retracing every line and stamping it on his memory. He was murmuring expressions of wonder and surprise as another boy might at an engine or an aeroplane. Finally he wound up with:

"Whew! That's something like dancing, isn't it?"

The wickets were put up again that evening. The boy bowled delightedly for three-quarters of an hour. As before, his bowling got faster and faster towards the end, but this time also wilder and wilder. The tutor thought it time to make an end. But Philip pleaded for one more over.

"Just six of my special, please!"

The tutor giving in to the plea, the boy went back for a slightly longer run, made a special show of ferocity, ran fast up to the wicket and then, instead of bowling, drew back his arm and threw the ball with all his strength straight at the tutor's head. The tutor ducked sharply and called out "Here, steady!" and when he recovered his balance, he saw that the boy was standing stock still, white in the face, as if scared out of his wits. Acting instinctively, the tutor made a joke of it.

"You'll have to be careful, young man, you don't know your own strength."

The boy was still standing uncertain and a bit dazed, as if he was horrified at what he had done; the ball had rebounded off the shed door and lay in the middle of the pitch; the tutor went over and picked it up and threw it to the boy, but he simply let it fall without moving.

"Come on, give me your six specials, but not as special as that last."

Philip turned round and put his hands in his pockets: "I don't want to play any more."

The tutor went and picked up the ball, took it across and forced it into the boy's hands. For the first time in a month he spoke with a firmness which wasn't to be denied: "You're going to take this and bowl me six more before we knock off. Here you are."

The tutor went back and took up his stance; he saw the boy walk back irresolutely and then lollop up to the wicket to bowl the feeblest kind of ball at him. But the second one was a little more in the boy's real style; the third quite in it; and, by the time he had bowled a couple of overs, he was back again in his best mood, self-confident, skilful and smilingly showing off. When they had finished, he ragged the tutor and began a fight with him. He escaped from his grasp and pranced across the lawn. He seized a stump and, holding it as a spear, imitated the young dancer on the Greek plate, stamping, twisting and turning, in a pirouette that was more violent than classical.

The tutor was surprised to find Mrs. Moroney in the drawing-room when he had packed the boy off to have a bath. She had come back early and turned towards him now from the window.

"I've been watching you two," she said coldly.

"But did you see him dance?" The tutor was too excited to notice her coolness.

"Dance?" She turned back to the window: "I saw him capering like a guttersnipe."

The tutor was dashed, but he persisted: "He's coming alive."

"He's getting very rough, I've noticed. Don't you think you indulge him too much? Personally I think you should start being a little stricter."

The tutor was young enough to find his temper insufficiently under control. He said nothing for a moment or two and then: "You gave me a free hand, you remember."

"Within reason," she now emended, "we don't want to turn him into a hooligan."

"You wanted him alive, and you didn't care how," he reminded her.

But she wasn't listening. "You didn't know Philip before," she continued with her thoughts. "So I suppose it's not unnatural for you to expect him to turn into any other noisy scrapping little boy. But Philip was never like that. Never. Even his father, who wouldn't have so much minded, recognized that. He takes after me."

The tutor considered that. He was wondering whether he should tell her about Philip's renewed interest in the Greek figures. But instead he spoke deliberately:

"If you startd interfering, I don't know what would happen. I'm not sure that I know what will, if you don't. But I think it may be what you want."

"And what *do* you think I want?" she suddenly turned round to face him with.

"That he should be free—free from whatever it is that damped him down," the tutor tried to recall her to her original purpose.

"Fighting and throwing balls at people—is that the way you hope to do it?"

"Wait and see," he pleaded, catching up his temper in deference to a loyalty to the boy's interests. "Please wait and see."

"I'm not sure that I've quite the confidence that I had," she said going past him without looking him full in the face.

In the subsequent days Mrs. Moroney began throwing in her weight, and in so exasperating a manner that it became unbearable for the tutor.

She nagged and fussed and interfered. She wanted to hear what they had been learning and criticized the choice. She made suggestions of her own as if she wanted now to enter their life on level terms. She took to playing on the piano, in the evenings, the pieces to which Philip had danced as a child and recalled, as she played, the way he had responded to them. She took to coming over in the mornings "to join in their reading" and suggested that she might reasonably be invited to accompany them on their walks. She was impervious both to the tutor's disapproval and to the boy's hostility, expressed now in a more active sentiment of dislike. He was no longer accepting her, and, if the hostility had not yet reached the stage of action or even of speech, it was abundantly clear to the tutor in looks and grimaces behind her back, in turnings away and sulky silences, in stampings and kickings when she had left.

The tutor was impossibly placed. If he was to be even superficially loyal to her, he couldn't be loyal to the boy; if he was to be loyal to the boy, he couldn't even superficially put up with her interference; and, as he felt committed to the boy's recovery, not hers, he worked himself more and more into a suppressed temper with her. So far was she from giving him his free hand, she was threatening to undo all he felt he had, even if unconsciously, done. He would have to have it out with her he felt one evening, after a particularly unnecessary piece of nagging at tea. She was really impossible; he'd have to tell her so straight. Her sensitiveness didn't evidently extend to other people's feelings: hints and indications were lost on her. There was only one thing to do and that was to have it straight out; and the cumulative effect of her general impossibility was to make him feel that having it out might well lead to a flaming row—and he really rather hoped it would; he knew what he would say.

He went downstairs thoroughly worked up for it. But he couldn't find her in the house. He went out into the garden and there, from one of the potting sheds, he heard sounds which drew his attention; it sounded as if someone was crying. It was a long dark shed, and when he came and stood at the side of the door, he made out his pupil at the far end, intent apparently on some private purpose which the tutor felt justified in watching. The boy's left arm was stretched out, holding something on the angle of a low shelf and the wall, and this something, the tutor, as his eyes became accustomed to the dark, saw to be a cat. The boy was holding it roughly by its neck and was forcing it down on its back while it cried and hissed and fought and whimpered. This was the crying that had drawn his attention and it was caused, he finally forced himself to realize, by the boy's holding in his right hand a lighted cigarette which he kept bringing up towards its face and eyes, so that he was singeing the fur.

The tutor's first and natural instinct to interfere was, for some reason that he had no time to analyse, held back. He was to justify it later by reminding himself that interference would have been Mrs. Moroney's immediate reaction, and it was therefore by definition wrong. But at the time he was simply stuck there, silent and gaping, and increasingly involved. It simply struck him that this playing of the cigarette up towards the cat's face wasn't enough; they must go further; it must really be hurt. So identified was he with the boy that he was sweating, as the boy must have been sweating, his head was buzzing, as the boy's must have been buzzing, he was working himself up as the boy was visibly working himself up, jabbing the cigarette nearer and nearer, until suddenly with a grunt he took the decision and plunged the glowing end into the soft neck. The cat squealed and the boy, letting go with his left hand, hit it, swinging off his balance; the terrified animal shrunk back, and in an onset of fury the boy hit at it with both hands till it streaked away, howling, down the shed and out of the door past the tutor. The boy was after it, throwing something—a flower pot—and he too dashed towards the door past the tutor who put out his arms and caught him into them. The child was shaking and breathing in quick violent snorts through his nostrils.

"Steady," said the tutor. "Steady. It's well away by now.". . . .

The boy struggled and panted and then sagged against the young man's arms, turning his back, still panting. The tutor not knowing what to say, said nothing; he just hoped by his grip on the boy's shoulders to communicate his own share in the guilt. They stood for some minutes like that, and then the tutor turned the boy round and giving his cheek a friendly slap said:

"Come on, let's go and have a bath before dinner."

The speed with which the child's moods could change had several times surprised the tutor. The boy insisted on his going and talking to him while he had his bath; and he chattered now and splashed and laughed as if he had no connection with the concentrated figure at the end of the long dark potting shed.

That night Mrs. Moroney, after dinner, went as usual to the piano. This evening, the tutor noticed, the boy was not resisting. He was restless, his legs were moving, his hands fluttering; and then he got up and went out. Mrs. Moroney hadn't noticed, she went on playing. It was a mazurka, slavonic, romantic. The tutor was not yet quite reassured about the boy and he thought it best to keep an eye on him. Mrs. Moroney's special room was next door to the drawing room and it was in there that he found Philip. The music easily penetrated and the boy was standing in his steel-tipped shoes on the very centre of the sacred table; at the tutor's entrance he burst into a dance. It was the dance of the young warrior on the Attic plate; the boy was alive and grinning; he was triumphant. He spun and twisted, leapt and stamped, and the delicate surface of the wood tore and splintered; it creaked and cracked—but it held. The music was approaching its finale, and the dance—while the tutor simply watched—gathered strength and violence, until with the last chords, the boy attempted an *entrechat* and failed to come down in the centre of the table. As the music stopped he landed on one leaf which gave beneath his weight. He threw himself into the tutor's arms, panting and laughing and crying out:

"That was something like a dance, that was. That was something like a dance."

(4)

There was less awkwardness than there might have been about the tutor's departure—which took place the following day—because he made the arrangements exclusively with Mr. Moroney. Mrs. Moroney was, in the circumstances, remarkably restrained, but she was too grieved to act. Mr. Moroney's dash-in with a metaphorical uplifted cane had been intercepted by the tutor; he took the blame on himself and, quietly in the study, persuaded the husband that if the boy went back to school he would make a first-class left-handed bowler.

The good-bye between boy and tutor was quite unemotional; even, the tutor thought, a little surprisingly so. He felt at Philip's nonchalant "So long!" that he less than ever understood children. The boy talked all the way to the station about his school, his friends there, and the one particularly nice master who admired his bowling; he was dying to get back. The tutor stepped into his compartment and shut the door. The boy waited as the train gathered speed, and the last the tutor saw of him was a small sturdy figure with hands in pockets, apparently whistling a tune and idly kicking a piece of clinker.

CHAPTER eleven

The Abnormal Personality
in Childhood

Dynamic psychology has emphasized the crucial importance of infancy and childhood in the development of personality disturbances. Investigation of children during these early ages offers the opportunity to observe pathology *in statu nascendi*. In fact, most of the disorders described in adults are also found in children, although some childhood variants of pathology are less fixed and others are somewhat atypical.

So as to take advantage of this special formative period, the literary examples for this section were chosen not to emphasize these differences in outward forms of pathology, but because they artfully illustrate some of the environmental patterns and conflicts that contribute to disturbances in development.

a. A brief and sensitive portrayal of the formative impact of early life experiences is presented by William Carlos Williams. Speaking through a young medical student he is able to convey the conflict between a humanistic appreciation for the important aspects of a child's development, and the cut-and-dried approach of physically oriented medicine. Williams underlines in his excerpt not only the tragedy of medical disinterest, but also the enormity of the problems that successful preventive therapy involves.

THE INSANE

William Carlos Williams (1883–1963)

What are they teaching you now, son? said the old Doc brushing the crumbs from his vest.

Have one, Dad? Yeah. Throw it to me. I got matches.

I wish you wouldn't do that, said his wife trying hard to scowl. It was the usual Saturday evening dinner, the young man, a senior in medical school, out for his regular weekend siesta, in the suburbs.

I'm curious, said the old Doc glancing at his wife. Then to his son, Anything new? She placed an ash tray at his elbow.

I go on Medicine Monday, said the boy. We finished Pediatrics and Psychiatry today.

Psychiatry, eh? That's one you won't regret, said his father. Or do you like it, maybe?

Not particularly. But what can we learn in a few weeks? The cases we get are so advanced, just poor dumb clucks, there's nothing to do for them anyway. I can see though that there must be a lot to it.

What are you two talking about? said his mother.

Insanity, Ma.

Oh.

Any new theories as to cause? said the older man. I mean, not the degenerative cases, with a somatic background, but the schizophrenics especially. Have they learned anything new about that in recent years?

Oh, Dad, there are all sorts of theories. It starts with birth in most cases, they tell us. Even before birth sometimes. That's what we're taught. Unwanted children, conflicts of one sort or another. You know.

No. I'm curious. What do they tell you about Freud?

Sex as the basis for everything? The boy's mother looked up at him a moment and then down again.

It's largely a reflection of his own personality, most likely. I mean it's all right to look to sex as a cause, but that's just the surface aspect of the thing. Not the thing itself. Don't you think?

That's what I'm asking you.

But everybody has a different theory. One thing I can understand though, even from my little experiencee, and that is why insanity is increasing so rapidly here today.

Really? said his mother.

I mean from my Pediatric work. He paused. Of the twenty-five children I saw in the clinic this week only two can be said to be really free from psychoneurotic symptoms. Two! Out of twenty-five. And maybe a more careful history would have found something even in those two.

Do you mean that those children all showed signs of beginning insanity? said his mother.

Potentially, yes.

Not a very reassuring comment on modern life, is it?

Go ahead, son, said his father.

Take a funny-faced little nine-year-old guy with big glasses I saw in the clinic this afternoon. His mother brought him in for stealing money.

How old a child, did you say?

Nine years. The history was he'd take money from her purse. Or if she sent him to the store to buy something, he'd come back without it and use the money for something he wanted himself.

Do you have to treat those cases, too? asked his mother.

Anything that comes in. We have to get the history, do a physical, a complete physical—you know what that means, Dad—make a diagnosis and prescribe treatment.

What did you find?

The story is this. The lad's father was a drunk who died two years ago when the boy was just seven. A typical drunk. The usual bust up. They took him to the hospital and he died.

But before that—to go back, this boy had been a caesarian birth. He has a brother, three years younger, an accident. After that the woman was sterilized. But I'll tell you about him later.

Anyhow, when she came home, on the ninth day after her caesarian, she found her husband under the influence, dead drunk as usual and he started to take her over—that's the story.

What's that?

Oh, you know, Mother. Naturally she put up a fight and as a result he knocked her downstairs.

What! Nine days after her confinement?

Yes, nine days after the section. She had to return to the hospital for a check up. And naturally when she came out again she hated her husband and the baby too because it was his child.

Terrible.

And the little chap had to grow up in that atmosphere. They were always battling. The old man beat up his wife regularly and the child had to witness it for his entire existence up to two years ago.

As I say, she had a second child—three years old now, which, though she hated it, came between the older boy and his mother forcing them apart still further. That one has tuberculosis which doesn't make things any easier.

Imagine such people!

They're all around you, Mother, if you only knew it. Oh, I forgot to tell you the older kid was the dead spit of his dad who had always showered all kinds of attentions on him. His favorite. All the love the kid ever knew came from his old man.

So when the father died the only person the boy could look to for continued affection was his mother—who hated him.

Oh, no!

As a result the child doesn't eat, has lost weight, doesn't sleep, constipation and all the rest of it. And in school, whereas his marks had always been good—because he's fairly bright—after his father died they went steadily down, down and down to complete failure.

Poor baby.

And then he began to steal—from his mother—because he couldn't get the love he demanded of her. He began to steal from her to compensate for what he could not get otherwise, and which his father had given him formerly.

Interesting. Isn't it, dear?

So young!

The child substitutes his own solution for the reality which he needs and cannot obtain. Unreality and reality become confused in him. Finally he loses track. He doesn't know one from the other and we call him insane.

What will become of him in this case? asked the mother.

In this case, said her son, the outcome is supposed to be quite favorable. We'll explain the mechanism to the woman—who by the way isn't in such good condition herself—and if she follows up what she's told to do the boy is likely to be cured.

Strange, isn't it? said the old Doc.

But what gets me, said his son. Of course we're checked up on all these cases; they're all gone over by a member of the staff. And when we give a history like that, they say, Oh those are just the psychiatric findings. That gripes me. Why, it's the child's life.

Good boy, said his father. You're all right. Stick to it.

b.   Childhood disturbance begins within the disturbed family. Parental discord, divorce, and separation have lasting impact on children. Katherine Anne Porter demonstrates two of the typical areas of disturbance that family discord can create. Stephen, a kindergarten-age child, has been left with his grandmother during one of his parents' many protracted disagreements. Shifted about and caught in the crossfire of his parents' anger, he is unsure of anyone's love. Stephen, like all children, needs a foundation of love and security to initiate peer relationships. Like many such children, he steals to bribe his playmates to like him. But the central theme of Miss Porter's story "The Downward Path to Wisdom" is contained in the last vignette. There Stephen has found a refuge from his insecurity in hating, a downward path that his mother and other relatives have already traveled.

THE DOWNWARD PATH TO WISDOM
Katherine Anne Porter   (1890–   )

. . . In the afternoon at school Teacher handed out big wads of clay and told the children to make something out of it. Anything they liked. Stephen decided to make a cat, like Mama's Meeow at home. He did not like Meeow, but he thought it would be easy to make a cat. He could not get the clay to work at all. It simply fell into one lump after another. So he stopped, wiped his hands on his pull-over, remembered his balloons and began blowing one.

"Look at Stephen's horse," said Frances. "Just look at it."

"It's not a horse, it's a cat," said Stephen. The other children gathered around. "It looks like a horse, a little," said Martin.

"It is a cat," said Stephen, stamping his foot, feeling his face turning hot. The other children all laughed and exclaimed over Stephen's cat that looked like a horse. Teacher came down among them. She sat usually at the top of the room before a big table covered with papers and playthings. She picked up Stephen's lump of clay and turned it round and examined it with her kind eyes. "Now, children," she said, "everybody has the right to make anything the way he pleases. If Stephen says this is a cat, it *is* a cat. Maybe you were thinking about a horse, Stephen?"

"It's a *cat*," said Stephen. He was aching all over. He knew then he should have said at first, "Yes, it's a horse." Then they would have let him alone. They would never have known he was trying to make a cat. "It's Meeow," he said in a trembling voice, "but I forgot how she looks."

His balloon was perfectly flat. He started blowing it up again, trying not to cry. Then it was time to go home, and Old Janet came looking for him. While Teacher was talking to other grown-up people who came to take other children home, Frances said, "Give me your balloon; I haven't got a balloon." Stephen handed it to her. He was happy to give it. He reached in his pocket and took out the other. Happily, he gave her that one too. Frances took it, then handed it back. "Now you blow up one and

I'll blow up the other, and let's have a race," she said. When their balloons were only half filled Old Janet took Stephen by the arm and said, "Come on here, this is my busy day."

Frances ran after them, calling, "Stephen, you give me back my balloon," and snatched it away. Stephen did not know whether he was surprised to find himself going away with Frances' balloon, or whether he was surprised to see her snatching it as if it really belonged to her. He was badly mixed up in his mind, and Old Janet was hauling him along. One thing he knew, he liked Frances, he was going to see her again tomorrow, and he was going to bring her more balloons.

That evening Stephen boxed awhile with his uncle David, and Uncle David gave him a beautiful orange. "Eat that," he said, "it's good for your health."

"Uncle David, may I have some more balloons?" asked Stephen.

"Well, what do you say first?" asked Uncle David, reaching for the box on the top bookshelf.

"Please," said Stephen.

"That's the word," said Uncle David. He brought out two balloons, a red and a yellow one. Stephen noticed for the first time they had letters on them, very small letters that grew taller and wider as the balloon grew rounder. "Now that's all, fellow," said Uncle David. "Don't ask for any more because that's all." He put the box back on the bookshelf, but not before Stephen had seen that the box was almost full of balloons. He didn't say a word, but went on blowing, and Uncle David blew also. Stephen thought it was the nicest game he had ever known.

He had only one left, the next day, but he took it to school and gave it to Frances. "There are a lot," he said, feeling very proud and warm; "I'll bring you a lot of them."

Frances blew it up until it made a beautiful bubble, and said, "Look, I want to show you something." She took a sharp-pointed stick they used in working the clay; she poked the balloon, and it exploded. "Look at that," she said.

"That's nothing," said Stephen, "I'll bring you some more."

After school, before Uncle David came home, while Grandma was resting, when Old Janet had given him his milk and told him to run away and not bother her, Stephen dragged a chair to the bookshelf, stood upon it and reached into the box. He did not take three or four as he believed he intended; once his hands were upon them he seized what they could hold and jumped off the chair, hugging them to him. He stuffed them into his reefer pocket where they folded down and hardly made a lump.

He gave them all to Frances. There were so many, Frances gave most of them away to the other children. Stephen, flushed with his new joy, the lavish pleasure of giving presents, found almost at once still another happiness. Suddenly he was popular among the children; they invited him specially to join whatever games were up; they fell in at once with his own notions for play, and asked him what he would like to do next. They had festivals of blowing up the beautiful globes, fuller and rounder and thinner, changing as they went from deep color to lighter, paler tones, growing glassy thin, bubbly thin, then bursting with a thrilling loud noise like a toy pistol.

For the first time in his life Stephen had almost too much of something he wanted, and his head was so turned he forgot how this fullness came about, and no longer thought of it as a secret. The next day was Saturday, and Frances came to visit him with her nurse. The nurse and Old Janet sat in Old Janet's room drinking coffee and gossiping, and the children sat on the side porch blowing balloons. Stephen chose an apple-colored one and Frances a pale green one. Between them on the bench lay a tumbled heap of delights still to come.

"I once had a silver balloon," said Frances, "a beyootiful silver one, not round like these; it was a long one. But these are even nicer, I think," she added quickly, for she did want to be polite.

"When you get through with that one," said Stephen, gazing at her with the pure bliss of giving added to loving, "you can blow up a blue one and then a pink one and a yellow one and a purple one." He pushed the heap of limp objects toward her. Her clear-looking eyes, with fine little rays of brown in them like the spokes of a wheel, were full of approval for Stephen. "I wouldn't want to be greedy, though, and blow up all your balloons."

"There'll be plenty more left," said Stephen, and his heart rose under his thin ribs. He felt his ribs with his fingers and discovered with some surprise that they stopped somewhere in front, while Frances sat blowing balloons rather halfheartedly. The truth was, she was tired of balloons. After you blow six or seven your chest gets hollow and your lips feel puckery. She had been blowing balloons steadily for three days now. She had begun to hope they were giving out. "There's boxes and boxes more of them, Frances," said Stephen happily. "Millions more. I guess they'd last and last if we didn't blow too many every day."

Frances said somewhat timidly, "I tell you what. Let's rest awhile and fix some liquish water. Do you like liquish?"

"Yes, I do," said Stephen, "but I haven't got any."

"Couldn't we buy some?" asked Frances. "It's only a cent a stick, the nice rubbery, twisty kind. We can put it in a bottle with some water, and shake it and shake it, and it makes foam on top like soda pop and we can drink it. I'm kind of thirsty," she said in a small, weak voice. "Blowing balloons all the time makes you thirsty, I think."

Stephen, in silence, realized a dreadful truth and a numb feeling crept over him. He did not have a cent to buy licorice for Frances and she was tired of his balloons. This was the first real dismay of his whole life, and he aged at least a year in the next minute, huddled, with his deep, serious blue eyes focused down his nose in intense speculation. What could he do to please Frances that would not cost money? Only yesterday Uncle David had given him a nickel, and he had thrown it away on gum-drops. He regretted that nickel so bitterly his neck and forehead were damp. He was thirsty too.

"I tell you what," he said, brightening with a splendid idea, lamely trailing off on second thought, "I know something we can do, I'll—I . . ."

"I *am* thirsty," said Frances with gentle persistence. "I think I'm so thirsty maybe I'll have to go home." She did not leave the bench, though, but sat, turning her grieved mouth toward Stephen.

Stephen quivered with the terrors of the adventure before him, but he said boldly, "I'll make some lemonade. I'll get sugar and lemon and some ice and we'll have lemonade."

"Oh, I love lemonade," cried Frances. "I'd rather have lemonade than liquish."

"You stay right here," said Stephen, "and I'll get everything."

He ran around the house, and under Old Janet's window he heard the dry, chattering voices of the two old women whom he must outwit. He sneaked on tiptoe to the pantry, took a lemon lying there by itself, a handful of lump sugar and a china teapot, smooth, round, with flowers and leaves all over it. These he left on the kitchen table while he broke a piece of ice with a sharp metal pick he had been forbidden to touch. He put the ice in the pot, cut the lemon and squeezed it as well as he could—a lemon was tougher and more slippery than he had thought—and mixed sugar and water. He decided there was not enough sugar so he sneaked back and took another handful. He was back on the porch in an astonish-ingly short time, his face tight, his knees trembling, carrying iced lemon ade to thirsty Frances with both his devoted hands.

A pace distant from her he stopped, literally stabbed through with a thought. Here he stood in broad daylight carrying a teapot with lemon-ade in it, and his grandma or Old Janet might walk through the door at any moment.

"Come on, Frances," he whispered loudly. "Let's go round to the back behind the rose bushes where it's shady." Frances leaped up and ran like a deer beside him, her face wise with knowledge of why they ran; Stephen ran stiffly, cherishing his teapot with clenched hands.

It was shady behind the rose bushes, and much safer. They sat side by side on the dampish ground, legs doubled under, drinking in turn from the slender spout. Stephen took his just share in large, cool, delicious swal-lows. When Frances drank she set her round pink mouth daintily to the spout and her throat beat steadily as a heart. Stephen was thinking he had really done something pretty nice for Frances. He did not know where his own happiness was; it was mixed with the sweet-sour taste in his mouth and a cool feeling in his bosom because Frances was there drinking his lemonade which he had got for her with great danger.

Frances said, "My, what big swallows you take," when his turn came next.

"No bigger than yours," he told her downrightly. "You take awfully big swallows."

"Well," said Frances, turning this criticism into an argument for her rightness about things, "that's the way to drink lemonade anyway." She peered into the teapot. There was quite a lot of lemonade left and she was beginning to feel she had enough. "Let's make up a game and see who can take the biggest swallows."

This was such a wonderful notion they grew reckless, tipping the spout into their opened mouths above their heads until lemonade welled up and ran over their chins in rills down their fronts. When they tired of this there was still lemonade left in the pot. They played first at giving the rose bush a drink and ended by baptizing it. "Name father son holygoat," shouted Stephen, pouring. At this sound Old Janet's face appeared over the low hedge, with the tan, disgusted-looking face of Frances' nurse hanging over her shoulder.

"Well, just as I thought," said Old Janet. "Just as I expected." The bag under her chin waggled.

"We were thirsty," he said; "we were awfully thirsty." Frances said nothing, but she gazed steadily at the toes of her shoes.

"Give me that teapot," said Old Janet, taking it with a rude snatch. "Just because you're thirsty is no reason," said Old Janet. "You can ask for things. You don't have to steal."

"We didn't steal," cried Frances suddenly. "We didn't. We didn't!"

"That's enough from you, missy," said her nurse. "Come straight out of there. You have nothing to do with this."

"Oh, I don't know," said Old Janet with a hard stare at Frances' nurse. "*He* never did such a thing before, by himself."

"Come on," said the nurse to Frances, "this is no place for you." She held Frances by the wrist and started walking away so fast Frances had to run to keep up. "Nobody can call *us* thieves and get away with it."

"You don't have to steal, even if others do," said Old Janet to Stephen, in a high carrying voice. "If you so much as pick up a lemon in somebody else's house you're a little thief." She lowered her voice then and said, "Now I'm going to tell your grandma and you'll see what you get."

"He went in the icebox and left it open," Janet told Grandma, "and he got into the lump sugar and spilt it all over the floor. Lumps everywhere underfoot. He dribbled water all over the clean kitchen floor, and he baptized the rose bush, blaspheming. And he took your Spode teapot."

"I didn't either," said Stephen loudly, trying to free his hand from Old Janet's big hard fist.

"Don't tell fibs," said Old Janet; "that's the last straw."

"Oh, dear," said Grandma. "He's not a baby any more." She shut the book she was reading and pulled the wet front of his pull-over toward her. "What's this sticky stuff on him?" she asked and straightened her glasses.

"Lemonade," said Old Janet. "He took the last lemon."

They walked in the big dark room with the red curtains. Uncle David walked in from the room with the bookcases, holding a box in his uplifted hand. "Look here," he said to Stephen. "What's become of all my balloons?"

Stephen knew well that Uncle David was not really asking a question.

Stephen, sitting on a footstool at his grandma's knee, felt sleepy. He leaned heavily and wished he could put his head on her lap, but he might go to sleep, and it would be wrong to go to sleep while Uncle David was still talking. Uncle David walked about the room with his hands in his pockets, talking to Grandma. Now and then he would walk over to a lamp and, leaning, peer into the top of the shade, winking in the light, as if he expected to find something there.

It's simply in the blood, I told her," said Uncle David. "I told her she would simply have to come and get him, and keep him. She asked me if I meant to call him a thief and I said if she could think of a more exact word I'd be glad to hear it."

"You shouldn't have said that," commented Grandma calmly.

"Why not? She might as well know the facts. . . . I suppose he can't help it," said Uncle David, stopping now in front of Stephen and dropping his chin into his collar, "I shouldn't expect too much of him, but you can't begin too early—"

"The trouble is," said Grandma, and while she spoke she took Stephen by the chin and held it up so that he had to meet her eye; she talked steadily in a mournful tone, but Stephen could not understand. She ended, "It's not just about the balloons, of course."

"It *is* about the balloons," said Uncle David angrily, "because balloons now mean something worse later. But what can you expect? His father—well, it's in the blood. He—"

"That's your sister's husband you're talking about," said Grandma, "and there is no use making things worse. Besides, you don't really *know*."

"I *do* know," said Uncle David. And he talked again very fast, walking up and down. Stephen tried to understand, but the sounds were strange and floating just over his head. They were talking about his father, and they did not like him. Uncle David came over and stood above Stephen and Grandma. He hunched over them with a frowning face, a long, crooked shadow from him falling across them to the wall. To Stephen he looked like his father, and he shrank against his grandma's skirts.

"The question is, what to do with him now?" asked Uncle David. "If we keep him here, he'd just be a—I won't be bothered with him. Why can't they take care of their own child? That house is crazy. Too far gone already, I'm afraid. No training. No example."

"You're right, they must take him and keep him," said Grandma. She ran her hands over Stephen's head; tenderly she pinched the nape of his neck between thumb and forefinger. "You're your Grandma's darling," she told him, "and you've had a nice long visit, and now you're going home. Mama is coming for you in a few minutes. Won't that be nice?"

"I want my mama," said Stephen, whimpering, for his grandma's face frightened him. There was something wrong with her smile.

Uncle David sat down. "Come over here, fellow," he said, wagging a forefinger at Stephen. Stephen went over slowly, and Uncle David drew him between his wide knees in their loose, rough clothes. "You ought to be ashamed of yourself," he said, "stealing Uncle David's balloons when he had already given you so many."

"It wasn't that," said Grandma quickly. "Don't say that. It will make an impression—"

"I hope it does," said Uncle David in a louder voice; "I hope he remembers it all his life. If he belonged to me I'd give him a good thrashing."

Stephen felt his mouth, his chin, his whole face jerking. He opened his mouth to take a breath, and tears and noise burst from him. "Stop that, fellow, stop that," said Uncle David, shaking him gently by the shoulders, but Stephen could not stop. He drew his breath again and it came back in a howl. Old Janet came to the door.

"Bring me some cold water," called Grandma. There was a flurry, a commotion, a breath of cool air from the hall, the door slammed, and Stephen heard his mother's voice. His howl died away, his breath sobbed and fluttered, he turned his dimmed eyes and saw her standing there. His heart turned over within him and he bleated like a lamb, "Maaaaama," running toward her. Uncle David stood back as Mama swooped in and fell on her knees beside Stephen. She gathered him to her and stood up with him in her arms.

"What are you doing to my baby?" she asked Uncle David in a thickened voice. "I should never have let him come here. I should have known better—"

"You always should know better," said Uncle David, "and you never do. And you never will. You haven't got it here," he told her, tapping his forehead.

"David," said Grandma, "that's your—"

"Yes, I know, she's my sister," said Uncle David. "I know it. But if she must run away and marry a—"

"Shut up," said Mama.

"And bring more like him into the world, let her keep them at home. I say let her keep—"

Mama set Stephen on the floor and, holding him by the hand, she said to Grandma all in a rush as if she were reading something, "Good-by, Mother. This is the last time, really the last. I can't bear it any longer. Say good-by to Stephen; you'll never see him again. You let this happen. It's your fault. You know David was a coward and a bully and a self-righteous little beast all his life and you never crossed him in anything. You let him bully me all my life and you let him slander my husband and call my baby a thief, and now this is the end. . . . He calls my baby a thief over a few horrible little balloons because he doesn't like my husband. . . ."

She was panting and staring about from one to the other. They were all standing. Now Grandma said, "Go home, daughter. Go away, David. I'm sick of your quarreling. I've never had a day's peace or comfort from either of you. I'm sick of you both. Now let me alone and stop this noise. Go away," said Grandma in a wavering voice. She took out her handkerchief and wiped first one eye and then the other and said, "All this hate, hate—what is it for? . . . So this is the way it turns out. Well, let me alone."

"You and your little advertising balloons," said Mama to Uncle David. "The big honest businessman advertises with balloons and if he loses one he'll be ruined. And your beastly little moral notions . . ."

Grandma went to the door to meet Old Janet, who handed her a glass of water. Grandma drank it all, standing there.

"Is your husband coming for you, or are you going home by yourself?" she asked Mama.

"I'm driving myself," said Mama in a far-away voice as if her mind had wandered. "You know he wouldn't set foot in this house."

"I should think not," said Uncle David.

"Come on, Stephen darling," said Mama. "It's far past his bedtime," she said, to no one in particular. "Imagine keeping a baby up to torture him about a few miserable little bits of colored rubber." She smiled at Uncle David with both rows of teeth as she passed him on the way to the door, keeping between him and Stephen. "Ah, where would we be without high moral standards," she said, and then to Grandma, "Good night, Mother," in quite her usual voice. "I'll see you in a day or so."

"Yes, indeed," said Grandma cheerfully, coming out into the hall with Stephen and Mama. "Let me hear from you. Ring me up tomorrow. I hope you'll be feeling better."

"I feel very well now," said Mama brightly, laughing. She bent down and kissed Stephen. "Sleepy, darling? Papa's waiting to see you. Don't go to sleep until you've kissed your papa good night."

Stephen woke with a sharp jerk. He raised his head and put out his chin a little. "I don't want to go home," he said; "I want to go to school. I don't want to see Papa, I don't like him."

Mama laid her palm over his mouth softly. "Darling, don't."

Uncle David put his head out with a kind of snort. "There you are," he said. "There you've got a statement from headquarters."

Mama opened the door and ran, almost carrying Stephen. She ran across the sidewalk, jerking open the car door and dragging Stephen in after her. She spun the car around and dashed forward so sharply Stephen was almost flung out of the seat. He sat braced then with all his might, hands digging into the cushions. The car speeded up and the trees and houses whizzed by all flattened out. Stephen began suddenly to sing to himself, a quiet, inside song so Mama would not hear. He sang his new secret; it was a comfortable, sleepy song: "I hate Papa, I hate Mama, I hate Grandma, I hate Uncle David, I hate Old Janet, I hate Marjory, I hate Papa, I hate Mama . . ."

His head bobbed, leaned, came to rest on Mama's knee, eyes closed. Mama drew him closer and slowed down, driving with one hand.

C.   Rosalind is a preadolescent girl whose feelings and thoughts are captured as she experiences one of the deepest emotional currents of childhood. Disturbances in this area begin in infancy, and can lead to the most severe forms of pathology. Elizabeth Bowen in this story has tapped many of the deeper fantasies and emotions connected with this central human concern, *separation* from mother. Rosalind's intense attachment is symbolized in her nickname for mother, "Darlingest." Her attachment is so intense that she experiences it almost as a physical union or fusion. This attachment must be finally resolved in adolescence so that the child can develop a separate and independent identity. The unusual insight of this story is its capturing of the usually obscure factors in the underlying dread evoked by a brief separation from mother; namely, that separation means to the primitive part of the person that mother is dead and that there can be no security in life. Psychoanalytic experience suggests that part of this child's fear for the mother's safety is based on her own anger and resentment at having been deserted, even momentarily. Thus, as Miss Bowen demonstrates, separation from mother is both a disappointment in love and a precipitant of hate.

COMING HOME

Elizabeth Bowen   (1899–   )

. . . As soon as she entered the hall she knew that the house was empty. Clocks ticked very loudly; upstairs and downstairs the doors were a little open, letting through pale strips of light. Only the kitchen door was shut, down the end of the passage, and she could hear Emma moving about behind it. There was a spectral shimmer of light in the white panelling. On the table was a bowl of primroses; Darlingest must have put them there that morning. The hall was chilly; she could not think why the primroses gave her such a feeling of horror, then she remembered the wreath of primroses, and the scent of it, lying on the raw new earth of that grave. . . . The pair of grey gloves were gone from the bowl of visiting-cards. Darlingest had spent the morning doing those deathly primroses, and then taken up her grey gloves and gone out, at the end of the afternoon, just when she knew her little girl would be coming in. A quarter-past four. It was unforgivable of Darlingest: she had been a mother for more than twelve years, the mother exclusively of Rosalind, and still, it seemed, she knew no better than to do a thing like that. Other people's mothers had terrible little babies: they ran quickly in and out to go to them, or they had smoky husbands who came in and sat, with big feet. There was something distracted about other people's mothers. But Darlingest, so exclusively one's own. . . .

Darlingest could never have really believed in her. She could never have really believed that Rosalind would do anything wonderful at school, or she would have been more careful to be in to hear about it. Rosalind flung herself into the drawing-room; it was honey-coloured and lovely in the pale spring light, another little clock was ticking in the corner, there were more bowls of primroses and black-eyed, lowering anemones. The tarnished mirror on the wall distorted and reproved her angry face in its mild mauveness. Tea was spread on the table by the window, tea for two that the two might never . . . Her work and an open book lay on the tumbled cushions of the window-seat. All the afternoon she had sat there waiting and working, and now—poor little Darlingest, perhaps she had gone out because she was lonely.

People who went out sometimes never came back again. Here she was, being angry with Darlingest, and all the time . . . Well, she had drawn on those grey gloves and gone out wandering along the roads, vague and beautiful, because she was lonely, and then?

Ask Emma? No, she wouldn't; fancy having to ask *her!*

"Yes, your mother'll be in soon, Miss Rosie. Now run and get your things off, there's a good girl—" Oh no, intolerable.

The whole house was full of the scent and horror of the primroses. Rosalind dropped the exercise-book on the floor, looked at it, hesitated, and putting her hands over her mouth, went upstairs, choking back her sobs. She heard the handle of the kitchen door turn; Emma was coming out. O God! Now she was on the floor by Darlingest's bed, with the branches swaying and brushing outside the window, smothering her face in the eiderdown, smelling and tasting the wet satin. Down in the hall she heard Emma call her, mutter something, and slam back into the kitchen.

How could she ever have left Darlingest? She might have known, she might have known. The sense of insecurity had been growing on her year by year. A person might be part of you, almost part of your body, and yet once you went away from them they might utterly cease to be. That sea of horror ebbing and flowing round the edges of the world, whose tides were charted in the newspapers, might sweep out a long wave over them and they would be gone. There was no security. Safety and happiness were a game that grown-up people played with children to keep them from understanding, possibly to keep themselves from thinking. But they did think, that was what made grown-up people—queer. Anything might happen, there was no security. And now Darlingest—

This was her dressing-table, with the long beads straggling over it, the little coloured glass barrels and bottles had bright flames in the centre. In front of the looking-glass, filmed faintly over with a cloud of powder, Darlingest had put her hat on—for the last time. Supposing all that had ever been reflected in it were imprisoned somewhere in the back of a looking-glass. The blue hat with the drooping brim was hanging over the corner of a chair. Rosalind had never been kind about that blue hat, she didn't think it was becoming. And Darlingest had loved it so. She must have gone out wearing the brown one; Rosalind went over to the wardrobe and stood on tip-toe to look on the top shelf. Yes, the brown hat was gone. She would never see Darlingest again, in the brown hat, coming down the road to meet her and not seeing her because she was thinking about something else. Peau d'Espagne crept faintly from among the folds of the dresses; the blue, the gold, the soft furred edges of the tea-gown dripping out of the wardrobe. She heard herself making a high, whining noise at the back of her throat, like a puppy, felt her swollen face distorted by another paroxysm.

"I can't bear it, I can't bear it. What have I done? I did love her, I did so awfully love her.

"Perhaps she was all right when I came in; coming home smiling. Then I stopped loving her, I hated her and was angry. And it happened.

She was crossing a road and something happened to her. I was angry and she died. I killed her.

"I don't know that she's dead. I'd better get used to believing it, it will hurt less afterwards. Supposing she does come back this time; it's only for a little. I shall never be able to keep her; now I've found out about this I shall never be happy. Life's nothing but waiting for awfulness to happen and trying to think about something else.

"If she could come back just this once—Darlingest."

Emma came half-way upstairs; Rosalind flattened herself behind the door.

"Will you begin your tea, Miss Rosie?"

"No. Where's mother?"

"I didn't hear her go out. I have the kettle boiling—will I make your tea?"

"No. *No.*"

Rosalind slammed the door on the angry mutterings, and heard with a sense of desolation Emma go downstairs. The silver clock by Darlingest's bed ticked; it was five o'clock. They had tea at a quarter-past four; Darlingest was never, never late. When they came to tell her about *It*, men would come, and they would tell Emma, and Emma would come up with a frightened, triumphant face and tell her.

She saw the grey-gloved hands spread out in the dust.

A sound at the gate. "I can't bear it, I can't bear it. Oh, save me, God!"

Steps on the gravel.

Darlingest.

She was at the window, pressing her speechless lips together.

Darlingest came slowly up the path with the long ends of her veil, untied, hanging over her shoulders. A paper parcel was pressed between her arm and her side. She paused, stood smiling down at the daffodils. Then she looked up with a start at the windows, as though she heard somebody calling. Rosalind drew back into the room.

She heard her mother's footsteps cross the stone floor of the hall, hesitate at the door of the drawing-room, and come over to the foot of the stairs. The voice was calling "Lindie! Lindie, duckie!" She was coming upstairs.

Rosalind leaned the weight of her body against the dressing-table and dabbed her face with the big powder-puff; the powder clung in paste to her wet lashes and in patches over her nose and cheeks. She was not happy, she was not relieved, she felt no particular feeling about Darlingest, did not even want to see her. Something had slackened down inside her, leaving her a little sick.

"Oh, you're *there*," said Darlingest from outside, hearing her movements. "Where did, where were—?"

She was standing in the doorway. Nothing had been for the last time, after all. She had come back. One could never explain to her how wrong she had been. She was holding out her arms; something drew one towards them.

"But my little *Clown*," said Darlingest, wiping off the powder. "But, oh—" She scanned the glazed, blurred face. "Tell me why," she said.

"You were late."

"Yes, it was horrid of me; did you mind? . . . But that was silly, Rosalind, I can't be always in."

"But you're my mother."

Darlingest was amused; little trickles of laughter and gratification ran out of her. "You weren't *frightened*, Silly Billy." Her tone changed to distress. "Oh, Rosalind, don't be cross."

"I'm not," said Rosalind coldly.

"Then come—"

"I was wanting my tea."

"Rosalind, *don't* be—"

Rosalind walked past her to the door. She was hurting Darlingest, beautifully hurting her. She would never tell her about that essay. Everybody would be talking about it, and when Darlingest heard and asked her about it she would say: "Oh, that? I didn't think you'd be interested." That would hurt. She went down into the drawing-room, past the primroses. The grey gloves were back on the table. This was the mauve and golden room that Darlingest had come back to, from under the Shadow of Death, expecting to find her little daughter. . . . They would have sat together on the window-seat while Rosalind read the essay aloud, leaning their heads closer together as the room grew darker.

That was all spoilt.

Poor Darlingest, up there alone in the bedroom, puzzled, hurt, disappointed, taking off her hat. She hadn't known she was going to be hurt like this when she stood out there on the gravel, smiling at the daffodils. The red essay-book lay spread open on the carpet. There was the paper bag she had been carrying, lying on a table by the door; macaroons, all squashy from being carried the wrong way, disgorging, through a tear in the paper, a little trickle of crumbs.

The pathos of the forgotten macaroons, the silent pain! Rosalind ran upstairs to the bedroom.

Darlingest did not hear her; she had forgotten. She was standing in the middle of the room with her face turned towards the window, looking at something a long way away, smiling and singing to herself and rolling up her veil.

d.   Traumatic events have a particularly lasting effect when they occur in childhood. The young person has fewer resources to cope with the anxiety that trauma inevitably produces. Isaac Babel describes an incredibly terrifying series of experiences in his understated story called "First Love." The child, caught in an episode of religious persecution, has his newly bought pet pigeons crushed against his face, sees his grandfather's murdered body, his father's humiliation, and at last finds refuge in the home of a woman who has been the object of his erotic fantasies. This combination of events leads to the onset of a massive conversion reaction, and Babel tells us, shaped the boy's later pathology as well.

First Love

Isaac Babel   (1894–1939?)

When I was ten years old I fell in love with a woman called Galina. Her surname was Rubtsov. Her husband, an officer, went off to the Russo-Japanese War and returned in October, 1905. He brought a great many trunks back with him. These trunks, which weighed nearly half a ton, contained Chinese souvenirs such as screens and costly weapons. Kuzma the yardman used to tell us that Rubtsov had bought all these things with money he had embezzled while serving in the engineer corps of the Manchurian Army. Other people said so too. The Rubtsovs were happy, so it was hard for people not to gossip about them. Their house adjoined our place, and their glass veranda jutted out over our premises, but father didn't make a fuss about it. The elder Rubtsov, who was a tax-inspector, had a reputation in our town for being a fair-minded man: he was friendly with Jews. When the officer, the old man's son, returned from the war, we could see how well he and his wife got on together.

Galina would hold her husband's hand all day long. She stared at him incessantly, for she had not seen him in a year and a half. But her gaze frightened me, and I would turn away and shiver, glimpsing that obscure and shameful side of human existence. I longed to fall into a strange sleep, to forget about this life that surpassed all my fancies. Galina would glide through the rooms with her braid hanging down her back, wearing elegant red shoes and a Chinese robe. Under the lace of her deep-cut slip one could see the swelling of her white breasts squeezed downward, and the depression between them. On her robe were embroidered pink silk dragons, birds, trees with hollows in their trunks.

The whole day long she sauntered about with a meaningless smile on her moist lips, brushing against the trunks that had not yet been unpacked and the ladders for doing physical exercises strewn about the floor. Galina would bruise herself, pull her robe above her knee, and say to her husband: "Kiss baby better." The officer would bend his long legs in their narrow dragoon's trousers, in their smooth, taut leather boots with spurs, and crawling across the littered floor on his knees, smile and kiss the bruised flesh, just where a little bulge rose above the garter.

I saw those kisses from my window, and they caused me agony. Unbounded fantasies tormented me—but what's the use of talking about it? The love and the jealousy of a ten-year-old boy are in every way the same as the love and jealousy of a grownup. I stopped going near the window and avoided Galina for two weeks, and then an event brought us together.

It was the pogrom against the Jews that broke out in 1905 in Nikolayev and other towns where Jews were permitted to live. A mob of hired murderers plundered my father's store and killed Grandfather Shoyl. All this happened when I was out. That sad morning I had bought some pigeons from Ivan Nikodimych the fancier. For five of my ten years I had dreamed with my whole soul about pigeons. But when I finally bought them, Makarenko the cripple smashed them against my temples. Then Kuzma found me and took me to the Rubtsovs'. On their gate a cross had been chalked. Nobody molested them, and they hid my parents in their house. Kuzma led me to the glass veranda. My mother and Galina were there in the green rotunda.

"Now we must wash," Galina said. "We must wash, my little rabbi. Our face is covered with feathers, and the feathers are bloody."

She put her arms around me and led me along a hallway full of pungent odors. My head leaned against her hip, her hip that moved and breathed. We went into the kitchen, and Galina put my head under the tap. A goose was frying on the tiled stove, glowing pots and pans hung on the wall, and next to them, in the cook's corner, was Tsar Nicholas decorated with paper flowers. Galina washed off the last smear of pigeon sticking to my cheek. "You'll look like a bridegroom now, my sweet boy," she said, kissing my mouth with her full lips and turning away.

"Your dad has troubles, you see," she suddenly whispered. "He roams the streets all day long with nothing to do. Fetch your dad home."

I saw through the window the empty street under the vast sky, and my redheaded father walking along in the roadway. He walked bareheaded, his soft red hair fluttering, his paper dickey askew and fastened to the wrong button. Vlasov, a drunken workman dressed in a soldier's wadded rags, was stubbornly pursuing him.

"Babel," Vlasov was saying in a hoarse, emotional voice, "we don't need freedom so that the Jews can corner all the business. Shine a light in the workingman's life, for his toil, for his great burdens. That's what you should do, my friend. D'you hear?"

The workman was begging my father for something, grabbing at his arm. Flashes of pure drunken inspiration and a gloomy sleepiness appeared in his face interchangeably. "We should live like the Molokan Sect," he mumbled, swaying on his weak legs. "We should live like the Molokans, but without that old God of the Old Believers. Only Jews get anything from him, nobody else."

Vlasov yelled in wild desperation against the God of the Old Believers who took pity only on the Jews. Vlasov wailed, stumbled and tried to catch up with his Unknown God, but at that moment a Cossack patrol rode by, barring his way. An officer with stripes on his trousers and a parade belt of silver rode in front of the patrol, a tall peaked cap set stiffly on his head. The officer rode slowly, not looking right or left. He rode as though through a mountain pass, where one can only look ahead.

"Captain," my father mumbled when the Cossacks came abreast of him, "captain," my father said, grasping his head in his hands and kneeling in the mud.

"Do what I can," the officer answered, still looking straight ahead, and raising his hand in its lemon-colored chamois glove to the peak of his cap.

Right in front of them, at the corner of Fish Street, the mob was looting and smashing up our store, throwing out into the street boxes filled with nails, machines, and my new photo in school uniform.

"Look," my father said, still on his knees, "they are destroying everything dear to me. Captain, why is it?"

The officer murmured something, and again put the lemon glove to his cap. He touched the reins, but his horse did not move. My father crawled in front of the horse on his knees, rubbing up against its short, kindly, tousled legs.

"At your service," the officer said, tugged at the reins, and rode off, the Cossacks following. They sat passionless on their high saddles, riding through their imaginary mountain pass and disappearing into Cathedral Street.

Galina again gently pushed me to the window.

"Fetch father home," she said. "He hasn't had anything to eat since morning."

I leaned out of the window.

My father turned when he heard my voice.

"My little son," he stuttered with immeasurable tenderness.

He and I went on to the Rubtsovs' veranda where my mother was lying in the green rotunda. Near her couch dumbbells and gymnastic apparatus were scattered.

"That cursed money," my mother cried at us. "You gave up every-thing for it. Human life, the children, our wretched little bit of happiness. Cursed money!" she cried out in a hoarse voice quite unlike her real voice. She jerked on the couch and fell silent.

And then in the stillness my hiccups were heard. I was standing by the wall with my cap pulled down over my forehead, and I couldn't stop hiccuping.

"You shouldn't do that, my sweet boy," Galina said with her disdain-ful smile, flipping me with her stiff robe. She went to the window in her red shoes and began to hang Chinese curtains on the weird cornice. Her bare arms were drowned in silk, and her braid was alive, swinging down over her hip. Enchanted, I stared at her.

I was a bookish boy, and I looked at her as at a distant scene glar-ingly limelighted. Then I imagined that I was Miron, son of the coalman who had his shop on our corner. I imagined myself to be a member of the Jewish Defense Corps. Like Miron, I am wearing torn shoes tied together with string, and on my shoulder a useless rifle hangs by a green cord. I am kneeling by a wooden fence shooting at the murderers. Behind the fence an empty lot stretches, heaps of dusty coal lie there. The antiquated rifle shoots badly. The murderers have beards and white teeth, they approach stealthily. I have a proud feeling of imminent death, and in the skies, in the world's blueness, I see Galina. I see a loophole cut in the wall of a gigantic house built of myriads of bricks. This purple house weighs heavily on the valley where the gray earth is loosely stamped. In the highest loophole stands Galina. From the loophole, out of reach, she smiles mockingly. Her husband, the officer, half-dressed, stands behind her kiss-ing her neck.

Trying to halt my hiccups, I imagined all this so that I might love Galina with a bitterer, warmer, more hopeless love, or perhaps because for a ten-year-old boy the measure of sorrow was too great. O foolish fancies that helped me forget the death of the pigeons, and Shoyl's death!

Maybe I would have forgotten those murderers if Kuzma had not come to the veranda with Aba, the repulsive Jew.

It was dusk when they came. On the veranda a poor bent lamp was burning. Its flame blinked, flickering companion of unhappiness.

"I put the shroud on Grandfather," Kuzma said as he entered. "He's a treat to look at now, lying there. And I've brought the sexton along. Let him gab a bit over the dead."

Kuzma pointed to Aba the shammes.

"Let him whine awhile," the yardman said amiably. "If the sexton gets his belly filled, he'll pester God all night long."

Kuzma was standing on the threshold, his friendly broken nose twisted in all directions, and he wanted to tell us with as much feeling as he could how he had bound the dead man's chin. But my father interrupted old Kuzma.

"Please, Reb Aba," my father said, "pray for the deceased. I will pay you."

"But I'm scared you won't pay," answered Aba in his tedious voice, and he placed his bearded, squeamish face on the tablecloth. "I'm afraid you'll take my rouble and go off with it to the Argentine, to Buenos Aires. You'll start a wholesale business with my rouble . . . a wholesale business," said Aba, champing his disdainful lips and dragging the newspaper across the table to him. In the paper a story was printed about the Tsar's manifesto of October 17, about the proclamation of freedom.

"Citizens of free Russia," Aba read syllable by syllable, chewing a mouthful of his beard, "citizens of free Russia, greetings on this blessed Sunday . . ."

The old shammes held the swaying paper sideways. He read drowsily in his singsong voice, strangely accentuating the unfamiliar Russian words. Aba's accent resembled the confused mumblings of a Negro who has just come to a Russian port from his native land. It made even my mother laugh.

"I am committing a sin," she exclaimed, leaning forward from her rotunda. "I am laughing, Aba. You'd better tell me how you're getting on, you and your family."

"Ask me something else," growled Aba, not easing the grip of his teeth on his beard, and he went on reading the paper.

"Ask him something else," said my father, echoing Aba's words, and he stepped to the center of the room. His eyes, smiling at us through his tears, suddenly turned in their sockets and focused on a point we could not see.

"Oy, Shoyl," my father said in a level, lying voice that was on the verge of bursting, "oy, Shoyl, you dear man . . ."

We saw that he would be shouting any moment, but mother forestalled us.

"Manus," she cried, her hair disheveled in an instant, and she started tearing at her husband's breast. "See how sick our boy is! Can't you hear how he's hiccuping? Why can't you, Manus?"

My father stopped.

"Rachel," he said timidly, "I can't tell you how sad I am for Shoyl."

He went to the kitchen and came back with a glass of water.

"Drink, little play actor," said Aba, coming over to me. "Drink the water. It will help you as a censer helps a dead man."

He was right: the water did not help me. My hiccups increased. A howl escaped from my breast. A swelling, pleasant to touch, rose on my throat. It breathed, expanded, spread on my throat and bulged over my collar. Inside the swelling bubbled my torn and gasping breath, bubbling like water on the boil. And when toward night I was no longer the lop-eared lad I had been all my life, but a writhing mass, my mother covered herself with a shawl and, grown taller and shapelier, approached the paralyzed Galina.

"Dear Galina," said my mother in a strong, ringing voice, "how we are disturbing you and your whole family! I am so ashamed, dear Galina."

Her cheeks burning, mother pushed Galina toward the door. Then she hurried back to me and stuffed my mouth with her shawl to muffle my groans.

"Try to stand it," she whispered. "Try to stand it for mother's sake."

But even had it been possible to stand I should not have tried to do so, for I no longer felt any shame.

So began my illness. I was then ten years old. Next morning they took me to the doctor's. The pogrom continued, but we were not interfered with. The doctor, a fat man, diagnosed nervous trouble.

He told us to go to Odessa as soon as possible to consult experts, and to wait there for the warm weather and the sea-bathing.

And so we did. A few days later I went with mother to Odessa, to Grandfather Leivi-Itzkhok's and Uncle Simon's. We went by the morning steamer, and already by noon the brown waters of the Bug had given place to the heavy green swell of the sea. Life at crazy Grandfather Leivi-Itzkhok's opened out before me, and I said goodbye for ever to Nikolayev, where ten years of my childhood had passed. And now, remembering those sorrowful years, I find in them the beginning of the ills that torment me, the cause of my early fading.

CHAPTER twelve

Psychiatry
and the Law

The law excuses from criminal and civil responsibility
individuals who are judged insane. Insanity is a legal concept
and is determined by legal procedures, using as precedents
the famous M'Naghten decision of 1843 and the *State* vs.
Thomson, 1834. These decisions, the former English and the
latter American, centered on two criteria: did the accused know
right from wrong? Was his behavior determined by an
uncontrollable impulse? These questions seem simple and
straightforward, but when one adds that all behavior is at least
in part influenced by impulses and that these impulses can be
conscious or unconscious, the questions begin to become obscure
and unanswerable. In fact, the findings of modern dynamic
psychiatry have outmoded the simple definitions of the law.
Unfortunately, nothing adequate has been found to replace this
obsolete definition which would suit both the purposes of the
law and the findings of psychiatry. The court has been left
responsible to decide these questions. But the ambiguities
remain. How abnormal does an individual have to be in order to
be treated rather than punished? How do we really define
whether the criminal was conscious of what he was doing; that
is, his intent? Shiga Naoya, a contemporary Japanese writer,
explores these issues in his study of the motivation for what is
either a murder or an accident.

Han's Crime

Shiga Naoya   (1883–   )

Much to everyone's astonishment, the young Chinese juggler, Han, severed his wife's carotid artery with one of his heavy knives in the course of a performance. The young woman died on the spot. Han was immediately arrested.

At the scene of the event were the director of the theatre, Han's Chinese assistant, the announcer, and more than three hundred spectators. There was also a policeman who had been stationed behind the audience. Despite the presence of all these witnesses, it was a complete mystery whether the killing had been intentional or accidental.

Han's act was as follows: his wife would stand in front of a wooden board about the size of a door, and from a distance of approximately four yards, he would throw his large knives at her so that they stuck in the board about two inches apart, forming a contour around her body. As each knife left his hand, he would let out a staccato exclamation as if to punctuate his performance.

The examining judge first questioned the director of the theatre.

"Would you say that this was a very difficult act?"

"No, Your Honor, it's not as difficult as all that for an experienced performer. But to do it properly, you need steady nerves and complete concentration."

"I see. Then assuming that what happened was an accident, it was an extremely unlikely type of accident?"

"Yes indeed, Your Honor. If accidents were not so very unlikely, I should never have allowed the act in my theatre."

"Well then, do you consider that this was done on purpose?"

"No, Your Honor, I do not. And for this reason: an act of this kind performed at a distance of twelve feet requires not only skill but at the same time a certain—well, intuitive sense. It is true that we all thought a mistake virtually out of the question, but after what has happened, I think we must admit that there was always the possibility of a mistake."

"Well then, which do you think it was—a mistake or on purpose?"

"That I simply cannot say, Your Honor."

The judge felt puzzled. Here was a clear case of homicide, but whether it was manslaughter or premeditated murder it was impossible to tell. If a murder, it was indeed a clever one, thought the judge.

"Han's Crime" by Shiga Naoya. Translated by Ivan Morris. Reprinted by the permission of the author, Shiga Naoya, and the translator, Ivan Morris.

Next the judge decided to question the Chinese assistant, who had worked with Han for many years past.

"What was Han's normal behavior?" he asked.

"He was always very correct, Your Honor; he didn't gamble or drink or run after women. Besides, last year he took up Christianity. He studied English and in his free time always seemed to be reading collections of sermons—the Bible and that sort of thing."

"And what about his wife's behavior?"

"Also very correct, Your Honor. Strolling players aren't always the most moral people, as you know. Mrs. Han was a pretty little woman and quite a few men used to make propositions to her, but she never paid the slightest attention to that kind of thing."

"And what sort of temperaments did they have?"

"Always very kind and gentle, sir. They were extremely good to all their friends and acquaintances and never quarreled with anyone. But . . ." He broke off and reflected a moment before continuing. "Your Honor, I'm afraid that if I tell you this, it may go badly for Han. But to be quite truthful, these two people, who were so gentle and unselfish to others, were amazingly cruel in their relations to each other."

"Why was that?"

"I don't know, Your Honor."

"Was that the case ever since you first knew them?"

"No, Your Honor. About two years ago Mrs. Han was pregnant. The child was born prematurely and died after about three days. That marked a change in their relations. They began having terrible rows over the most trivial things, and Han's face used to turn white as a sheet. He always ended by suddenly growing silent. He never once raised his hand against her or anything like that—I suppose it would have gone against his principles. But when you looked at him, Your Honor, you could see the terrible anger in his eyes! It was quite frightening at times.

"One day I asked Han why he didn't separate from his wife, seeing that things were so bad between them. Well, he told me that he had no real grounds for divorce, even though his love for her had died. Of course, she felt this and gradually stopped loving him too. He told me all this himself. I think the reason he began reading the Bible and all those sermons was to calm the violence in his heart and stop himself from hating his wife, whom he had no real cause to hate. Mrs. Han was really a pathetic woman. She had been with Han nearly three years and had traveled all over the country with him as a strolling player. If she'd ever left Han and gone back home, I don't think she'd have found it easy to get married. How many men would trust a woman who'd spent all that time traveling about? I suppose that's why she stayed with Han, even though they got on so badly."

"And what do you really think about this killing?"

"You mean, Your Honor, do I think it was an accident or done on purpose?"

"That's right."

"Well, sir, I've been thinking about it from every angle since the day it happened. The more I think, the less I know what to make of it. I've talked about it with the announcer, and he also says he can't understand what happened."

"Very well. But tell me this: at the actual moment it did happen, did it occur to you to wonder whether it was accidental or on purpose?"

"Yes, sir, it did. I thought . . . I thought, 'He's gone and killed her.' "

"On purpose, you mean?"

"Yes, sir. However the announcer says that he thought, 'His hand's slipped.' "

"Yes, but he didn't know about their everyday relations as you did."

"That may be, Your Honor. But afterwards I wondered if it wasn't just because I did know about those relations that I thought, 'He's killed her.' "

"What were Han's reactions at the moment?"

"He cried out, 'Ha.' As soon as I heard that, I looked up and saw blood gushing from his wife's throat. For a few seconds she kept standing there, then her knees seemed to fold up under her and her body swayed forward. When the knife fell out, she collapsed on the floor, all crumpled in a heap. Of course there was nothing any of us could do—we just sat there petrified, staring at her. . . . As to Han, I really can't describe his reactions, for I wasn't looking at him. It was only when the thought struck me, 'He's finally gone and killed her,' that I glanced at him. His face was dead white and his eyes closed. The stage manager lowered the curtain. When they picked up Mrs. Han's body she was already dead. Han dropped to his knees then, and for a long time he went on praying in silence."

"Did he appear very upset?"

"Yes, sir, he was quite upset."

"Very well. If I have anything further to ask you, I shall call for you again."

The judge dismissed the Chinese assistant and now summoned Han himself to the stand. The juggler's intelligent face was drawn and pale; one could tell right away that he was in a state of nervous exhaustion.

"I have already questioned the director of the theatre and your assistant," said the judge when Han had taken his place in the witness box. "I now propose to examine you."

Han bowed his head.

"Tell me," said the judge, "did you at any time love your wife?"

"From the day of our marriage until the child was born I loved her with all my heart."

"And why did the birth of the child change things?"

"Because I knew it was not mine."

"Did you know who the other man was?"

"I had a very good idea. I think it was my wife's cousin."

"Did you know him personally?"

"He was a close friend. It was he who first suggested that we get married. It was he who urged me to marry her."

"I presume that his relations with her occurred prior to your marriage."

"Yes, sir. The child was born eight months after we were married."

"According to your assistant, it was a premature birth."

"That is what I told everyone."

"The child died very soon after birth, did it not? What was the cause of death?"

"He was smothered by his mother's breasts."

"Did your wife do that on purpose?"

"She said it was an accident."

The judge was silent and looked fixedly at Han's face. Han raised his head but kept his eyes lowered as he awaited the next question. The judge continued,

"Did your wife confess these relations to you?"

"She did not confess, nor did I ever ask her about them. The child's death seemed like retribution for everything and I decided that I should be as magnanimous as possible, but . . ."

"But in the end you were unable to be magnanimous?"

"That's right. I could not help thinking that the death of the child was insufficient retribution. When apart from my wife, I was able to reason calmly, but as soon as I saw her, something happened inside me. When I saw her body, my temper would begin to rise."

"Didn't divorce occur to you?"

"I often thought that I should like to have a divorce, but I never mentioned it to my wife. My wife used to say that if I left her she could no longer exist."

"Did she love you?"

"She did not love me."

"Then why did she say such things?"

"I think she was referring to the material means of existence. Her home had been ruined by her elder brother, and she knew that no serious man would want to marry a woman who had been the wife of a strolling player. Also her feet were too small for her to do any ordinary work."

"What were your physical relations?"

"I imagine about the same as with most couples."

"Did your wife have any real liking for you?"

"I do not think she really liked me. In fact, I think it must have been very painful for her to live with me as my wife. Still, she endured it. She endured it with a degree of patience almost unthinkable for a man. She used to observe me with a cold, cruel look in her eyes as my life gradually went to pieces. She never showed a flicker of sympathy as she saw me struggling in agony to escape into a better, truer sort of existence."

"Why could you not take some decisive action—have it out with her, or even leave her if necessary?"

"Because my mind was full of all sorts of ideals."

"What ideals?"

"I wanted to behave towards my wife in such a way that there would be no wrong on my side. . . . But in the end it didn't work."

"Did you never think of killing your wife?"

Han did not answer and the judge repeated his question. After a long pause, Han replied,

"Before the idea of killing her occurred to me, I often used to think it would be a good thing if she died."

"Well, in that case, if it had not been against the law, don't you think you might have killed her?"

"I wasn't thinking in terms of the law, sir. That's not what stopped me. It was just that I was weak. At the same time I had this overmastering desire to enter into a truer sort of life."

"Nevertheless you did think of killing your wife, did you not—later on, I mean?"

"I never made up my mind to do it. But, yes, it is correct to say that I did think about it once."

"How long was that before the event?"

"The previous night. . . . Or perhaps even the same morning."

"Had you been quarreling?"

"Yes, sir."

"What about?"

"About something so petty that it's hardly worth mentioning."

"Try telling me about it."

"It was a question of food. I get rather short-tempered when I haven't eaten for some time. Well, that evening my wife had been dawdling and our supper wasn't ready when it should have been. I got very angry."

"Were you more violent than usual?"

"No, but afterwards I still felt worked up, which was unusual. I suppose it was because I'd been worrying so much during those past weeks about making a better existence for myself, and realizing there was nothing I could do about it. I went to bed but couldn't get to sleep. All sorts of upsetting thoughts went through my mind. I began to feel that whatever I did, I should never be able to achieve the things I really wanted—that however hard I tried, I should never be able to escape from all the hateful aspects of my present life. This sad, hopeless state of affairs all seemed connected with my marriage. I desperately wanted to find a chink of light to lead me out of my darkness, but even this desire was gradually being extinguished. The hope of escape still flickered and sputtered within me, and I knew that if ever it should go out I would to all intents and purposes be a dead person.

"And then the ugly thought began flitting through my mind, 'If only she would die! If only she would die! Why should I not kill her?' The practical consequence of such a crime meant nothing to me any longer. No doubt I would go to prison, but life in prison could not be worse—could only be better—than this present existence. And yet somehow I had the feeling that killing my wife would solve nothing. It would have been a shirking of the issue, in the same way as suicide. I must go through each day's suffering as it came, I told myself; there was no way to circumvent that. That had become my true life: to suffer.

"As my mind raced along these tracks, I almost forgot that the cause of my suffering lay beside me. Utterly exhausted, I lay there unable to sleep. I fell into a blank state of stupefaction, and as my tortured mind turned numb, the idea of killing my wife gradually faded. Then I was overcome by the sad empty feeling that follows a nightmare. I thought of all my fine resolutions for a better life, and realized that I was too weak-hearted to attain it. When dawn finally broke I saw that my wife also, had not been sleeping. . . ."

"When you got up, did you behave normally towards each other?"

"We did not say a single word to each other."

"But why didn't you think of leaving her, when things had come to this?"

"Do you mean, Your Honor, that that would have been a solution of my problem? No, no, that too would have been a shirking of the issue! As I told you, I was determined to behave towards my wife so that there would be no wrong on my side."

Han gazed earnestly at the judge, who nodded his head as a sign for him to continue.

"Next day I was physically exhausted and of course my nerves were ragged. It was agony for me to remain still, and as soon as I had got dressed I left the house and wandered aimlessly about the deserted parts of town. Constantly the thought kept returning that I must do something to solve my life, but the idea of killing no longer occurred to me. The truth is that there was a chasm between my thoughts of murder the night before and any actual decision to commit a crime! Indeed, I never even thought about that evening's performance. If I had, I certainly would have decided to leave out the knife-throwing act. There were dozens of other acts that could have been substituted.

"Well, the evening came and finally it was our turn to appear on the stage. I did not have the slightest premonition that anything out of the ordinary was to happen. As usual, I demonstrated to the audience the sharpness of my knives by slicing pieces of paper and throwing some of the knives at the floor boards. Presently my wife appeared, heavily made up and wearing an elaborate Chinese costume; after greeting the audience with her charming smile, she took up her position in front of the board. I picked up one of the knives and placed myself at the distance from her.

"That's when our eyes met for the first time since the previous evening. At once I understood the risk of having chosen this particular act for that night's performance! Obviously I would have to master my nerves, yet the exhaustion which had penetrated to the very marrow of my bones prevented me. I sensed that I could no longer trust my own arm. To calm myself I closed my eyes for a moment, and I sensed that my whole body was trembling.

"Now the time had come! I aimed my first knife above her head; it struck just one inch higher than usual. My wife raised her arms and I prepared to throw my next two knives under each of her arms. As the first one left the ends of my fingers, I felt as if something were holding it back; I no longer had the sense of being able to determine the exact destination of my knives. It was now really a matter of luck if the knife struck at the point intended; each of my movements had become deliberate and self-conscious.

"I threw one knife to the left of my wife's neck and was about to throw another to the right when I saw a strange expression in her eyes. She seemed to be seized by a paroxysm of fear! Did she have a presentiment that this knife, that in a matter of seconds would come hurtling towards her, was going to lodge in her throat? I felt dizzy, as if about to faint. Forcing the knife deliberately out of my hand, I as good as aimed it into space. . . ."

The judge was silent, peering intently at Han.

"All at once the thought came to me, 'I've killed her,'" said Han abruptly.

"On purpose, you mean?"

"Yes. Suddenly I felt that I had done it on purpose."

"After that I understood you knelt down beside your wife's body and prayed in silence."

"Yes, sir. That was a rather cunning device that occurred to me on the spur of the moment. I realized that everyone knew me as a believer in Christianity. But while I was making a pretense of praying, I was in fact carefully calculating what attitude to adopt."

"So you were absolutely convinced that what you had done was on purpose?"

"I was. But I realized at once that I should be able to pretend it had been an accident."

"And why did you think it had been on purpose?"

"I had lost all sense of judgment."

"Did you think you'd succeeded in giving the impression it was an accident?"

"Yes, though when I thought about it afterwards it made my flesh creep. I pretended as convincingly as I could to be grief-stricken, but if there'd been just one really sharp-witted person about, he'd have realized right away that I was only acting. Well, that evening I decided that there was no good reason why I should not be acquitted; I told myself very calmly that there wasn't a shred of material evidence against me. To be sure, everyone knew how badly I got on with my wife, but if I persisted in saying that it was an accident, no one could prove the contrary. Going over in my mind everything that had happened, I saw that my wife's death could be explained very plausibly as an accident.

"And then a strange question came to my mind: why did I myself believe that it had *not* been an accident? The previous night I had thought about killing her, but might it not be that very fact which now caused me to think of my act as deliberate? Gradually I came to the point that I myself did not know what actually had happened! At that I became very happy—almost unbearably happy. I wanted to shout at the top of my lungs."

"Because you had come to consider it an accident?"

"No, that I can't say: because I no longer had the slightest idea as to whether it had been intentional or not. So I decided that my best way of being acquitted would be to make a clean breast of everything. Rather than deceive myself and everyone else by saying it was an accident, why not be completely honest and say I did not know what happened? I cannot declare it was a mistake; on the other hand I can't admit it was intentional. In fact, I can plead neither 'guilty' nor 'not guilty.'"

Han was silent. The judge, too, remained silent for a long moment before saying softly, reflectively, "I believe that what you have told me is true. Just one more question: do you not feel the slightest sorrow for your wife's death?"

"None at all! Even when I hated my wife most bitterly in the past, I never could have imagined I would feel such happiness in talking about her death."

"Very well," said the judge. "You may stand down."

Han silently lowered his head and left the room. Feeling strangely moved, the judge reached for his pen. On the document which lay on the table before him he wrote down the words, "Not guilty."